PRAISE FOR ANDREW HINTON

From "AI Basics for Managers:"

"a beacon, guiding non-tech leaders through the often murky waters of artificial intelligence"

— KIRAN

"this book is your ticket to understanding AI's potential and implementing it effectively"

— KAM

"the book was written in an easy-to-understand style, with enough info to make it interesting and informational, but not too much technical data ... the futuristic images, nice touch and beautifully reflects the topic of the book"

— SHAMSA K

"book's holistic approach, ranging from AI's history to its potential impact on contemporary business, is truly commendable"

— AES

AI MASTERY TRILOGY

AI MASTERY TRILOGY

A COMPREHENSIVE GUIDE TO AI BASICS FOR MANAGERS, ESSENTIAL MATHEMATICS FOR AI, AND CODING PRACTICES FOR MODERN PROGRAMMERS IN THE AI ERA (3-IN-1 COLLECTION)

AI FUNDAMENTALS

ANDREW HINTON

Book Bound
STUDIOS

To the pioneers of the past, the innovators of the present, and the visionaries of the future—may this trilogy serve as a beacon on your journey to mastering the art and science of artificial intelligence.

In the pursuit of learning, every day something is acquired.
In the pursuit of AI, every day something is understood.

— ADAPTED FROM LAO TZU

CONTENTS

AI AND ML FOR CODERS

$10.99 FREE EBOOK

Receive Your Free Copy of The Power of AI

SCAN ME

Or visit:
bookboundstudios.wixsite.com/andrew-hinton

AI BASICS FOR MANAGERS

A COMPREHENSIVE GUIDE FOR
MANAGERS TO IMPLEMENT, MEASURE,
AND OPTIMIZE AI IN BUSINESS
OPERATIONS WITHIN THE AI
REVOLUTION

INTRODUCTION TO AI FOR MANAGERS

The dawn of the 21st century has witnessed a technological revolution unlike any other in human history. At the forefront of this revolution is artificial intelligence (AI), a rapidly evolving field that has the potential to transform every aspect of our lives. As a manager in today's fast-paced business environment, it is crucial to understand the basics of AI and embrace its potential to drive innovation, efficiency, and growth within your organization.

The AI revolution is already well underway, with countless industries and sectors reaping the benefits of this groundbreaking technology. From healthcare and finance to manufacturing and retail, AI is reshaping the way we live, work, and interact with one another. As a manager, you are uniquely positioned to harness AI's power and lead your team into a future defined by data-driven decision-making, automation, and unparalleled efficiency.

However, embracing the AI revolution has its challenges. As with any disruptive technology, potential pitfalls and obstacles exist. This book aims to provide you with the knowledge and tools necessary to navigate the complex world of AI, ensuring you are well-equipped to make informed decisions and implement effective strategies within your organization.

In the following chapters, we will delve into the fundamentals of AI, exploring its history, key concepts, and various applications in the business world. We will also examine the ethical considerations and potential risks associated with AI and the steps you can take to mitigate these concerns. Finally, we will provide practical guidance on successfully integrating AI into your management practices, empowering you to lead your team into a future driven by artificial intelligence.

As you embark on this journey, remember that the AI revolution should not be feared or resisted. Rather, it is an opportunity to embrace change, foster innovation, and propel your organization to new heights. By understanding the basics of AI and adopting a multifaceted approach to its implementation, you can ensure that your team is well-prepared to thrive in a world increasingly defined by artificial intelligence. So, let us begin our exploration of AI for managers and unlock the potential of this transformative technology.

The Emergence of AI in the Business World

The dawn of the digital age has brought about a paradigm shift in the way businesses operate, and at the forefront of this revolution is Artificial Intelligence (AI). The concept of AI, which was once confined to science fiction, has now become an integral part of our daily lives. From virtual assistants like Siri and Alexa to advanced analytics and automation tools, AI has permeated various aspects of the business world, transforming industries and redefining how we work.

The emergence of AI in the business world can be traced back to the mid-20th century when computer scientists and mathematicians began exploring the idea of creating machines that could mimic human intelligence. This pursuit led to the development of early AI systems, such as the General Problem Solver and ELIZA, which laid the foundation for future advancements in the field. However, it was only with the advent of the internet and the exponential growth of computing power that AI became a disruptive force in the business landscape.

In recent years, the rapid advancements in AI technologies, such as machine learning, natural language processing, and computer vision, have enabled businesses to harness the power of AI to streamline operations, enhance decision-making, and drive innovation. The proliferation of big data has further accelerated the adoption of AI, as organizations now have access to vast amounts of information that can be analyzed and leveraged to gain valuable insights and improve business outcomes.

As AI continues to evolve, it is reshaping the business world in several ways. For instance, AI-powered automation is transforming how businesses manage their supply chains, optimize logistics, and handle customer service. In addition, AI-driven analytics enables organizations to make data-driven decisions, identify trends, and uncover hidden patterns that can lead to new opportunities and competitive advantages.

Moreover, AI is also playing a crucial role in developing innovative products and services, as companies can now leverage AI technologies to create personalized experiences, enhance user engagement, and drive customer satisfaction. Furthermore, AI is fostering new business models and strategies, as organizations can now harness the power of AI to create value, differentiate themselves from competitors, and stay ahead of the curve in an increasingly competitive and dynamic business environment.

In conclusion, the emergence of AI in the business world has ushered in a new era of innovation, efficiency, and growth. As AI technologies advance and become more accessible, businesses across industries must adapt and embrace the AI revolution to stay relevant and thrive in the digital age. This book aims to empower managers with the knowledge and tools they need to navigate the AI landscape, harness its potential to drive success and create a future driven by artificial intelligence.

Empowering Managers to Navigate the AI Landscape

The dawn of the AI revolution has brought forth many opportunities and challenges for businesses across the globe. As managers, staying ahead of the curve and adapting to this rapidly evolving landscape is crucial. This book aims to empower you, the modern manager, with the knowledge and tools necessary to navigate the complex world of artificial intelligence.

In today's competitive business environment, relying solely on traditional management techniques is no longer enough. Integrating AI into various aspects of business operations has become necessary for organizations seeking to maintain a competitive edge. This book aims to comprehensively understand AI fundamentals, its applications in the business world, and the strategies required for successful implementation.

By delving into the core concepts of AI, this book will enable managers to make informed decisions about adopting and integrating AI technologies within their organizations. Furthermore, it will provide insights into AI's ethical considerations and potential pitfalls, ensuring managers are well-equipped to address any challenges.

This book will engage readers and facilitate a deeper understanding of AI in management through a multifaceted approach that combines expository, descriptive, narrative, and persuasive writing styles. The narrative style will bring the concepts to life by presenting real-world examples and case studies. At the same time, the persuasive elements will encourage readers to embrace the potential of AI in their organizations.

In conclusion, this book aims to empower managers with the knowledge and confidence to navigate the AI landscape, ensuring that they are well-prepared for a future driven by artificial intelligence. By understanding the fundamentals of AI, its applications in the business world, and the strategies for successful implementation, managers will be better equipped to lead their organizations into the new era of AI-driven innovation.

From AI Fundamentals to Implementation Strategies

As we embark on this journey to explore the world of artificial intelligence, it is crucial to understand the scope of this book and how it aims to empower managers like you. Our goal is to provide a comprehensive guide that covers the fundamentals of AI and delves into practical implementation strategies that can be applied in various business contexts.

To begin with, we will lay the foundation by discussing AI's core concepts and principles. This includes an overview of its history, the different types of AI, and the underlying technologies that drive its development, such as machine learning, deep learning, and natural language processing. By grasping these essential concepts, you will be better equipped to appreciate the potential of AI and its relevance to your organization.

Next, we will explore the various applications of AI across different industries and business functions. From marketing and customer service to finance and human resources, AI has the potential to revolutionize the way we work and make decisions. By examining real-world case studies and success stories, you will gain valuable insights into how AI can be harnessed to drive innovation, efficiency, and competitive advantage.

As a manager, it is vital to understand the ethical and legal implications of AI adoption. Therefore, we will dedicate a section discussing the potential risks, challenges, and ethical considerations of integrating AI into your business operations. This will enable you to make informed decisions and ensure that your organization complies with relevant regulations and industry standards.

Once you understand the AI landscape, we will delve into the practical aspects of implementing AI in your organization. This includes identifying the right AI solutions for your business needs, building a robust AI strategy, and managing the change process effectively. We will also discuss the importance of fostering a culture of innovation and collaboration and developing the necessary skills and competencies within your team to harness the full potential of AI.

Finally, we will look toward the future and explore the emerging trends and developments in AI. By staying informed about the latest advancements and anticipating the potential impact on your industry, you can position your organization at the forefront of the AI revolution and ensure long-term success.

In conclusion, this book aims to provide a multifaceted approach to AI in management, equipping you with the knowledge, tools, and strategies necessary to navigate the rapidly evolving AI landscape. By embracing the power of artificial intelligence, you can unlock new opportunities, drive innovation, and lead your organization into a future driven by AI.

Preparing for a Future Driven by Artificial Intelligence

As we stand on the precipice of a new era in business, it is crucial for managers to not only understand the transformative power of artificial intelligence but also embrace it wholeheartedly. The AI revolution is upon us, rapidly reshaping how we work, communicate, and make decisions. In this ever-evolving landscape, managers well-versed in AI fundamentals and implementation strategies will be better equipped to lead their organizations into a prosperous and innovative future.

Throughout this book, we have explored the various facets of AI, delving into its history, current applications, and potential to revolutionize industries across the globe. We have also examined the challenges and ethical considerations of integrating AI into the workplace. By providing a comprehensive and multifaceted approach to AI in management, this book aims to empower managers with the knowledge and tools necessary to navigate the complex world of artificial intelligence.

As we move forward, managers need to remain adaptable and open-minded, embracing the potential of AI to enhance their decision-making processes, streamline operations, and foster a culture of innovation within their organizations. By doing so, they will be better prepared to face the challenges of an increasingly competitive business environment and seize the opportunities that AI presents.

In conclusion, the future of business is undeniably intertwined with the advancements in artificial intelligence. As managers, we are responsible for staying informed, adapting, and leading our teams through this transformative period. By embracing the AI revolution and harnessing its potential, we can ensure that our organizations thrive in the dynamic and exciting world that lies ahead.

1

UNDERSTANDING ARTIFICIAL INTELLIGENCE: KEY CONCEPTS AND TERMINOLOGY

A digital brain with glowing circuits, surrounded by floating holographic screens displaying binary code and AI algorithms, set against a backdrop of deep space.

I n today's rapidly evolving technological landscape, artificial intelligence (AI) has emerged as a driving force behind innovation and progress in various industries. As a manager, it is crucial to stay informed and knowledgeable about AI, as it has the potential to revolutionize the way businesses operate and compete in the global market. This chapter aims to comprehensively understand AI, its key concepts, and terminology, enabling managers to make informed decisions and effectively integrate AI into their business strategies.

The importance of AI knowledge for managers cannot be overstated. As AI advances and becomes more integrated into our daily lives, managers need to understand its potential applications and implications. This understanding will not only help managers identify opportunities for AI implementation but also enable them to address potential challenges and ethical considerations that may arise.

Moreover, having a solid grasp of AI concepts and terminology will empower managers to communicate effectively with technical teams and make informed decisions when investing in AI technologies. This knowledge will also help managers to stay ahead of the curve, as they will be better equipped to anticipate and adapt to the ever-changing AI landscape.

This chapter will provide a comprehensive overview of artificial intelligence, exploring its origins, development, and current state. Next, we will delve into the key AI concepts, such as machine learning, deep learning, and neural networks, which form the foundation of modern AI systems. To ensure that managers are well-versed in the technical jargon associated with AI, we will also provide a guide to essential AI terminology.

Finally, we will examine real-world applications of AI, showcasing how it transforms business operations across various industries. By the end of this chapter, managers will have a solid understanding of AI and its potential impact on their organizations, enabling them to embrace AI and confidently prepare for the future.

Defining Artificial Intelligence: A Comprehensive Overview

In today's rapidly evolving technological landscape, artificial intelligence (AI) has emerged as a game-changing force, revolutionizing how businesses operate and managers make decisions. But what exactly is AI, and how can we define it in a way that is both comprehensive and accessible to managers? In this section, we will delve into the fascinating world of AI, providing a clear and concise overview of its core principles and components.

At its most fundamental level, artificial intelligence refers to developing computer systems that can perform tasks that typically require human intelligence. These tasks include learning, reasoning, problem-solving, perception, and understanding natural language. The ultimate goal of AI is to create machines that can think, learn, and adapt independently, thereby enhancing human capabilities and improving our ability to solve complex problems.

To better understand AI, it is helpful to break it down into two main categories: narrow AI and general AI. Narrow AI, or weak AI, refers to systems designed to perform specific tasks without possessing true intelligence or consciousness. Examples of narrow AI include speech recognition software, recommendation algorithms, and autonomous vehicles. These systems are highly specialized and excel at their designated tasks, but they lack the ability to think or reason beyond their programming.

On the other hand, general AI, or strong AI, refers to systems that possess human-like intelligence and can perform any intellectual task that a human being can do. While this level of AI remains a theoretical concept, it represents the ultimate aspiration of AI researchers and developers. Achieving general AI would mean creating machines that can perform tasks and understand and reason about the world in the same way humans do.

Now that we have a basic understanding of AI let's explore

some key concepts underpinning its development and functionality. In the next section, we will delve into the fascinating realms of machine learning, deep learning, and neural networks, shedding light on the mechanisms that enable AI systems to learn and adapt over time. By grasping these foundational concepts, managers will be better equipped to harness the power of AI in their organizations and navigate the challenges and opportunities that this transformative technology presents.

Key AI Concepts: Machine Learning, Deep Learning, and Neural Networks

As a manager, it is crucial to have a solid understanding of the key concepts that underpin artificial intelligence. This will not only help you make informed decisions but also enable you to communicate effectively with your technical team. This section will delve into three fundamental AI concepts: machine learning, deep learning, and neural networks.

Machine Learning: Teaching Computers to Learn

At the heart of artificial intelligence lies machine learning, a subset of AI that focuses on developing algorithms and statistical models that enable computers to learn from and make predictions or decisions based on data. In other words, machine learning allows computers to identify patterns and trends without being explicitly programmed to do so.

There are three main types of machine learning:

- **Supervised Learning:** In this approach, the algorithm is trained on a labeled dataset, which means that the input data is paired with the correct output. The algorithm learns to map inputs to outputs and can then make predictions on new, unseen data.

- **Unsupervised Learning:** Unlike supervised learning, unsupervised learning deals with unlabeled data. The algorithm must identify patterns and relationships within the data with guidance on the output. This is often used for tasks such as clustering and dimensionality reduction.
- **Reinforcement Learning:** This type of learning is inspired by how humans and animals learn from their environment. The algorithm learns by interacting with its environment and receiving feedback through rewards or penalties. The goal is to maximize the cumulative reward over time.

Deep Learning: Unleashing the Power of Neural Networks

Deep learning is a more advanced subset of machine learning that utilizes artificial neural networks to model and solve complex problems. These networks mimic how the human brain processes information, allowing computers to recognize patterns and make decisions with minimal human intervention.

The term "deep" refers to the multiple layers of interconnected nodes or neurons within the network. Each layer is responsible for processing different aspects of the input data, and the depth of the network allows it to learn more abstract and complex features.

Neural Networks: The Building Blocks of Deep Learning

Neural networks are the foundation of deep learning and consist of interconnected nodes or neurons that process and transmit information. These networks are organized into layers, each receiving input from the previous one and passing its output to the next.

There are three main types of layers in a neural network:

- **Input Layer:** This is the first layer of the network and is responsible for receiving the raw data. Each node in this layer represents a single input data feature or attribute.
- **Hidden layer(s):** These are the layers between the input and output layers. They perform complex computations and transformations on the input data, allowing the network to learn abstract features and representations.
- **Output Layer:** The final layer of the network produces the output or prediction based on the processed input data. The number of nodes in this layer depends on the problem being solved, such as the number of classes in a classification task.

In conclusion, understanding these key AI concepts - machine learning, deep learning, and neural networks - is essential for managers who wish to harness the power of artificial intelligence in their organizations. By grasping these fundamental ideas, you will be better equipped to make informed decisions, communicate with your technical team, and ultimately drive your business forward in the rapidly evolving world of AI.

Essential AI Terminology: A Manager's Guide to Technical Jargon

As a manager, it is crucial to have a firm grasp of the key terms and concepts related to artificial intelligence. This understanding will not only help you communicate effectively with your technical team but also enable you to make informed decisions about AI implementation in your organization. This section will explore some of the most important AI terminology that every manager should be familiar with.

- **Algorithm:** An algorithm is a set of rules or instructions a computer follows to solve a problem or complete a task. In AI, algorithms process data, identify patterns, and make predictions or decisions based on that data.

- **Supervised Learning:** This is a type of machine learning where the algorithm is trained on a labeled dataset, which means that the input data is paired with the correct output. The algorithm learns from this data and then applies it to new, unlabeled data.

- **Unsupervised Learning:** Unlike supervised learning, unsupervised learning algorithms are not provided with labeled data. Instead, they must independently identify patterns and relationships within the data. This type of learning is often used for tasks such as clustering and dimensionality reduction.

- **Reinforcement Learning:** In reinforcement learning, an AI agent learns by interacting with its environment and receiving feedback through rewards or penalties. The agent's goal is maximizing its cumulative reward over time, often involving learning an optimal strategy through trial and error.

- **Natural Language Processing (NLP):** NLP is a subfield of AI that focuses on enabling computers to understand, interpret, and generate human language. This technology is used in chatbots, sentiment analysis, and machine translation applications.

- **Computer Vision:** This is another subfield of AI that enables computers to interpret and understand visual information from the world, such as images and videos. Computer vision is used in facial recognition, object detection, and autonomous vehicles.

- **Neural Network:** A neural network is a machine learning model inspired by the human brain's structure and function. It consists of interconnected nodes or neurons that process and transmit information. Neural networks are particularly effective at handling complex tasks like image and speech recognition.

- **Deep Learning:** Deep learning is a subset of machine learning that involves training large neural networks with multiple layers. These deep neural networks can learn hierarchical representations of data, which allows them to excel at tasks such as image and speech recognition, natural language processing, and game playing.
- **Transfer Learning:** Transfer learning is a technique in which a pre-trained neural network is fine-tuned for a new task or domain. This approach can save time and resources by leveraging the knowledge gained from previous training.
- **Bias and Fairness:** In the context of AI, bias refers to the presence of systematic errors in an algorithm's predictions, often stemming from biased training data. Fairness, on the other hand, is the equitable treatment of different groups by an AI system. Ensuring that AI systems are unbiased and fair is critical for managers implementing AI in their organizations.

In conclusion, understanding these essential AI terms and concepts will empower you as a manager to make informed decisions about AI implementation and effectively communicate with your technical team. By embracing AI and staying informed about its developments, you will be better prepared to lead your organization into the future.

Real-World Applications: How AI is Transforming Business Operations

As a manager, it is crucial to understand the practical applications of artificial intelligence (AI) in today's business landscape. By grasping the transformative power of AI, you can better position your organization for success and capitalize on the opportunities it presents. This section will explore some real-world applications of

AI and how they revolutionize various aspects of business operations.

Customer Service and Support

One of the most visible applications of AI in business is using chatbots and virtual assistants to enhance customer service and support. These AI-powered tools can handle various tasks, from answering frequently asked questions to guiding customers through complex processes. By automating routine customer interactions, businesses can reduce response times, improve customer satisfaction, and free up human agents to focus on more complex issues.

Sales and Marketing

AI is also transforming the way businesses approach sales and marketing. Machine learning algorithms can analyze vast amounts of data to identify patterns and trends, enabling businesses to understand their customers better and target their marketing efforts more effectively. AI-powered tools can also help sales teams prioritize leads, predict customer behavior, and personalize their interactions, leading to increased sales and improved customer relationships.

Supply Chain Management

In supply chain management, AI is used to optimize logistics and streamline operations. Machine learning algorithms can analyze historical data to predict demand, allowing businesses to make more informed decisions about inventory levels and production schedules. AI can also help identify inefficiencies in the supply chain, such as bottlenecks or underutilized resources, enabling managers to make data-driven decisions that improve overall efficiency.

Human Resources

AI is making its mark on human resources (HR) by automating repetitive tasks and providing valuable insights into employee performance and engagement. AI-powered tools can help HR professionals sift through large numbers of job applications, identify top candidates, and predict which applicants are most likely to succeed in a given role. Additionally, AI can analyze employee feedback and sentiment, helping managers identify areas for improvement and fostering a more positive work environment.

Decision-Making and Strategy

Finally, AI plays an increasingly important role in decision-making and strategy development. Businesses can uncover hidden patterns and insights that inform strategic decisions by leveraging machine learning algorithms and advanced analytics. AI can also help managers simulate various scenarios and predict the potential outcomes of different strategies, enabling them to make more informed choices and better prepare for the future.

In conclusion, AI transforms business operations in many ways, from enhancing customer service to streamlining supply chain management. As a manager, embracing AI and understanding its potential applications within your organization is essential. By doing so, you can position your business for success and ensure you are prepared to navigate the rapidly evolving landscape of AI-driven innovation.

Embracing AI as a Manager and Preparing for the Future

As we reach the end of this enlightening journey through the world of artificial intelligence, it is crucial for managers to not only understand the key concepts and terminology but also to embrace AI and its potential impact on the future of business operations. In this concluding section, we will discuss the importance of adopting AI as a manager and outline the steps to prepare for the inevitable AI-driven future.

The rapid advancements in AI technology have made it an essential component of modern business strategies. As a manager, embracing AI means recognizing its potential to transform your organization and industry and actively seeking ways to integrate it into your operations. This proactive approach will help you stay ahead of the competition and ensure that your organization remains relevant and agile in the ever-evolving business landscape.

To prepare for the future, managers must take the following steps:

- **Stay informed:** Stay updated on AI trends, research, and developments. This will enable you to make informed decisions about adopting and implementing AI technologies in your organization.
- **Develop a strategic vision:** Identify the areas within your organization where AI can have the most significant impact and create a strategic vision for its integration. This vision should be aligned with your organization's overall goals and objectives.
- **Foster a culture of innovation:** Encourage a culture of innovation and experimentation within your organization. This will help your team members to be more open to new ideas and technologies, including AI.
- **Invest in education and training:** Ensure your team members have the skills and knowledge to use AI technologies. This may involve investing in training programs, workshops or even hiring AI experts to guide your team.
- **Collaborate with AI experts:** Establish partnerships with AI experts, researchers, and technology providers to gain insights into the latest AI developments and best practices. This will help you make informed decisions

about adopting and implementing AI technologies in your organization.

- **Monitor and evaluate AI initiatives:** Regularly monitor and evaluate the performance of your AI initiatives to ensure that they deliver the desired results. This will help you identify areas that require improvement and adjust your AI strategy.

In conclusion, the future of business is undeniably intertwined with artificial intelligence. As a manager, it is your responsibility to embrace AI and prepare your organization for the inevitable changes it will bring. By staying informed, developing a strategic vision, fostering a culture of innovation, investing in education and training, collaborating with AI experts, and monitoring and evaluating AI initiatives, you will be well-equipped to navigate the challenges and opportunities presented by AI and lead your organization into a successful and prosperous future.

Chapter Summary

- Artificial intelligence (AI) is a driving force behind innovation and progress in various industries, making it crucial for managers to stay informed and knowledgeable about its potential applications and implications.
- AI can be categorized into narrow AI (weak AI) and general AI (strong AI), with narrow AI focusing on specific tasks without true intelligence or consciousness and general AI aiming to achieve human-like intelligence across all intellectual tasks.
- Key AI concepts include machine learning, deep learning, and neural networks, which form the foundation of modern AI systems and enable them to learn and adapt over time.

- Understanding essential AI terminology, such as supervised learning, unsupervised learning, reinforcement learning, natural language processing, and computer vision, is crucial for managers to make informed decisions and communicate effectively with technical teams.
- Real-world applications of AI are transforming business operations across various industries, including customer service, sales and marketing, supply chain management, human resources, and decision-making and strategy.
- Embracing AI as a manager involves recognizing its potential to transform organizations and industries, actively seeking ways to integrate it into operations, and staying informed about the latest AI trends and developments.
- Preparing for the AI-driven future requires developing a strategic vision for AI integration, fostering a culture of innovation, investing in education and training, collaborating with AI experts, and monitoring and evaluating AI initiatives.
- By understanding and embracing AI, managers can position their organizations for success, navigate the rapidly evolving AI landscape, and lead their teams into a successful and prosperous future.

2

THE EVOLUTION OF AI: A BRIEF HISTORY AND ITS IMPACT ON BUSINESS

A visual journey of AI evolution, starting from an abacus, transforming into an old computer, then a modern laptop, and finally morphing into a futuristic neural network.

I n today's fast-paced world of technology, artificial intelligence (AI) has surfaced as a critical catalyst in the transformation of diverse industries. As companies aim to remain competitive and ahead of the game, it's essential to grasp the fundamentals of AI and its possible uses for effective management. This chapter thoroughly reviews AI's evolution, its influence on business procedures, and the potential future trends that managers need to be aware of.

The concept of AI has been around for decades, but only in recent years have we witnessed its true potential unfold. From automating mundane tasks to revolutionizing decision-making processes, AI has proven to be a game-changer in how businesses operate. As a manager, it is essential to recognize the value of AI and its potential to reshape the business landscape.

In the following sections, we will delve into the early beginnings of AI, exploring the pioneering concepts and visionaries that laid the foundation for this groundbreaking technology. We will then examine the AI boom, highlighting the technological advancements that have propelled AI into the forefront of business operations. Furthermore, we will discuss the modern era of AI, focusing on machine learning, deep learning, and their practical applications in various industries.

As we venture into the future of AI, we will explore emerging trends and their potential impacts on business strategies. By understanding the trajectory of AI's development and its implications for the business world, managers can better prepare themselves and their organizations for transformative changes.

In conclusion, this chapter will provide managers with a solid understanding of AI's history, current applications, and potential future developments. By embracing the AI revolution and staying informed about its progress, managers can ensure that their businesses remain agile, innovative, and ready to face the challenges of an increasingly AI-driven world.

The Dawn of Artificial Intelligence: Early Concepts and Pioneers

As we embark on this journey to explore the fascinating world of artificial intelligence (AI), it is essential to understand its origins and the visionaries who laid the groundwork for the AI revolution. The dawn of AI can be traced back to the mid-20th century when the concept of creating intelligent machines first captured the imagination of scientists, mathematicians, and philosophers.

The Birth of an Idea: Turing and the Turing Test

The story of AI begins with the brilliant British mathematician and logician Alan Turing. In 1950, Turing published a groundbreaking paper titled "Computing Machinery and Intelligence," he proposed a test to determine if a machine could exhibit intelligent behavior indistinguishable from that of a human. This test, now known as the Turing Test, laid the foundation for the field of AI and sparked a debate on the possibility of machine intelligence that continues to this day.

The Pioneers: McCarthy, Minsky, and the Birth of AI as a Discipline

The 1950s saw the emergence of several key figures who would shape the field of AI. Among them were John McCarthy, an American computer scientist, and Marvin Minsky, a cognitive scientist and co-founder of the Massachusetts Institute of Technology's (MIT) Media Lab. In 1956, McCarthy and Minsky, along with other leading researchers, organized the Dartmouth Conference, which marked the birth of AI as a distinct discipline. The conference aimed to explore the potential of machines to simulate various aspects of human intelligence, such as learning, problem-solving, and language understanding.

Early AI Programs: Chess, Language, and Problem Solving

The 1960s and 1970s witnessed the development of several early AI programs that demonstrated the potential of machines to perform tasks previously thought to be the exclusive domain of human intelligence. Among these were chess-playing programs, such as IBM's Deep Blue, which defeated the reigning world champion, Garry Kasparov, in 1997. Another notable example was SHRDLU, a natural language understanding program developed by Terry Winograd at MIT, which could interpret and respond to simple English sentences.

The AI Winter: Challenges and Lessons Learned

Despite these early successes, the field of AI faced significant challenges in the 1970s and 1980s as researchers grappled with the limitations of their approaches and the complexity of simulating human intelligence. Funding for AI research dwindled, and the field entered a period of stagnation known as the "AI winter." However, this period also provided valuable lessons and insights that would later contribute to the resurgence of AI in the 1990s and beyond.

In conclusion, the early days of AI were marked by groundbreaking ideas, pioneering researchers, and ambitious projects that sought to push the boundaries of what machines could achieve. While the path was not without its challenges, these early efforts laid the foundation for the future AI boom, transforming how businesses operate and setting the stage for a future where AI plays an increasingly central role in our lives.

The AI Boom: Technological Advancements and Their Influence on Business Operations

As the sun began to rise on the horizon of artificial intelligence, a new era of technological advancements emerged, casting a transformative light on the business world. As it came to be known, the AI boom was characterized by rapid innovation and the development of cutting-edge tools and techniques that would forever change how businesses operate. In this section, we will delve into the key milestones of the AI boom and explore how these breakthroughs have shaped the modern business landscape.

The Birth of Machine Learning: Paving the Way for AI in Business

The AI boom can be traced back to the advent of machine learning, a revolutionary approach to AI that enabled computers to learn from data and improve their performance over time. This groundbreaking concept was first introduced by Arthur Samuel in 1959, who demonstrated the potential of machine learning through a simple yet powerful example: a computer program that could teach itself to play checkers.

As machine learning algorithms grew more sophisticated, businesses began to recognize the immense value of harnessing this technology to optimize their operations. From predicting customer behavior to automating complex decision-making processes, machine learning opened the door to a new world of possibilities for businesses seeking a competitive edge.

The Rise of Deep Learning: Unleashing the Power of Neural Networks

The next major milestone in the AI boom came with the rise of deep learning, a subset of machine learning that leverages artificial neural networks to mimic the human brain's ability to process and interpret vast amounts of information. Pioneered by Geoffrey Hinton and his team in the late 2000s, deep learning has since become the driving force behind many of the most advanced AI applications in business today.

Deep learning has enabled businesses to tackle previously insurmountable challenges, such as image and speech recognition, natural language processing, and even original content creation. By harnessing the power of deep learning, businesses have streamlined their operations, enhanced their products and services, and delivered more personalized experiences to their customers.

AI in Action: Real-World Business Applications

The AI boom has given rise to many practical applications that have transformed how businesses operate across various industries. Some notable examples include:

- **Customer Service:** AI-powered chatbots and virtual assistants have revolutionized customer service by providing instant, personalized support, reducing response times, and freeing human agents to focus on more complex tasks.
- **Marketing and Sales:** AI-driven analytics and predictive modeling have enabled businesses to understand their customers better, tailor their marketing campaigns, and optimize their sales strategies.
- **Supply Chain Management:** AI has been instrumental in optimizing supply chain operations, from demand forecasting and inventory management to route optimization and quality control.
- **Human Resources:** AI has streamlined recruitment by automating candidate screening, skill assessment, and even conducting preliminary interviews.
- **Finance:** AI has enhanced financial decision-making through advanced risk assessment, fraud detection, and algorithmic trading.

The AI Boom: A Catalyst for Business Transformation

The AI boom has undoubtedly left an indelible mark on the business world, driving innovation and fostering a culture of continuous improvement. As AI technologies evolve, businesses must adapt and embrace these advancements to stay ahead of the curve and capitalize on the opportunities they present. By harnessing the power of AI, businesses can unlock new levels of efficiency, agility, and growth, paving the way for a brighter, more prosperous future.

AI in the Modern Era: Machine Learning, Deep Learning, and Business Applications

As we venture into the modern era of artificial intelligence, it is essential to understand the key concepts that have shaped the AI landscape and their implications for businesses. This section will delve into machine learning, deep learning, and their various applications in the business world.

Machine Learning: The Driving Force Behind AI

Machine learning, a subset of AI, has emerged as a game-changing technology that enables computers to learn from data and improve their performance over time. This is achieved through algorithms that iteratively learn from data, allowing the system to make predictions or decisions without being explicitly programmed.

In the business context, machine learning has opened up many opportunities for organizations to gain insights from vast amounts of data, automate processes, and enhance decision-making. Some common applications of machine learning in business include:

- **Customer segmentation:** By analyzing customer data, machine learning algorithms can identify patterns and group customers based on their preferences, behaviors, and demographics. This enables businesses to tailor their marketing strategies and improve customer engagement.

- **Fraud detection:** Machine learning can help businesses detect unusual patterns and anomalies in transactions, which may indicate fraudulent activities. This allows organizations to prevent financial losses and protect their reputation proactively.
- **Inventory management:** Machine learning can optimize inventory levels by predicting demand and identifying trends, ensuring businesses maintain the right stock to meet customer needs while minimizing costs.

Deep Learning: Taking AI to New Heights

Deep learning, a more advanced subset of machine learning, has further revolutionized the AI landscape. It involves using artificial neural networks inspired by the human brain's structure and function. These networks can process vast amounts of data and identify complex patterns, enabling machines to perform tasks that were once considered impossible for computers.

Deep learning has particularly succeeded in image and speech recognition, natural language processing, and autonomous vehicles. In the business world, deep learning has found applications in:

- **Sentiment analysis:** By analyzing text data from sources like social media, customer reviews, and emails, deep learning algorithms can determine the sentiment behind the text, allowing businesses to gauge customer satisfaction and respond accordingly.
- **Chatbots and virtual assistants:** Deep learning has enabled the development of more sophisticated

chatbots and virtual assistants that can understand and respond to natural language queries, providing customers with personalized support and improving the overall customer experience.

- **Predictive maintenance:** Deep learning can analyze sensor data from equipment and machinery to predict potential failures, allowing businesses to schedule maintenance and avoid costly downtime.

Harnessing the Power of AI in Business

The modern era of AI, characterized by machine learning and deep learning, has created many opportunities for businesses to enhance operations, drive innovation, and gain a competitive edge. By understanding and embracing these technologies, organizations can unlock the full potential of AI and prepare for a transformative future.

In the next section, we will explore the emerging trends in AI and their potential impacts on business strategies, ensuring that managers are well-equipped to navigate the ever-evolving AI landscape.

The Future of AI: Emerging Trends and Potential Impacts on Business Strategies

As we venture into the uncharted territory of the future, artificial intelligence (AI) continues evolving at an unprecedented pace, shaping how businesses operate and strategize. In this section, we will explore the emerging trends in AI and their potential impacts on business strategies, providing managers with valuable insights to navigate the transformative landscape ahead.

The Rise of AI-Driven Decision Making

One of the most significant trends in AI is the increasing reliance on data-driven decision-making. As AI algorithms become more sophisticated, they can analyze vast amounts of data and generate actionable insights, enabling businesses to make informed decisions based on empirical evidence. This shift towards AI-driven decision-making will require managers to adapt their strategies, placing greater emphasis on data collection, analysis, and interpretation.

The Integration of AI Across Business Functions

As AI technologies become more accessible and affordable, businesses will increasingly integrate AI across various functions, from marketing and sales to human resources and customer service. This widespread adoption of AI will necessitate reevaluating traditional business processes, as managers must determine how to leverage AI best to streamline operations, enhance efficiency, and drive innovation.

The Emergence of AI Ethics and Regulations

As AI becomes more ingrained in our daily lives, ethical considerations and regulatory frameworks will play a crucial role in shaping the future of AI in business. Managers must stay informed about the evolving ethical and legal landscape surrounding AI, ensuring that their organizations adhere to best practices and comply with relevant regulations. This will involve developing robust AI governance structures and fostering a culture of ethical AI use within the organization.

The Growing Importance of AI Talent and Education

As AI transforms the business landscape, the demand for skilled AI professionals will grow exponentially. To stay competitive, businesses must invest in AI education and training, cultivating a workforce capable of harnessing the power of AI to drive growth and innovation. This may involve partnering with educational institutions, offering in-house training programs, or providing employees access to online resources and courses.

The Need for Human-AI Collaboration

While AI has the potential to automate many tasks, it is essential to recognize that human expertise and intuition remain invaluable assets in the business world. The future of AI in business will likely involve a symbiotic relationship between humans and machines, each complementing the other's strengths and weaknesses. Managers must balance AI-driven automation and human ingenuity, fostering a collaborative environment where both can thrive.

In conclusion, the future of AI presents both challenges and opportunities for businesses. By staying informed about emerging trends and adapting their strategies accordingly, managers can harness the power of AI to drive growth, innovation, and success in the ever-evolving business landscape. Embracing the AI revolution and preparing for a transformative future will be essential for businesses to remain competitive and thrive in the age of artificial intelligence.

Embracing the AI Revolution and Preparing for a Transformative Future

As we have journeyed through the fascinating evolution of artificial intelligence, it is evident that AI has come a long way since its early conceptualizations. From the pioneering work of Alan Turing and John McCarthy to the groundbreaking advancements in machine learning and deep learning, AI has transformed how businesses operate and strategize. As we stand on the cusp of a new era, managers must embrace the AI revolution and prepare for a transformative future.

The AI revolution is not a distant dream but a present reality. Companies across industries are harnessing the power of AI to streamline operations, enhance customer experiences, and gain a competitive edge. As a manager, it is essential to recognize the potential of AI in your organization and identify areas where it can be effectively implemented. This may involve investing in AI-driven tools and technologies, upskilling your workforce, or collaborating with AI experts to develop tailored solutions.

Embracing the AI revolution also requires a shift in mindset. Managers must be open to experimentation and willing to adapt to new working methods. This includes fostering a culture of innovation and encouraging employees to think creatively about how AI can be leveraged to solve complex business challenges. By nurturing an environment that embraces change, managers can ensure that their organizations remain agile and responsive to the ever-evolving AI landscape.

As we look to the future, it is clear that AI will continue to shape the world of business in profound ways. Emerging trends such as natural language processing, autonomous systems, and AI-driven decision-making will further revolutionize how companies operate and interact with their customers. To stay ahead of the curve, managers must proactively monitor these developments and assess their potential impact on business strategies.

In conclusion, the AI revolution presents immense business opportunities and challenges. By embracing this transformative technology and preparing for its future advancements, managers can position their organizations for success in the rapidly evolving world of AI. As we continue to witness the remarkable progress of artificial intelligence, it is crucial for managers not only to adapt but also to lead the way in shaping a future where AI and human ingenuity work hand in hand to drive growth, innovation, and prosperity.

Chapter Summary

- The concept of AI has been around for decades, but its true potential has only been realized in recent years, revolutionizing various industries and transforming business operations.
- The early days of AI were marked by groundbreaking ideas and pioneering researchers, laying the foundation for the AI boom that followed and changed the way businesses operate.
- Machine learning, a subset of AI, has enabled computers to learn from data and improve their performance over time, opening up numerous opportunities for businesses to optimize their operations.
- Deep learning, a more advanced subset of machine learning, has further revolutionized the AI landscape, enabling machines to perform tasks that were once considered impossible for computers.
- AI has found practical applications in various industries, such as customer service, marketing and sales, supply chain management, human resources, and finance.
- Emerging trends in AI, such as AI-driven decision-making, integration of AI across business functions, AI ethics and regulations, and the growing importance of AI talent and education, will shape the future of AI in business.
- The future of AI in business will likely involve a symbiotic relationship between humans and machines, each complementing the other's strengths and weaknesses.
- Embracing the AI revolution and preparing for a transformative future is essential for businesses to

remain competitive and thrive in the age of artificial intelligence.

3

AI TECHNOLOGIES: MACHINE LEARNING, DEEP LEARNING, AND NATURAL LANGUAGE PROCESSING

A futuristic computer lab with glowing blue neural networks visualizing machine learning processes.

I n today's rapidly evolving business landscape, artificial intelligence (AI) has emerged as a game-changing technology that is transforming how organizations operate and compete. As a manager, it is crucial to understand the basics of AI technologies and their potential applications in your industry. This chapter will provide a comprehensive overview of the key AI technologies, namely machine learning, deep learning, and natural language processing, and how they can be integrated into your business strategy.

AI technologies have the potential to revolutionize various aspects of management, from automating routine tasks and enhancing decision-making processes to improving customer experiences and driving innovation. By leveraging these cutting-edge tools, managers can unlock new opportunities for growth, efficiency, and competitive advantage.

To begin our exploration of AI technologies, let us first clearly understand what artificial intelligence is. At its core, AI refers to developing computer systems that can perform tasks that typically require human intelligence. These tasks include learning from experience, recognizing patterns, understanding natural language, and making decisions based on complex data.

Now that we have a foundational understanding of AI let us delve deeper into the three primary technologies that drive its capabilities: machine learning, deep learning, and natural language processing. Each of these technologies offers unique benefits and applications, and together, they form the backbone of AI's transformative potential in the management world.

Machine Learning: The Foundation of AI

As a manager, you may have heard the term "machine learning" thrown around in discussions about artificial intelligence. But what exactly is machine learning, and why is it considered the foundation of AI? This section will delve into the fascinating world of machine learning, explore its various types, and understand its significance in AI.

Machine learning is a subset of artificial intelligence that focuses on developing algorithms and statistical models that enable computers to learn and improve from experience without being explicitly programmed. In simpler terms, it is the process through which machines can analyze vast amounts of data, identify patterns, and make decisions or predictions based on that information.

There are three primary types of machine learning: supervised learning, unsupervised learning, and reinforcement learning. We've briefly discussed them in chapter one, but as each type has its unique approach to learning and problem-solving, we must go deeper.

- **Supervised Learning:** In supervised learning, the machine is provided with a labeled dataset, which means that the input data is paired with the correct output. The machine uses this dataset to learn the relationship between the input and output and then applies this knowledge to make predictions on new, unseen data. Supervised learning is commonly used in applications such as image recognition, speech recognition, and financial forecasting.
- **Unsupervised Learning:** Unlike supervised learning, unsupervised learning deals with unlabeled data. The machine finds patterns, relationships, or structures within the data without prior knowledge of the desired output. Unsupervised learning is often used for tasks such as clustering (grouping similar data points) and dimensionality reduction (reducing the number of variables in a dataset while preserving its essential information).
- **Reinforcement Learning:** Reinforcement learning is a unique approach to machine learning, where an agent

learns to make decisions by interacting with its environment. The agent receives feedback through rewards or penalties and adjusts its actions accordingly to maximize the cumulative reward. This type of learning is beneficial in situations where the optimal solution is not known in advance and must be discovered through trial and error, such as in robotics and game-playing.

Machine learning is often called the foundation of AI because it allows computers to learn, adapt, and evolve without human intervention. By harnessing the power of machine learning, AI systems can analyze vast amounts of data, uncover hidden patterns, and make predictions with remarkable accuracy. This ability to learn from data and improve over time is what sets AI apart from traditional rule-based systems. It has led to groundbreaking advancements in computer vision, natural language processing, and robotics.

In conclusion, machine learning is a crucial component of artificial intelligence that enables machines to learn from experience and make data-driven decisions. As a manager, understanding the basics of machine learning and its various types will help you appreciate the potential of AI technologies and make informed decisions about their implementation in your organization. The next section will dive deeper into AI by exploring deep learning and its transformative impact on neural networks.

Deep Learning: Unleashing the Power of Neural Networks

As a manager, you may have heard the term "deep learning" thrown around in discussions about artificial intelligence. But what exactly is deep learning, and how does it differ from machine learning? How can you harness its power to drive your business forward? This section will delve into the fascinating world of deep learning, explore its potential applications, and provide the knowledge you need to make informed decisions about incorporating this cutting-edge technology into your organization.

Deep learning is a subset of machine learning that uses artificial neural networks to process and analyze data. These networks are inspired by the structure and function of the human brain, with interconnected nodes or "neurons" working together to process information and generate insights. The term "deep" refers to the multiple layers of neurons that make up these networks, allowing them to learn and recognize complex patterns and relationships in the data.

While both machine learning and deep learning involve the use of algorithms to analyze data and make predictions, there are some key differences between the two. Traditional machine learning algorithms often require manual feature extraction, meaning that a human expert must identify and select the most relevant variables for the algorithm to consider. On the other hand, deep learning can automatically discover and extract relevant features from raw data, making it more efficient and less reliant on human intervention.

Another significant difference is the ability of deep learning models to handle unstructured data, such as images, audio, and text. Traditional machine learning algorithms typically struggle with this type of data, whereas deep learning models excel at identifying patterns and relationships within them. This makes deep learning particularly well-suited for tasks such as image recognition, natural language processing, and speech recognition.

The power of deep learning to process and analyze vast amounts of complex data has opened up a world of possibilities for businesses across various industries. Some of the most promising applications of deep learning include:

- **Customer segmentation:** By analyzing customer data, deep learning models can identify patterns and trends that help businesses better understand their target audience and tailor their marketing strategies accordingly.

- **Fraud detection:** Deep learning algorithms can quickly and accurately identify suspicious transactions or activities, helping businesses protect themselves from financial losses and maintain their reputation.
- **Product recommendation:** By analyzing customer preferences and purchase history, deep learning models can generate personalized product recommendations, increasing customer satisfaction and loyalty.
- **Predictive maintenance:** Deep learning can analyze sensor data from equipment and machinery to predict when maintenance is needed, reducing downtime and increasing operational efficiency.
- **Sentiment analysis:** Deep learning models can gauge public sentiment towards a brand or product by processing and analyzing customer reviews and social media posts. This allows businesses to make data-driven decisions about their marketing and public relations strategies.

As a manager, it's essential to recognize the potential of deep learning and consider how it can be integrated into your organization's strategy. Begin by identifying areas where deep learning could have the most significant impact, such as improving customer service, streamlining operations, or enhancing product offerings. Next, collaborate with your IT and data teams to assess your organization's current infrastructure and determine the resources needed to implement deep learning solutions. Finally, consider partnering with AI and deep learning experts to ensure your organization is leveraging the latest advancements in this rapidly evolving field.

In conclusion, deep learning represents a powerful tool for businesses looking to harness the full potential of artificial intelligence. By understanding the basics of deep learning and its applications, you, as a manager, can make informed decisions about incorporating this technology into your organization's strategy and embracing the future of AI in management.

Natural Language Processing: Bridging the Gap Between Humans and Machines

As we delve deeper into artificial intelligence, managers must understand the significance of Natural Language Processing (NLP) and its potential impact on businesses. NLP, a subfield of AI, focuses on the interaction between humans and computers through natural language. In simpler terms, it enables machines to understand, interpret, and generate human language in a meaningful and useful way. This section will provide an overview of NLP, its applications, and how it can be integrated into your business strategy.

Understanding Natural Language Processing

At its core, NLP aims to bridge the gap between human communication and computer understanding. It involves various techniques and algorithms that allow machines to process and analyze large volumes of text or speech data. This is achieved by breaking down sentences into words, phrases, or symbols and then analyzing their structure, meaning, and context. By doing so, NLP enables computers to extract valuable insights and information from unstructured data, such as emails, social media posts, customer reviews, and more.

Applications of Natural Language Processing

NLP has various applications across various industries, making it an essential tool for businesses leveraging AI technologies. Some of the most common applications include:

- **Sentiment Analysis:** By analyzing the sentiment behind customer feedback, businesses can gain valuable insights into their products and services, allowing them to make data-driven decisions and improve customer satisfaction.
- **Chatbots and Virtual Assistants:** NLP-powered chatbots and virtual assistants can understand and respond to customer queries in real time, providing personalized support and enhancing the overall customer experience.
- **Text Classification:** NLP can be used to categorize and organize large volumes of text data, such as emails, documents, or articles, making it easier for businesses to manage and access information.
- **Machine Translation:** NLP enables translating text or speech from one language to another, breaking down language barriers and facilitating global communication.
- **Speech Recognition:** By converting spoken language into written text, NLP allows for voice-activated commands, transcription services, and more.

Integrating NLP into Your Business Strategy

To harness the power of NLP, managers must first identify the areas within their business where language processing can provide the most value. This may involve analyzing customer feedback, streamlining communication channels, or automating routine tasks. Once the potential applications have been identified, businesses can explore various NLP tools and platforms available in the market or even consider developing custom solutions tailored to their needs.

In conclusion, Natural Language Processing is a powerful AI technology that has the potential to revolutionize the way businesses interact with their customers, employees, and data. By understanding the basics of NLP and its applications, managers can make informed decisions on how to integrate this technology into their business strategy, ultimately driving growth and success in the age of AI.

Integrating AI Technologies into Your Business Strategy

As a manager, understanding the potential of AI technologies is only the first step in harnessing their power for your organization. The real challenge lies in effectively integrating machine learning, deep learning, and natural language processing into your business strategy. This section will explore the key considerations and best practices for incorporating AI technologies into your organization's operations and decision-making processes.

Identify the right opportunities

Before diving into AI implementation, it is crucial to identify the areas within your organization where AI technologies can have the most significant impact. Start by analyzing your business processes, customer interactions, and data management systems to pinpoint areas that could benefit from automation, enhanced decision-making, or improved efficiency. Some common use cases for AI technologies include customer service, fraud detection, marketing, and supply chain optimization.

Develop a clear AI strategy

Once you have identified the opportunities for AI integration, develop a comprehensive AI strategy outlining your organization's goals, objectives, and desired outcomes. This strategy should include an AI implementation roadmap detailing the necessary resources, timelines, and milestones. It is also essential to establish a system for measuring the success of your AI initiatives, using key performance indicators (KPIs) that align with your organization's overall objectives.

Assemble a cross-functional AI team

Successful AI integration requires collaboration between various departments and stakeholders within your organization. Assemble a cross-functional team that includes representatives from IT, data science, business operations, and other relevant departments. This team will oversee the AI implementation process, ensuring all stakeholders are aligned and working towards the same goals.

Invest in the right infrastructure and tools

Implementing AI technologies requires a robust infrastructure that can handle the demands of data processing, storage, and analysis. Invest in the necessary hardware, software, and cloud-based solutions to support your AI initiatives. Additionally, ensure your organization can access the right tools and platforms for machine learning, deep learning, and natural language processing, such as TensorFlow, Keras, and NLTK.

Foster a culture of AI adoption

For AI technologies to truly transform your organization, fostering a culture of AI adoption among your employees is essential. Encourage a mindset of continuous learning and innovation, providing training and resources to help your team members understand and embrace AI technologies. Empowering your employees to leverage AI in their daily tasks and decision-making processes can drive greater efficiency, productivity, and overall success for your organization.

Monitor, evaluate, and iterate

AI integration is an ongoing process that requires continuous monitoring, evaluation, and iteration. Regularly assess the performance of your AI initiatives, using the KPIs established in your AI strategy to determine their effectiveness. Be prepared to make adjustments and improvements as needed, ensuring that your AI technologies continue to deliver value and drive positive outcomes for your organization.

In conclusion, integrating AI technologies into your business strategy is a complex but rewarding endeavor. By identifying the right opportunities, developing a clear AI strategy, assembling a cross-functional team, investing in the necessary infrastructure and tools, fostering a culture of AI adoption, and continuously monitoring and iterating, you can unlock the full potential of AI for your organization and embrace the future of AI in management.

Embracing the Future of AI in Management

As we reach the end of this enlightening journey through the world of artificial intelligence, managers need to recognize the transformative potential of AI technologies in business. Machine learning, deep learning, and natural language processing are not just buzzwords or fleeting trends; they are powerful tools that can revolutionize the way organizations operate, compete, and thrive in an increasingly digital and data-driven world.

The key to harnessing the full potential of AI lies in understanding its capabilities and limitations and developing a strategic approach to its implementation. Managers must be proactive in staying informed about the latest advancements in AI technologies and be prepared to adapt their business strategies accordingly. This requires a willingness to embrace change, invest in continuous learning, and foster a culture of innovation within the organization.

One of the most critical aspects of integrating AI technologies into your business strategy is identifying the areas where these tools can have the most significant impact. This may involve automating repetitive tasks, enhancing decision-making processes, or improving customer experiences. By pinpointing the specific challenges that AI can help address, managers can ensure that their investments in these technologies yield tangible results and drive long-term growth.

Moreover, managers must recognize that successfully implementing AI technologies goes beyond merely acquiring the right tools and software. It also involves cultivating the necessary skills and expertise within the organization. This may entail hiring new talent, upskilling existing employees, or partnering with external experts to bridge knowledge gaps. By fostering a workforce well-versed in AI, managers can ensure that their organizations are well-equipped to navigate the complexities of this rapidly evolving landscape.

Finally, it is essential for managers to approach the integration of AI technologies with a sense of responsibility and ethical awareness. As powerful as these tools may be, they have risks and challenges. Issues such as data privacy, algorithmic bias, and the potential displacement of human workers must be carefully considered and addressed to ensure that the adoption of AI technologies is both sustainable and socially responsible.

In conclusion, the future of AI in management is undoubtedly bright, filled with opportunities for growth, innovation, and competitive advantage. By embracing these technologies with a strategic, informed, and responsible approach, managers can lead their organizations into a new digital transformation and success era. The time to act is now – the future of AI is already here, and it is up to today's leaders to seize the moment and shape the course of their organizations for years to come.

Chapter Summary

- Artificial intelligence (AI) technologies, including machine learning, deep learning, and natural language processing, can revolutionize various management aspects and drive innovation, efficiency, and competitive advantage.

- Machine learning is a subset of AI that focuses on developing algorithms and statistical models that enable computers to learn and improve from experience without being explicitly programmed.

- Deep learning is a subset of machine learning that uses artificial neural networks to process and analyze data, excelling at identifying patterns and relationships within unstructured data such as images, audio, and text.

- Natural Language Processing (NLP) is a subfield of AI that enables machines to understand, interpret, and generate human language in a meaningful and useful way, with applications such as sentiment analysis, chatbots, and machine translation.

- To integrate AI technologies into a business strategy, managers should identify the right opportunities, develop a clear AI strategy, assemble a cross-functional AI team, invest in the necessary infrastructure and tools, and foster a culture of AI adoption.

- Continuous monitoring, evaluation, and iteration are essential for successful AI integration, ensuring that AI technologies continue to deliver value and drive positive outcomes for the organization.

- Cultivating the necessary skills and expertise within the organization is crucial for successful AI implementation, which may involve hiring new talent, upskilling existing employees, or partnering with external experts.

- Managers should approach the integration of AI technologies with a sense of responsibility and ethical awareness, addressing issues such as data privacy, algorithmic bias, and the potential displacement of human workers to ensure sustainable and socially responsible adoption.

4

THE ROLE OF DATA IN AI: COLLECTION, PROCESSING, AND ANALYSIS

A neon matrix of flowing data streams in a dark cybernetic environment.

In today's swiftly changing business environment, artificial intelligence (AI) has surfaced as a revolutionary technology that is reshaping how organizations function and make choices. As a manager, comprehending the essential role of data in creating and applying AI solutions is vital. This chapter intends to offer an all-inclusive review of the importance of data in AI and how managers can utilize its potential to propel innovation and success within their organizations.

Data is often called the "fuel" that powers AI systems. Without data, AI algorithms would be unable to learn, adapt, and improve their performance over time. Data serves as the raw material that AI systems use to identify patterns, make predictions, and generate insights that can inform strategic decision-making. As a manager, recognizing the value of data in AI initiatives is the first step toward unlocking the full potential of this transformative technology.

The process of leveraging data in AI projects can be broadly divided into three main stages: data collection, data processing, and data analysis. Each stage plays a critical role in ensuring the success of AI-driven solutions and requires careful planning and execution.

In the following sections, we will delve deeper into the various strategies and techniques involved in data collection, processing, and analysis and how they can be effectively integrated into management practices. By gaining a solid understanding of these concepts, managers will be better equipped to make informed decisions about AI projects and ensure that their organizations remain at the forefront of innovation.

As we explore the world of data and its role in AI, it is important to remember that the ultimate goal is to create value for your organization. By embracing data-driven AI solutions and fostering a culture of continuous learning and improvement, managers can unlock new opportunities for growth and success in an increasingly competitive business environment.

Data Collection: Strategies and Techniques for AI Projects

In today's rapidly evolving business landscape, the ability to harness the power of artificial intelligence (AI) is no longer a luxury but a necessity for managers. One of the most critical aspects of AI implementation is data collection, as it forms the foundation upon which AI systems are built and trained. In this section, we will explore various strategies and techniques for data collection that can help managers successfully integrate AI into their projects.

Identifying Data Needs

Before diving into data collection, it is essential for managers to identify the specific data needs of their AI projects. This involves determining the type of data required, the volume of data needed, and the desired level of data quality. By clearly defining these parameters, managers can ensure their data collection efforts are targeted and efficient.

Primary and Secondary Data Sources

Data collection can be broadly categorized into two types: primary and secondary. Primary data refers to information that is collected directly from the source, such as through surveys, interviews, or observations. Conversely, secondary data is information that has already been collected and is available for use, such as existing databases, reports, or research studies. Managers should consider primary and secondary data sources when planning their AI projects, as each offers unique advantages and limitations.

Data Collection Techniques

Numerous data collection techniques are available to managers, each with its own set of benefits and drawbacks. Some of the most common techniques include:

- **Surveys and Questionnaires:** These tools allow managers to gather large amounts of data quickly and cost-effectively. However, they may be subject to biases and inaccuracies if not designed and administered properly.

- **Interviews:** Conducting one-on-one or group interviews can provide rich, in-depth insights into a particular topic. However, this method can be time-consuming and may not be feasible for large-scale data collection efforts.
- **Observations:** By observing and recording events or behaviors, managers can collect data that is free from the biases that may be present in self-reported data. However, this method can be labor-intensive and require specialized training to ensure accurate and consistent data collection.
- **Web Scraping:** This technique involves extracting data from websites and online sources, making it an excellent option for quickly collecting large volumes of data. However, web scraping may raise ethical and legal concerns, and the data quality may vary.

Ensuring Data Quality

Data quality is a crucial factor in the success of AI projects, as poor-quality data can lead to inaccurate or unreliable AI models. Managers should implement quality control measures throughout the data collection process, such as validating data sources, using standardized data collection tools, and regularly reviewing and cleaning the data.

Ethical Considerations

In addition to ensuring data quality, managers must also consider the ethical implications of their data collection efforts. This includes obtaining informed consent from participants, protecting the privacy and confidentiality of the data, and adhering to relevant laws and regulations.

In conclusion, data collection is a vital component of AI

projects, and managers must carefully plan and execute their data collection efforts to ensure the success of their AI initiatives. By understanding the various strategies and techniques available and the importance of data quality and ethical considerations, managers can confidently navigate the complex world of AI data collection and lay the groundwork for AI-driven success in their organizations.

Data Processing: Preparing and Cleaning Data for AI Systems

In the world of artificial intelligence, data is the lifeblood that fuels the decision-making capabilities of AI systems. As a manager, understanding the process of data preparation and cleaning is crucial to ensure the success of AI projects within your organization. In this section, we will delve into the importance of data processing, the steps involved in preparing and cleaning data, and the role managers play in overseeing this critical aspect of AI implementation.

Data processing is transforming raw data into a structured format that AI systems can easily understand and analyze. This step is essential because AI algorithms rely on clean, accurate, and well-organized data to make informed decisions and predictions. Only accurate or complete data can lead to better decision-making, reduced efficiency, and even financial losses for your organization. As a manager, you are responsible for ensuring that the data used in AI projects is of the highest quality and has undergone thorough processing.

- **Data Exploration:** The first step in data processing is to explore the raw data and understand its structure, content, and potential issues. This involves examining the data's format, identifying missing or inconsistent values, and assessing the overall quality of the data.
- **Data Cleaning:** Once the data has been explored, the next step is to clean it by addressing any inconsistencies,

errors, or missing values. This may involve correcting typos, filling in missing data points, or removing duplicate entries. Data cleaning is an iterative process, and it may require multiple rounds of review and correction to ensure the data is accurate and consistent.

- **Data Transformation:** After cleaning the data, it must be transformed into a format that AI algorithms can easily understand. This may involve converting data types, scaling or normalizing values, or encoding categorical variables into numerical values. Data transformation ensures that AI systems can effectively analyze and interpret data.

- **Feature Engineering:** The final step in data processing is feature engineering, which involves selecting the most relevant variables or attributes from the data to be used as input for AI algorithms. This may involve creating new variables, combining existing variables, or reducing the dimensionality of the data. Feature engineering is crucial for improving the performance and accuracy of AI systems.

As a manager, your role in the data processing stage of AI projects is to oversee and guide the process, ensuring that the data is accurate, consistent, and well-structured. This may involve:

- Collaborating with data scientists and engineers to establish data processing goals and strategies.
- Allocating resources and setting timelines for data processing tasks.
- Monitoring the progress of data processing and addressing any issues or challenges that arise.
- Ensuring data processing meets industry standards, legal requirements, and ethical guidelines.
- Evaluating the quality of processed data and making informed decisions about its suitability for AI projects.

In conclusion, data processing is a critical aspect of AI implementation that managers must understand and oversee. Ensuring that your organization's data is properly prepared and cleaned can lay the foundation for successful AI projects that drive efficiency, innovation, and growth. Embrace the power of data and harness its potential to transform your management practices and elevate your organization's performance.

Data Analysis: Extracting Insights and Patterns for AI Decision-Making

In artificial intelligence, data is the lifeblood that fuels the decision-making process. As a manager, understanding the role of data analysis in AI is crucial to harnessing its full potential and driving your organization toward success. This section will explore the data analysis process, exploring how insights and patterns can be extracted to inform AI decision-making.

Data analysis examines, cleans, transforms, and models data to extract valuable information, draw conclusions, and support decision-making. In the context of AI, data analysis is essential for identifying patterns and trends that can be used to train and improve machine learning models. The primary goal of data analysis in AI is to uncover hidden relationships and insights that can be leveraged to make better decisions and predictions.

Several techniques and tools are used in data analysis, which can be broadly categorized into descriptive and predictive analytics.

Descriptive Analytics: This type of analysis focuses on summarizing and understanding the past. It involves the use of historical data to identify patterns, trends, and relationships that can provide insights into the current state of a business or system. Descriptive analytics techniques include data visualization, summary statistics, and clustering. These methods help managers understand the underlying structure of their data and identify areas of interest or concern.

Predictive Analytics: On the other hand, predictive analytics uses historical data to make predictions about future events or outcomes. This type of analysis is particularly relevant to AI, as it involves the use of machine learning algorithms to identify patterns and relationships in data that can be used to make informed decisions. Predictive analytics techniques include regression analysis, classification, and time series forecasting. These methods enable managers to anticipate future trends, identify potential risks, and make data-driven decisions that can improve the performance of their AI systems.

As a manager, it is essential to recognize the importance of data analysis in the AI decision-making process. By extracting insights and patterns from your data, you can better understand the factors influencing your organization's performance and make more informed decisions. Furthermore, data analysis can help you identify areas where AI can be most effectively applied, allowing you to prioritize resources and maximize the impact of your AI initiatives.

In conclusion, data analysis is a critical component of AI decision-making, providing the foundation for informed, data-driven decisions that can drive your organization toward success. By embracing the power of data analysis and incorporating it into your management practices, you can unlock the full potential of AI and position your organization for a successful future in the rapidly evolving world of artificial intelligence.

Implementing Data-Driven AI Solutions in Management Practices

In today's rapidly evolving business landscape, managers must be agile and adaptive to stay ahead of the curve. One of the most effective ways to achieve this is by implementing data-driven AI solutions in management practices. By leveraging the power of AI, managers can make more informed decisions, optimize processes, and drive innovation. This section will explore the key steps to integrate data-driven AI solutions into your management practices successfully.

- **Identify the problem or opportunity:** The first step in implementing AI solutions is clearly defining the problem or opportunity you wish to address. This could include improving customer satisfaction, streamlining supply chain operations, or enhancing employee productivity. You can better tailor your AI solution to meet your organization's needs by identifying the specific issue.

- **Set clear objectives:** Once you have identified the problem or opportunity, it is crucial to establish clear objectives for your AI project. These objectives should be SMART (Specific, Measurable, Achievable, Relevant, and Time-bound) to ensure your AI solution is focused and results-driven.

- **Assemble a cross-functional team:** Implementing AI solutions requires collaboration between various departments, including IT, data science, and business operations. By assembling a cross-functional team, you can ensure that all relevant stakeholders are involved in the decision-making process and that your AI solution is aligned with your organization's overall strategy.

- **Collect and process data:** As discussed in previous sections, data is the lifeblood of AI systems. To implement a successful AI solution, you must collect and process relevant data from various sources, such as customer interactions, internal databases, and external data providers. This data should be cleaned, organized, and transformed into a format that AI algorithms can easily analyze.

- **Develop and train AI models:** With your data, your team can now develop AI models tailored to your specific objectives. These models should be trained and tested using your processed data to ensure they can accurately predict outcomes, identify patterns, and make recommendations.

- **Integrate AI solutions into existing processes:** Once your AI models have been developed and tested, it is time to integrate them into your existing management practices. This may involve updating your software systems, retraining employees, or redefining workflows to accommodate the new AI-driven insights.
- **Monitor and evaluate performance:** After implementing your AI solution, it is essential to continuously monitor its performance and evaluate its impact on your organization. This will allow you to identify areas for improvement, fine-tune your AI models, and ensure that your AI solution remains effective and relevant in the face of changing business conditions.
- **Foster a data-driven culture:** Finally, to fully reap the benefits of AI in management practices, fostering a data-driven culture within your organization is crucial. This involves promoting data literacy, encouraging data-driven decision-making, and investing in ongoing AI education and employee training.

In conclusion, implementing data-driven AI solutions in management practices can significantly improve efficiency, decision-making, and innovation. By following the steps outlined above, managers can successfully integrate AI into their organizations and harness the power of data to drive business success.

Embracing Data as the Foundation of AI Success in Management

In conclusion, data plays a pivotal role in successfully implementing artificial intelligence (AI) in management practices. As managers, understanding the significance of data collection, processing, and analysis is crucial in harnessing the full potential of

AI to drive business growth and enhance decision-making processes. By embracing data as the foundation of AI success, managers can unlock new opportunities and stay ahead of the competition in today's rapidly evolving business landscape.

Throughout this chapter, we have explored the various aspects of data management in AI projects, from the strategies and techniques employed in data collection to preparing and cleaning data for AI systems. We have also delved into the importance of data analysis in extracting valuable insights and patterns that can inform AI-driven decision-making. By mastering these essential data management components, managers can ensure that their AI initiatives are built on a solid foundation.

Implementing data-driven AI solutions in management practices requires a shift in mindset and a willingness to adapt to new technologies. Managers must be open to learning and embracing the power of AI, as well as fostering a culture of innovation and collaboration within their teams. By doing so, they can create an environment where AI can thrive and deliver tangible results for the organization.

Moreover, managers need to stay informed about the latest AI and data management developments, as the field is constantly evolving. By staying up-to-date with the latest trends and best practices, managers can ensure that their AI initiatives remain relevant and effective in addressing the challenges faced by their organizations.

In summary, the role of data in AI cannot be overstated. By embracing data as the foundation of AI success in management, managers can unlock the full potential of AI to drive business growth, enhance decision-making processes, and stay ahead of the competition. As the world continues to embrace AI and its transformative capabilities, managers need to understand and harness the power of data to ensure the success of their AI initiatives.

Chapter Summary

- Data is the lifeblood of AI systems, serving as the raw material that AI algorithms use to identify patterns, make predictions, and generate insights for strategic decision-making.
- The process of leveraging data in AI projects involves three main stages: data collection, data processing, and data analysis, each playing a critical role in the success of AI-driven solutions.
- Data collection strategies and techniques include identifying data needs, using primary and secondary data sources, employing various data collection methods, ensuring data quality, and considering ethical implications.
- Data processing involves preparing and cleaning data for AI systems, including exploration, data cleaning, transformation, and feature engineering.
- Data analysis in AI focuses on extracting insights and patterns from data using descriptive and predictive analytics techniques, which help inform AI decision-making.
- Implementing data-driven AI solutions in management involves identifying problems or opportunities, setting clear objectives, assembling cross-functional teams, collecting and processing data, developing and training AI models, integrating AI solutions into existing processes, monitoring and evaluating performance, and fostering a data-driven culture.
- Embracing data as the foundation of AI success in management enables managers to unlock new opportunities, drive business growth, and stay ahead of the competition.

- Staying informed about the latest developments in AI and data management is crucial for managers to ensure that their AI initiatives remain relevant and effective in addressing their organization's challenges.

5

IMPLEMENTING AI IN BUSINESS: IDENTIFYING OPPORTUNITIES AND CHALLENGES

A futuristic office with AI robots performing business tasks under soft white lighting.

A rtificial intelligence (AI) has emerged as a game-changing force in today's rapidly evolving technological landscape, revolutionizing how businesses operate and compete. As a manager, it is crucial to understand the potential of AI and how it can be harnessed to drive innovation, efficiency, and growth within your organization. This chapter provides a comprehensive overview of the opportunities and challenges associated with implementing AI in business management, offering valuable insights and practical guidance for those seeking to embrace this transformative technology.

The AI revolution is already well underway, with companies across industries leveraging machine learning, natural language processing, and other AI technologies to streamline processes, enhance decision-making, and deliver more personalized customer experiences. From automating routine tasks to uncovering hidden patterns in vast datasets, AI enables businesses to operate more intelligently and effectively than ever.

However, the journey to AI-driven success has its challenges. Managers must navigate a complex landscape of technological, organizational, and ethical considerations to integrate AI into their business operations successfully. This requires a clear understanding of the potential benefits and risks associated with AI and a strategic approach to implementation that ensures alignment with broader business objectives.

In this chapter, we will explore how AI can transform your business, highlighting key opportunities for innovation and growth. We will also delve into the common challenges faced by organizations seeking to adopt AI, offering practical advice on overcoming these hurdles and maximizing the value of your AI investments. Through real-world case studies, we will demonstrate the power of AI in driving tangible business results, showcasing the successes of companies that have effectively harnessed this technology. Finally, we will outline best practices for AI integration and adoption, equipping you with the knowledge and tools needed to prepare for a future driven by AI in business management.

By understanding the fundamentals of AI and its potential applications in the business world, managers can position themselves at the forefront of this technological revolution, unlocking new growth and competitive advantage opportunities. Embracing AI in business management is no longer a choice but a necessity for those seeking to thrive in today's increasingly digital and data-driven landscape.

Identifying Opportunities: How AI Can Transform Your Business

As we explore the potential of artificial intelligence (AI) in business management, it is crucial to identify the opportunities that AI presents. By understanding how AI can transform your business, you can make informed decisions and strategically integrate AI solutions to enhance efficiency, productivity, and overall success.

Streamlining Operations and Enhancing Efficiency

One of AI's most significant opportunities is the ability to streamline operations and enhance efficiency. By automating repetitive tasks and processes, AI can free up valuable time and resources, allowing your team to focus on the business's more strategic and creative aspects. For instance, AI-powered chatbots can handle routine customer inquiries, while machine learning algorithms can optimize supply chain management by predicting demand patterns and identifying potential bottlenecks.

Data-Driven Decision Making

In today's data-driven world, businesses generate and collect vast information. AI can help managers make sense of this data by identifying patterns, trends, and insights that would otherwise remain hidden. Managers can make more informed decisions by leveraging AI-powered analytics tools, leading to improved business outcomes. For example, AI can help identify customer preferences and trends, enabling businesses to tailor their products and services better to meet customer needs.

Enhancing Customer Experience

AI has the potential to revolutionize the way businesses interact with their customers. By utilizing AI-powered tools such as chatbots, virtual assistants, and personalized recommendations, businesses can provide a more seamless and engaging customer experience. This improves customer satisfaction, fosters brand loyalty, and drives long-term growth.

Fostering Innovation and Creativity

AI can help businesses unlock their creative potential by automating routine tasks and providing valuable insights. With more time and resources, teams can focus on developing innovative products, services, and strategies that set them apart from the competition. Furthermore, AI can also assist in the creative process, offering suggestions and ideas based on data analysis and pattern recognition.

Expanding Market Reach

AI can help businesses expand their market reach by identifying new customer segments, untapped markets, and emerging trends. By leveraging AI-powered market research tools, businesses can gain a competitive edge and capitalize on new growth opportunities.

In conclusion, the opportunities presented by AI in business management are vast and varied. Businesses can transform their operations, enhance efficiency, and drive innovation by identifying these opportunities and strategically implementing AI solutions. In the following sections, we will delve deeper into the challenges of AI implementation and explore real-world examples of AI success in business management.

Overcoming Challenges: Addressing Common AI Implementation Hurdles

As businesses integrate AI into their operations, they will encounter various challenges. While the potential benefits of AI are immense, managers must be aware of these hurdles and develop strategies to overcome them. This section will discuss some of the most common challenges faced during AI implementation and provide practical solutions to address them.

Data Quality and Availability

One of the most significant challenges in implementing AI is data availability and quality. AI systems rely heavily on data to learn and make decisions. Therefore, it is essential to have access to accurate, relevant, and up-to-date data. To overcome this challenge, businesses should invest in robust data management systems and establish processes to ensure data quality and integrity. Additionally, collaborating with external data providers and leveraging open data sources can help enrich the available data pool.

Talent Acquisition and Retention

The demand for AI professionals, such as data scientists and machine learning engineers, has skyrocketed in recent years. Consequently, businesses face difficulties finding and retaining the right talent to develop and maintain AI systems. To address this challenge, organizations should invest in training and upskilling their existing workforce and partnering with academic institutions and research organizations to tap into a broader talent pool. Offering competitive compensation packages and fostering a culture of innovation can also help attract and retain top AI talent.

Integration with Existing Systems

Integrating AI solutions with existing business systems and processes can be complex and time-consuming. To ensure seamless integration, managers should involve all relevant stakeholders in the planning and implementation process, including IT teams, business analysts, and end-users. Adopting a modular and scalable approach to AI implementation can also help businesses gradually incorporate AI into their operations without disrupting existing workflows.

Ethical and Legal Considerations

AI systems can raise ethical and legal concerns like data privacy, algorithmic bias, and transparency. Managers should proactively address these concerns by establishing ethical guidelines for AI development and usage, conducting regular audits of AI systems, and ensuring compliance with relevant laws and regulations. Engaging with external experts and participating in industry forums can also help businesses stay informed about emerging ethical and legal issues related to AI.

Managing Expectations

Lastly, managers must manage expectations around AI implementation. While AI can benefit businesses significantly, it is not a magic solution that can solve all problems instantly. Managers should set realistic goals and timelines for AI projects and communicate them clearly to all stakeholders. By doing so, they can avoid disappointment and ensure that the organization remains committed to the long-term success of AI initiatives.

In conclusion, overcoming the challenges associated with AI implementation requires strategic planning, effective communication, and continuous learning. By addressing these hurdles head-on, businesses can successfully harness the power of AI to drive innovation and growth in their operations.

Case Studies: Real-World Examples of AI Success in Business Management

In this section, we will delve into real-world examples of how AI has been successfully implemented in various industries, showcasing the transformative power of this technology in business management. These case studies will provide valuable insights into the practical applications of AI, demonstrating how businesses have overcome challenges and reaped the benefits of AI integration.

Retail: Personalized Shopping Experiences with AI

One of the most prominent examples of AI success in business management can be found in the retail industry. E-commerce giant Amazon has been at the forefront of AI adoption, utilizing machine learning algorithms to analyze customer data and provide personalized product recommendations. This has not only improved customers' shopping experience but has also increased sales and customer loyalty. Similarly, clothing retailer Stitch Fix employs AI-powered algorithms to analyze customer preferences and deliver personalized clothing selections, resulting in higher customer satisfaction and retention rates.

Healthcare: Improved Diagnostics and Treatment Plans

AI has made significant strides in the healthcare industry, particularly in diagnostics and treatment planning. IBM's Watson, a powerful AI system, has assisted doctors in diagnosing and treating various medical conditions. By analyzing vast amounts of medical data, Watson can provide accurate diagnoses and recommend personalized treatment plans, leading to better patient outcomes. Additionally, AI-powered tools like Zebra Medical Vision's imaging analytics platform have been instrumental in detecting diseases such as cancer at early stages, enabling timely intervention and potentially saving lives.

Finance: Enhanced Fraud Detection and Risk Management

The finance industry has also embraced AI to improve its operations, particularly in fraud detection and risk management. Financial institutions like JPMorgan Chase and American Express have implemented AI-powered systems to analyze transaction data and identify patterns indicative of fraudulent activity. This has resulted in a significant reduction in financial losses due to fraud. Furthermore, AI-driven risk assessment tools have enabled banks and investment firms to make more informed decisions, leading to better portfolio management and increased returns on investment.

Manufacturing: Streamlined Production Processes and Quality Control

AI has revolutionized manufacturing by streamlining production processes and enhancing quality control measures. For instance, General Electric has employed AI-powered robots to inspect and repair jet engines, reducing inspection times by over 50% and minimizing human error. Similarly, Siemens has implemented AI-driven systems to optimize its production lines, increasing efficiency and reducing waste. These examples demonstrate how AI can significantly improve operational efficiency and product quality in the manufacturing sector.

Customer Service: AI-Powered Chatbots and Virtual Assistants

AI has also significantly impacted customer service with the advent of AI-powered chatbots and virtual assistants. Companies like Microsoft and Google have developed sophisticated AI systems that can understand and respond to customer queries in real time, providing quick and accurate assistance. This has improved customer satisfaction and reduced the workload on human customer service representatives, allowing them to focus on more complex tasks.

In conclusion, these case studies demonstrate the transformative potential of AI in various industries, highlighting the benefits of AI integration in business management. By learning from these real-world examples, managers can identify AI implementation opportunities in their organizations and develop strategies to overcome challenges and ensure successful AI adoption.

Best Practices: Strategies for Effective AI Integration and Adoption

As businesses increasingly embrace the potential of artificial intelligence (AI) to transform their operations, it is crucial to adopt best practices that ensure the successful integration and adoption of AI technologies. This section will explore strategies to help managers implement AI effectively in their organizations while minimizing potential risks and maximizing benefits.

Develop a Clear AI Strategy and Vision

Before embarking on the AI journey, it is essential for managers to have a clear understanding of their organization's goals and objectives in adopting AI technologies. This involves identifying the specific business problems that AI can help solve and the desired outcomes and key performance indicators (KPIs) that will be used to measure success. By establishing a well-defined AI strategy and vision, managers can ensure that their AI initiatives are aligned with the organization's overall business objectives and can effectively communicate the value of AI to stakeholders.

Foster a Culture of Innovation and Collaboration

Successful AI integration requires a culture encouraging innovation, experimentation, and collaboration. Managers should promote a mindset of continuous learning and improvement, where employees are encouraged to explore new ideas, share their knowledge, and work together to solve complex problems. This can be achieved through regular training sessions, workshops, and team-building activities that foster a sense of camaraderie and shared purpose. By creating an environment that supports innovation and collaboration, organizations can more effectively harness the power of AI to drive business growth.

Invest in Talent and Skills Development

As AI technologies evolve, organizations must invest in developing their workforce's skills and expertise. This includes hiring and retaining top talent in AI-related fields and providing ongoing training and development opportunities for existing employees. Managers should also consider partnering with educational institutions, industry associations, and other organizations to access specialized AI training programs and resources. By investing in talent and skills development, businesses can ensure they have the necessary expertise to implement AI technologies and stay ahead of the competition.

Establish Robust Data Management Practices

AI technologies rely heavily on data to function effectively, making it essential for organizations to have robust data management practices in place. This includes ensuring that data is accurate, complete, and up-to-date and implementing strong data security measures to protect sensitive information. Managers should also consider adopting data governance frameworks and tools that can help streamline data management processes and ensure compliance with relevant regulations. By establishing solid data management practices, organizations can maximize the effectiveness of their AI initiatives and minimize potential risks.

Monitor and Evaluate AI Performance

To ensure the ongoing success of AI initiatives, managers need to monitor and evaluate AI technologies' performance regularly. This involves tracking the progress of AI projects against predefined KPIs and conducting regular audits and assessments to identify areas for improvement. Managers should also be prepared to adjust their AI strategy and implementation plans as needed based on the insights gained from performance monitoring and evaluation. By maintaining a proactive approach to AI performance management, organizations can ensure their AI initiatives continue delivering value and driving business growth.

In conclusion, the successful integration and adoption of AI technologies in business management require a strategic approach, a culture of innovation and collaboration, investment in talent and skills development, robust data management practices, and ongoing performance monitoring and evaluation. By adopting these best practices, managers can effectively harness the power of AI to transform their organizations and prepare for a future driven by AI in business management.

Preparing for a Future Driven by AI in Business Management

As we conclude this enlightening journey through artificial intelligence and its impact on business management, we must reflect on the key takeaways and prepare ourselves for the inevitable AI-driven future. The transformative power of AI is undeniable, and as managers, it is our responsibility to harness this potential to drive innovation, efficiency, and growth in our organizations.

First and foremost, it is crucial to recognize that AI is not a fleeting trend or a mere buzzword; it is a powerful tool that is here to stay and will continue to revolutionize how we conduct business. Embracing the AI revolution means acknowledging its potential and proactively seeking opportunities to integrate AI into various aspects of your organization. This may include automating repetitive tasks, enhancing decision-making processes, or creating new products and services.

Identifying these opportunities requires a keen understanding of your organization's unique needs and challenges and a willingness to think creatively and strategically about how AI can address them. It is essential to stay informed about the latest advancements in AI technology and to collaborate with experts in the field to ensure that your organization remains at the forefront of innovation.

However, implementing AI in business management has its challenges. As with any significant change, there will be hurdles to overcome, such as addressing concerns about job displacement, ensuring data privacy and security, and navigating the complexities of AI integration. By anticipating and proactively addressing these challenges, managers can mitigate potential risks and create a smoother transition to an AI-driven business model.

The case studies presented in this chapter are powerful examples of how AI can be successfully integrated into various industries and business functions. By examining these real-world applications, managers can gain valuable insights into the strategies and best practices that have led to AI success. These lessons can then be applied to your organization, helping to guide your AI implementation journey.

In conclusion, the future of business management is undeniably intertwined with the advancements in artificial intelligence. As managers, we must prepare for this future by embracing AI, identifying opportunities for its integration, and overcoming the challenges that may arise along the way. By doing so, we can ensure that our organizations remain competitive, innovative, and poised for success in the rapidly evolving landscape of AI-driven business management.

Chapter Summary

- AI has the potential to revolutionize business management by streamlining operations, enhancing efficiency, fostering innovation, and improving customer experiences.
- Identifying opportunities for AI integration requires a clear understanding of an organization's unique needs and challenges and staying informed about the latest advancements in AI technology.
- Implementing AI in business management comes with challenges, such as data quality and availability, talent acquisition and retention, integration with existing systems, ethical and legal considerations, and managing expectations.
- Real-world case studies demonstrate the transformative potential of AI in various industries, highlighting the benefits of AI integration in business management and providing valuable insights into practical applications.
- Best practices for effective AI integration and adoption include developing a clear AI strategy and vision, fostering a culture of innovation and collaboration, investing in talent and skills development, establishing robust data management practices, and monitoring and evaluating AI performance.
- Overcoming the challenges associated with AI implementation requires strategic planning, effective communication, and continuous learning.

- Preparing for a future driven by AI in business management involves embracing AI, identifying opportunities for its integration, and overcoming the challenges that may arise along the way.
- The future of business management is undeniably intertwined with the advancements in artificial intelligence, and managers must adapt to ensure their organizations remain competitive, innovative, and poised for success in the rapidly evolving landscape of AI-driven business management.

6

AI ETHICS AND RESPONSIBLE MANAGEMENT: ENSURING FAIRNESS, TRANSPARENCY, AND ACCOUNTABILITY

A digital scale balancing a human brain and a circuit board, symbolizing AI ethics, under soft blue lighting.

Artificial intelligence (AI) has surfaced as a potent instrument for revolutionizing how businesses function and decide in the swiftly changing tech world today. As AI systems increasingly become a part of diverse management facets, managers must comprehend the ethical consequences of these technologies and embrace responsible practices to guarantee fairness, transparency, and accountability. This chapter offers a detailed review of AI ethics and responsible management, emphasizing the significance of these principles in the successful execution and management of AI systems.

AI ethics refers to the moral principles and guidelines that govern the design, development, and deployment of AI technologies. These principles are essential in addressing AI's potential risks and unintended consequences, such as biased decision-making, lack of transparency, and misuse of personal data. On the other hand, responsible management involves adopting ethical practices and policies for managers to ensure that AI systems are used in a manner that aligns with the organization's values and societal norms.

As AI continues to permeate various industries and sectors, managers must have the knowledge and skills to navigate the complex ethical landscape surrounding these technologies. This chapter will delve into the importance of fairness in AI decision-making, highlighting the need for unbiased algorithms and data sets to prevent discriminatory outcomes. We will also explore the concept of transparency in AI systems and processes, emphasizing the significance of clear communication and understanding of AI's inner workings for managers and stakeholders.

Furthermore, this chapter will discuss the critical aspect of accountability in AI implementation and management, outlining managers' responsibilities in ensuring that AI systems are used ethically and in compliance with relevant regulations. To provide a comprehensive understanding of these concepts, we will also present real-world examples and case studies of ethical AI management, showcasing the challenges and successes experienced by organizations in various industries.

In conclusion, this chapter will offer a glimpse into the future of AI ethics and responsible management, highlighting the potential developments and challenges as AI continues to revolutionize how we live and work. By understanding and embracing these ethical principles, managers can harness the power of AI to drive innovation and growth while ensuring that their organizations remain committed to upholding the highest standards of fairness, transparency, and accountability.

Understanding the Importance of Fairness in AI Decision-Making

In today's rapidly evolving technological landscape, artificial intelligence (AI) has become an essential tool for businesses and organizations across various industries. As AI systems grow in complexity and capability, managers must understand the importance of fairness in AI decision-making. This section will delve into fairness, its significance in AI applications, and the potential consequences of biased AI systems.

Defining Fairness in AI

Fairness in AI refers to an AI system's equitable treatment of all individuals and groups, ensuring that its decisions do not discriminate against any particular demographic. This involves carefully considering various factors, such as race, gender, age, and socioeconomic status, to guarantee that AI algorithms do not perpetuate existing biases or create new ones.

The Significance of Fairness in AI Applications

The importance of fairness in AI decision-making cannot be overstated. As AI systems become more integrated into our daily lives, they have the potential to significantly impact various aspects of society, from employment and education to healthcare and criminal justice. Ensuring fairness in AI applications is vital for several reasons:

- **Social Responsibility:** As managers, we are responsible for ensuring that the AI systems we implement do not perpetuate harmful biases or contribute to social inequality. By prioritizing fairness in AI decision-making, we can work towards creating a more just and equitable society.
- **Legal Compliance:** Many countries have enacted laws and regulations to prevent discrimination in various aspects of life. Fairness in AI systems can help organizations avoid legal repercussions and maintain a positive reputation.
- **Customer Trust:** Fair and unbiased AI systems can help build trust with customers and stakeholders as they demonstrate a commitment to ethical practices and social responsibility.

Consequences of Biased AI Systems

Ignoring the importance of fairness in AI decision-making can lead to severe consequences for individuals and organizations. Biased AI systems can:

- **Reinforce Stereotypes:** AI systems relying on biased data or algorithms can perpetuate harmful stereotypes, further marginalizing disadvantaged groups.
- **Limit Opportunities:** Unfair AI systems can restrict access to essential services, such as employment, education, and healthcare, for certain demographics.

- **Damage Reputation:** Organizations that employ biased AI systems may face public backlash, leading to a loss of trust and potential boycotts.
- **Legal Repercussions:** Companies that fail to ensure fairness in their AI systems may face legal penalties for discrimination, resulting in financial losses and damage to their reputation.

In conclusion, understanding the importance of fairness in AI decision-making is crucial for managers navigating the complex world of AI integration. By prioritizing fairness and working to eliminate biases in AI systems, managers can ensure that their organizations remain socially responsible, legally compliant, and trusted by customers and stakeholders.

Promoting Transparency and Ensuring Accountability in AI Systems and Processes

In today's rapidly evolving technological landscape, artificial intelligence (AI) has become integral to various industries, transforming how businesses operate and make decisions. As AI continues to permeate our daily lives, managers must understand the importance of promoting transparency and ensuring accountability in AI systems and processes. This section will delve into the concepts of transparency and accountability, their significance in AI, and practical steps managers can take to ensure that AI systems are transparent, accountable, and easily understandable.

Transparency in AI refers to the ability to understand and interpret the inner workings of an AI system, including its decision-making processes, algorithms, and data inputs. A transparent AI system allows users, stakeholders, and regulators to gain insights into how the system operates, the rationale behind its decisions, and the potential biases that may be present. On the other hand, accountability in AI systems refers to the ability to trace and explain the decision-making processes of AI algorithms and hold individuals and organizations responsible for the outcomes of these decisions.

Promoting transparency and ensuring accountability in AI systems and processes are essential for several reasons. Both foster trust between AI systems and their users, promote ethical decision-making and help organizations comply with regulations. Understanding the inner workings of an AI system allows managers to identify areas for improvement, leading to more accurate and efficient AI-driven processes.

Managers can take several practical steps to ensure transparency and accountability in their organization's AI systems. These include collaborating with AI developers, implementing explainable AI, documenting AI processes, conducting regular audits, and educating and training employees. Managers should also establish clear roles and responsibilities, implement robust documentation practices, conduct regular audits and reviews, and foster a culture of accountability within their organization.

Failing to promote transparency and ensure accountability in AI systems can have significant consequences for organizations, including loss of trust, legal and financial consequences, and ethical concerns. Therefore, it is critical to responsible AI management. By understanding the importance of transparency and accountability and taking practical steps, managers can build trust, ensure ethical decision-making, comply with regulations, and continuously improve their AI systems. As AI advances, transparency and accountability will remain vital to ethical and responsible AI management.

Real-World Examples and Case Studies of Ethical AI Management

This section will delve into real-world examples and case studies that demonstrate ethical AI management in action. These examples will provide valuable insights into how organizations can successfully implement AI systems while adhering to fairness, transparency, and accountability principles.

Google's AI Ethics Council

In 2019, Google established an AI Ethics Council to guide on ethical issues related to AI and other emerging technologies. The council, composed of experts from various fields, was tasked with ensuring that Google's AI projects align with the company's AI principles, which include being socially beneficial, avoiding unfair bias, and promoting transparency. Although the initial council faced some controversies and was eventually disbanded, Google's commitment to ethical AI management remains strong as they continue to seek external input and refine their approach to AI ethics.

IBM's AI Fairness 360 Toolkit

IBM has developed an open-source toolkit called AI Fairness 360, which provides a comprehensive set of metrics and algorithms to help organizations detect and mitigate bias in AI systems. The toolkit is designed to promote fairness in AI decision-making by enabling developers and data scientists to assess and improve their AI models throughout the development process. By making this toolkit available to the broader AI community, IBM demonstrates its commitment to fostering ethical AI management practices across the industry.

The Partnership on AI

The Partnership on AI is a collaborative initiative involving major tech companies, including Amazon, Apple, Google, Facebook, and Microsoft, as well as non-profit organizations and academic institutions. The partnership aims to develop best practices for AI ethics and promote transparency, fairness, and accountability in AI systems. Through research, public dialogue, and collaboration, the Partnership on AI seeks to address the global challenges posed by AI and ensure that AI technologies benefit all of humanity.

The European Union's AI Ethics Guidelines

In 2019, the European Union published AI ethics guidelines outlining key requirements for trustworthy AI systems. These guidelines emphasize the importance of human oversight, transparency, fairness, and accountability in AI development and deployment. By providing a clear framework for ethical AI management, the European Union aims to promote responsible AI innovation and ensure that AI technologies respect fundamental human rights and values.

The Case of Microsoft's Tay AI Chatbot

In 2016, Microsoft launched an AI chatbot named Tay, designed to learn from and engage with users on social media platforms. However, within hours of its release, Tay began to post offensive and inappropriate content, as it learned from the negative input it received from users. Microsoft quickly took Tay offline and apologized for the incident. This case study highlights the importance of ethical AI management, as it demonstrates the potential consequences of failing to consider AI systems' potential risks and biases.

In conclusion, these real-world examples and case studies illustrate the growing importance of ethical AI management in today's rapidly evolving technological landscape. By prioritizing fairness, transparency, and accountability, organizations can harness the power of AI while minimizing potential risks and ensuring that AI technologies serve the greater good. As AI continues to advance, managers must stay informed about ethical AI practices and actively work to promote responsible AI innovation within their organizations.

The Future of AI Ethics and Responsible Management

As we reach the end of our exploration into AI ethics and responsible management, it is crucial to reflect on the importance of these concepts in shaping the future of artificial intelligence. The rapid advancement of AI technologies has the potential to revolutionize various industries, streamline processes, and improve decision-making. However, without a strong ethical foundation and responsible management practices, these innovations may lead to unintended consequences, exacerbating existing inequalities and creating new ethical dilemmas.

The future of AI ethics and responsible management lies in managers, developers, policymakers, and other stakeholders, who must work together to ensure that AI systems are designed and implemented with fairness, transparency, and accountability at their core. By prioritizing these principles, organizations can harness the power of AI to drive positive change while minimizing the risks associated with its deployment.

One of the key challenges in achieving this goal is the need for continuous learning and adaptation. As AI technologies evolve, so must our understanding of their ethical implications and the best practices for managing them responsibly. This requires a commitment to ongoing education, collaboration, and dialogue among all stakeholders and the development of new tools and frameworks to guide ethical decision-making.

Moreover, the future of AI ethics and responsible management will depend on cultivating a diverse and inclusive workforce. By fostering a culture of diversity and inclusion, organizations can ensure that a wide range of perspectives and experiences are represented in the development and management of AI systems. This can help to identify and address potential biases, promote fairness, and enhance the overall effectiveness of AI technologies.

In addition to these efforts, the future of AI ethics and responsible management will be shaped by the emergence of new regulations and industry standards. Policymakers and industry leaders must work together to develop comprehensive guidelines that balance promoting innovation and protecting the rights and interests of individuals and communities affected by AI technologies. By establishing clear expectations and accountability mechanisms, these regulations can ensure that AI is used responsibly and ethically across all sectors.

Finally, the growing public awareness and engagement with AI-related issues will influence the future of AI ethics and responsible management. As more people become aware of AI's potential benefits and risks, they will play a critical role in holding organizations accountable for their actions and advocating for ethical AI practices. This increased public scrutiny will motivate organizations to prioritize ethical considerations in their AI strategies and decision-making processes.

In conclusion, AI ethics and responsible management future are promising and challenging. By embracing the principles of fairness, transparency, and accountability and fostering a culture of continuous learning, diversity, and public engagement, we can ensure that AI technologies are harnessed for the greater good. As managers, developers, policymakers, and citizens, we all have a role in shaping this future and creating a world where AI is a force for positive change rather than a source of harm or inequality.

Chapter Summary

- AI ethics and responsible management are crucial for ensuring fairness, transparency, and accountability in AI systems, which are increasingly integrated into various management and decision-making aspects.
- Fairness in AI decision-making involves treating all individuals and groups equitably, preventing biased algorithms and data sets from leading to discriminatory outcomes.

- Transparency in AI systems and processes is essential for building trust, ensuring ethical decision-making, maintaining compliance with regulations, and enabling continuous improvement.
- Accountability in AI implementation and management involves tracing and explaining AI decision-making processes and holding individuals and organizations responsible for the outcomes.
- Managers can promote ethical AI management by collaborating with developers, implementing explainable AI, documenting AI processes, conducting regular audits, and fostering a culture of accountability.
- Real-world examples and case studies, such as Google's AI Ethics Council and IBM's AI Fairness 360 Toolkit, demonstrate the importance of ethical AI management in practice.
- The future of AI ethics and responsible management depends on continuous learning, adaptation, diverse and inclusive workforces, new regulations and industry standards, and increased public awareness and engagement.
- By embracing the principles of fairness, transparency, and accountability and fostering a culture of continuous learning, diversity, and public engagement, AI technologies can be harnessed for the greater good and serve as a force for positive change.

7

BUILDING AN AI-READY WORKFORCE: TALENT ACQUISITION, RETENTION, AND TRAINING

A futuristic AI training center with neon blue lights, holographic screens, and robots learning tasks.

A rtificial intelligence (AI) has emerged as a game-changing force in today's rapidly evolving business land-scape, revolutionizing how organizations operate and compete. As AI continues to permeate various industries, managers must stay ahead of the curve by understanding the implications of this transformative technology and preparing their workforce to harness its full potential. This chapter provides a comprehensive guide for managers seeking to build an AI-ready workforce, focusing on talent acquisition, retention, and training strategies.

The AI revolution is not a distant reality; it is happening now. From automating mundane tasks to making data-driven decisions, AI is transforming how businesses function and creating new opportunities for growth and innovation. As a manager, it is crucial to recognize the impact of AI on your organization and take proactive steps to adapt to this new paradigm.

Building an AI-ready workforce is more than hiring a few data scientists or software engineers. It involves creating a culture that embraces AI, fostering collaboration between technical and non-technical teams, and investing in continuously developing your employees' skills. By doing so, you will ensure that your organization remains competitive in the age of AI and empower your employees to thrive in this dynamic environment.

The following sections will delve deeper into the key aspects of building an AI-ready workforce, including identifying and attracting AI-proficient candidates, implementing effective retention strategies, and cultivating AI expertise within your organization. Additionally, we will discuss the role of managers in fostering an AI-driven culture and embracing the future of AI in workforce management.

As you embark on this journey, remember that the AI revolution presents an exciting opportunity for managers to redefine their roles and drive meaningful change within their organizations. By equipping your workforce with the right skills and mindset, you can unlock the true potential of AI and pave the way for a more efficient, innovative, and successful future.

Talent Acquisition: Identifying and Attracting AI-Proficient Candidates

The demand for AI-proficient candidates is skyrocketing in today's rapidly evolving technological landscape. As a manager, it is crucial to understand the importance of identifying and attracting top talent in artificial intelligence. This section will delve into the key aspects of talent acquisition, focusing on the strategies and techniques to help you build an AI-ready workforce.

The first step in acquiring AI-proficient talent recognizes the skills and qualifications essential for success in this field. Some of the most sought-after skills include:

- **Programming languages:** Proficiency in languages such as Python, R, and Java is crucial for AI development and implementation.
- **Machine learning and deep learning:** A strong foundation in these areas is vital for creating and refining AI algorithms.
- **Data analytics and visualization:** The ability to analyze and interpret large datasets is essential for AI-driven decision-making.
- **Problem-solving and critical thinking:** AI professionals must be able to think creatively and strategically to develop innovative solutions.
- **Communication and collaboration:** AI projects often involve cross-functional teams, making strong interpersonal skills necessary.

Once you clearly understand the skills and qualifications required for AI proficiency, the next step is to source potential candidates. Some effective strategies for finding top AI talent include:

- **Networking:** Attend industry conferences, workshops, and meetups to connect with AI professionals and expand your network.
- **Social media:** Use platforms like LinkedIn and Twitter to identify and engage with AI experts and enthusiasts.
- **Online communities:** Participate in AI-focused forums, discussion boards, and blogs to discover potential candidates and learn about their expertise.
- **Educational institutions:** Partner with universities and research institutions to tap into a pool of fresh talent and gain access to cutting-edge AI research.
- **Recruitment agencies:** Collaborate with specialized recruitment firms that focus on AI and technology to streamline your talent acquisition process.

You must differentiate your organization from the rest in a competitive job market. To attract top AI talent, consider the following strategies:

- **Showcase your commitment to AI:** Highlight your organization's dedication to AI innovation through case studies, whitepapers, and thought leadership content.
- **Offer competitive compensation and benefits:** Ensure that your compensation packages are on par with industry standards and offer unique benefits that cater to the needs of AI professionals.
- **Provide growth and development opportunities:** Demonstrate your commitment to employee growth by offering ongoing training, mentorship, and opportunities for advancement within the AI field.

- **Foster a culture of innovation:** Encourage creativity, experimentation, and collaboration by creating an environment where AI professionals can thrive.
- **Highlight your organization's social impact:** Showcase how your AI initiatives contribute to the greater good, as many AI professionals are driven by a desire to impact society positively.

By understanding the skills and qualifications of AI-proficient candidates, sourcing talent from the right channels, and creating a compelling employer brand, you can successfully build an AI-ready workforce that will drive your organization forward in the age of artificial intelligence.

Retention Strategies: Keeping Your AI-Savvy Workforce Engaged and Loyal

As the AI revolution continues to reshape the business landscape, managers must focus on acquiring top talent and retaining their AI-proficient workforce. In this section, we will explore various retention strategies to help managers keep their AI-savvy employees engaged, motivated, and loyal.

Recognizing and Rewarding AI Expertise

One of the most effective ways to retain AI-proficient employees is by recognizing and rewarding their expertise. Managers should establish a system that acknowledges the contributions of AI experts to the organization's success. This can be done through various means, such as offering promotions, bonuses, or other incentives that reflect the value of their skills and knowledge. By doing so, managers can demonstrate their appreciation for their AI-savvy workforce's hard work and dedication, fostering a sense of loyalty and commitment to the organization.

Providing Opportunities for Growth and Advancement

AI-proficient employees are often driven to learn and grow in their field. Managers can support this by providing ample opportunities for professional development and career advancement. This may include offering training programs, workshops, or conferences that allow employees to expand their AI knowledge and skills. Additionally, managers should encourage internal mobility, enabling AI experts to explore different organizational roles and responsibilities. By promoting a culture of continuous learning and growth, managers can ensure that their AI-savvy workforce remains engaged and motivated to excel in their careers.

Fostering a Collaborative and Supportive Work Environment

A supportive and collaborative work environment is crucial for retaining AI-proficient employees. Managers should encourage open communication and knowledge sharing among team members, promoting a culture of collaboration and innovation. This can be achieved by organizing regular team meetings, brainstorming sessions, or informal gatherings where employees can discuss their ideas, challenges, and successes. Moreover, managers should provide the necessary resources and tools that enable AI experts to work efficiently and effectively. By fostering a positive work environment, managers can help their AI-savvy workforce feel valued and supported, increasing job satisfaction and loyalty.

Ensuring Work-Life Balance

Work-life balance is essential to employee retention, particularly for those working in demanding fields such as AI. Managers should be mindful of their AI-proficient employees' workload and stress levels, ensuring they have the necessary support and resources to maintain a healthy work-life balance. This may include offering flexible work arrangements, such as remote work or flexible hours, and promoting a culture that values personal well-being and self-care. By prioritizing work-life balance, managers can help their AI-savvy workforce maintain a sustainable and fulfilling career within the organization.

In conclusion, retaining an AI-proficient workforce requires a multifaceted approach that addresses these talented individuals' unique needs and aspirations. By recognizing and rewarding their expertise, providing opportunities for growth and advancement, fostering a collaborative and supportive work environment, and ensuring work-life balance, managers can keep their AI-savvy employees engaged, motivated, and loyal to the organization. Embracing these retention strategies will benefit the employees and contribute to the organization's overall success and competitiveness in the rapidly evolving world of AI.

Training and Development: Cultivating AI Expertise Within Your Organization

As the world continues to embrace the transformative power of artificial intelligence (AI), organizations must invest in the training and development of their workforce. This ensures that employees are equipped with the necessary skills to navigate the AI landscape and fosters a culture of continuous learning and innovation. This section will delve into the importance of cultivating AI expertise within your organization and explore various strategies to achieve this goal.

The rapid advancements in AI technology have led to a growing demand for professionals with AI proficiency. By investing in the training and development of your workforce, you can ensure that your organization remains competitive in the ever-evolving AI landscape. Moreover, a well-trained workforce can increase productivity, improve decision-making, and enhance customer experiences.

Before embarking on the journey of AI training and development, it is essential to identify your organization's specific needs.

This can be achieved by conducting a thorough skills gap analysis, which involves assessing the current AI capabilities of your workforce and comparing them with the desired level of expertise. This will help you pinpoint the areas where training is most needed and design targeted programs to address these gaps.

Once you have identified the AI training needs of your organization, the next step is to implement effective training programs. These can take various forms, such as workshops, seminars, online courses, and hands-on projects. It is important to choose the right mix of training methods that cater to your employees' diverse learning preferences and provide ample opportunities to apply their newly acquired skills in real-world scenarios.

In the fast-paced world of AI, fostering a culture of continuous learning within your organization is essential. This can be achieved by encouraging employees to stay updated on the latest AI trends and developments, providing access to relevant resources, and offering incentives for acquiring new skills. By promoting a growth mindset, you can ensure that your workforce remains agile and adaptable in the face of technological change.

To gauge the effectiveness of your AI training and development initiatives, it is crucial to establish key performance indicators (KPIs) and track them over time. These may include metrics such as employee engagement, skill acquisition, and the application of AI expertise in daily tasks. By regularly monitoring these KPIs, you can make data-driven decisions to refine your training programs and maximize their impact on your organization.

In conclusion, cultivating AI expertise within your organization is vital to building an AI-ready workforce. By identifying training needs, implementing targeted programs, fostering a culture of continuous learning, and measuring the impact of your initiatives, you can ensure that your employees are well-equipped to navigate the AI revolution and contribute to the success of your organization. As a manager, your role in this process is pivotal as you set the tone for a culture that embraces AI and encourages growth and innovation.

The Role of Managers in Fostering an AI-Driven Culture

As the world continues to embrace the transformative power of artificial intelligence (AI), managers must understand their role in fostering an AI-driven culture within their organizations. This section will delve into managers' responsibilities in cultivating an environment that encourages the adoption of AI technologies, promotes collaboration between AI and human talent, and supports continuous learning and innovation.

Managers play a pivotal role in driving the adoption of AI within their organizations. They must act as advocates for AI, educating their teams on the benefits and potential applications of these technologies. By clearly understanding AI's capabilities and limitations, managers can help dispel misconceptions and alleviate any fears or concerns that employees may have. This, in turn, will create a more receptive environment for AI integration and experimentation.

A successful AI-driven culture fosters collaboration between human and AI talent. Managers must work to break down silos and promote cross-functional teamwork, ensuring that employees with diverse skill sets and expertise can solve complex problems using AI. By encouraging open communication and knowledge sharing, managers can help their teams leverage the full potential of AI technologies and drive innovation.

As AI evolves rapidly, managers must prioritize continuous learning and professional development for their teams. This includes providing access to relevant training programs, workshops, and resources that can help employees stay up-to-date with AI advancements. Managers should also encourage their teams to experiment with new AI tools and techniques, fostering a culture of curiosity and innovation.

To further incentivize the adoption of AI, managers should recognize and reward employees who demonstrate exceptional AI-driven performance. This can include celebrating team successes, acknowledging individual contributions, and providing opportunities for career advancement within the organization. By recognizing and rewarding AI-driven success, managers can help reinforce the value of AI and motivate their teams to continue pushing the boundaries of what is possible with these technologies.

Finally, managers must lead by example, embracing AI and fostering an AI-driven culture. This means staying informed about the latest AI trends and developments, actively participating in AI-related initiatives, and demonstrating a willingness to adapt and evolve alongside these technologies. By embodying the principles of an AI-driven culture, managers can inspire their teams to follow suit and fully embrace the potential of AI in their work.

In conclusion, managers are critical in fostering an AI-driven culture within their organizations. By championing AI adoption, encouraging collaboration, supporting continuous learning, recognizing and rewarding AI-driven success, and leading by example, managers can help their organizations harness the power of AI and thrive in the rapidly evolving landscape of the digital age.

Embracing the Future of AI in Workforce Management

As we reach the end of our journey through the fascinating world of artificial intelligence and its impact on workforce management, it is essential to take a step back and reflect on the transformative power of this technology. The AI revolution is not a distant dream; it is happening now, and managers must be prepared to adapt and thrive in this new landscape. By focusing on talent acquisition, retention, and training, organizations can build an AI-ready workforce that will drive innovation and success in the future.

In this rapidly evolving environment, managers play a crucial role in fostering an AI-driven culture. They must be open to change, willing to learn, and proactive in seeking out opportunities to leverage AI for the betterment of their teams and organizations. This includes staying informed about the latest AI advancements, understanding the ethical implications of AI deployment, and promoting a culture of collaboration and continuous learning.

Embracing the future of AI in workforce management is challenging. Managers may face resistance from employees who fear job displacement or struggle to adapt to new technologies. However, by addressing these concerns head-on and demonstrating the value of AI in enhancing human capabilities, managers can help their teams see the potential benefits of this technology.

Moreover, it is essential to remember that AI is not a one-size-fits-all solution. Each organization will have unique needs and goals, and managers must be strategic in determining how AI can best support their specific objectives. This may involve experimenting with different AI applications, collaborating with AI experts, and continuously refining their approach based on feedback and results.

Ultimately, the future of AI in workforce management is full of promise and potential. By embracing this technology and investing in developing an AI-ready workforce, managers can position their organizations for long-term success in the age of artificial intelligence. The key is to approach this transformation with an open mind, a willingness to learn, and a commitment to empowering employees to harness the power of AI for the betterment of all.

As we conclude this chapter, let us remember that the AI revolution is not a threat to be feared but an opportunity to be seized. By understanding the fundamentals of AI, adopting effective talent acquisition, retention, and training strategies, and fostering an AI-driven culture, managers can lead their organizations into a future where humans and machines work together in harmony, unlocking new levels of productivity, innovation, and success.

Chapter Summary

- The AI revolution is transforming the business landscape, making it crucial for managers to understand its implications and prepare their workforce to harness its full potential.

- Building an AI-ready workforce involves creating a culture that embraces AI, fostering collaboration between technical and non-technical teams, and investing in continuously developing employees' skills.
- Talent acquisition for AI-proficient candidates requires recognizing essential skills, sourcing talent from the right channels, and creating a compelling employer brand.
- Retaining an AI-savvy workforce involves recognizing and rewarding expertise, providing opportunities for growth and advancement, fostering a collaborative and supportive work environment, and ensuring work-life balance.
- Cultivating AI expertise within an organization is vital for staying competitive. It involves identifying training needs, implementing targeted programs, fostering a culture of continuous learning, and measuring the impact of training initiatives.
- Managers play a critical role in fostering an AI-driven culture by championing AI adoption, encouraging collaboration, supporting continuous learning, recognizing and rewarding AI-driven success, and leading by example.
- Embracing the future of AI in workforce management involves staying informed about the latest AI advancements, understanding the ethical implications of AI deployment, and promoting a culture of collaboration and continuous learning.
- The future of AI in workforce management is full of promise and potential, and by embracing this technology and investing in the development of an AI-ready workforce, managers can position their organizations for long-term success in the age of artificial intelligence.

8

AI PROJECT MANAGEMENT: BEST PRACTICES AND STRATEGIES FOR SUCCESS

A futuristic AI robot managing multiple digital project boards in a high-tech office environment, with a color scheme of blues and silvers, under soft white lighting.

A rtificial intelligence (AI) has surfaced as a revolutionary force for businesses in diverse industries in today's fast-paced tech world. As a manager, staying at the forefront and utilizing AI's power to simplify processes, improve decision-making, and propel innovation within your organization is essential. This chapter offers a thorough guide to understanding the fundamentals of AI project management, equipping you with the tools and strategies to incorporate AI into your organization's project management practices successfully.

Integrating AI in project management is not merely a trend but a necessity for organizations seeking to maintain a competitive edge in the digital age. AI-powered tools and technologies have the potential to revolutionize the way projects are planned, executed, and monitored, resulting in increased efficiency, reduced costs, and improved outcomes. By embracing AI, managers can unlock new opportunities for growth and success while addressing the challenges and complexities of managing AI-driven projects.

This chapter will explore the various aspects of AI project management, beginning with identifying the right AI solutions for your organization. This will involve understanding your business's specific needs and goals and evaluating the available AI technologies and platforms that can help you achieve those objectives. Next, we will delve into building a strong AI project team, which is essential for ensuring the successful implementation and adoption of AI within your organization.

Once you have assembled your AI project team, we will guide you through the step-by-step process of implementing AI projects, from initial planning and development to deployment and ongoing maintenance. Along the way, we will discuss the potential challenges and risks associated with AI project management and provide practical strategies for overcoming and mitigating these obstacles.

Finally, we will conclude with a discussion on ensuring long-term success with AI in project management, emphasizing the importance of continuous learning, adaptation, and improvement as your organization navigates the ever-changing landscape of AI technology.

By the end of this chapter, you will have a solid understanding of the fundamentals of AI project management and be well-equipped to lead your organization toward a future where AI is integral to driving success and innovation. So, let us embark on this exciting journey together and discover the transformative potential of AI in project management.

Identifying the Right AI Solutions for Your Organization

Artificial intelligence (AI) has emerged as a game-changer for businesses across various industries in today's rapidly evolving technological landscape. As a manager, it is crucial to recognize the potential of AI in enhancing your organization's efficiency, productivity, and overall competitiveness. However, with many AI solutions in the market, identifying the right one for your organization can take time and effort. This section will explore the key factors to consider when selecting the most suitable AI solution for your organization.

Define Your Objectives and Goals

Before diving into the world of AI, it is essential to have a clear understanding of your organization's objectives and goals. What specific problems are you trying to solve? How can AI help you achieve your desired outcomes? By answering these questions, you can establish a solid foundation for your AI project and ensure that the chosen solution aligns with your organization's strategic vision.

Assess Your Organization's AI Readiness

Before implementing AI solutions, evaluating your organization's readiness for AI adoption is crucial. This includes assessing your existing infrastructure, data quality, and the skill sets of your team members. Identifying gaps or areas that require improvement can better prepare your organization for a smooth and successful AI integration.

Research and Evaluate AI Solutions

Once you clearly understand your objectives and your organization's AI readiness, it is time to explore the various AI solutions available in the market. Conduct thorough research to identify the most promising solutions catering to your needs. Consider factors such as ease of integration, scalability, and the solution's track record in similar industries. Additionally, evaluating the solution's cost-effectiveness is essential, ensuring that it provides a good return on investment.

Consult with AI Experts

As AI technology advances, staying updated on the latest trends and best practices can be challenging. Therefore, consulting with AI experts who can provide valuable insights and guidance in selecting the most suitable AI solution for your organization is highly recommended. These experts can also help you navigate the complexities of AI implementation and ensure that your project is set up for success.

Conduct a Pilot Project

Before fully committing to an AI solution, conducting a pilot project to test its effectiveness and compatibility with your organization's processes is advisable. This will allow you to identify potential issues or challenges and make necessary adjustments before scaling up the implementation. A successful pilot project can also serve as a powerful, persuasive tool, showcasing the benefits of AI adoption to stakeholders and team members.

In conclusion, identifying the right AI solution for your organization is a critical step in ensuring the success of your AI project. By defining your objectives, assessing your organization's AI readiness, researching and evaluating AI solutions, consulting with experts, and conducting a pilot project, you can confidently select the most suitable AI solution to drive your organization toward greater efficiency and success.

Building a Strong AI Project Team

In the rapidly evolving world of artificial intelligence, having a strong AI project team is crucial for successfully implementing and integrating AI solutions within your organization. A well-rounded team possesses the technical expertise to navigate the complexities of AI and the ability to communicate effectively, collaborate seamlessly, and adapt to the ever-changing landscape of AI technology. In this section, we will explore the key roles and responsibilities of an AI project team and strategies for assembling a team that is equipped to tackle the unique challenges of AI project management.

Key Roles and Responsibilities in an AI Project Team

Project Manager: The project manager is responsible for overseeing the entire AI project, ensuring that it stays on track, within budget, and meets the organization's objectives. They must possess strong leadership, communication, and organizational skills and a solid understanding of AI technology and its potential impact on the business.

- **AI Architect:** The AI architect is responsible for designing the overall structure and framework of the AI solution, ensuring that it aligns with the organization's goals and requirements. They must have a deep understanding of AI algorithms, data structures, and programming languages and the ability to translate complex technical concepts into actionable plans.

- **Data Scientist:** The data scientist plays a crucial role in the development and optimization of AI models, using their expertise in statistics, machine learning, and data analysis to extract valuable insights from large datasets. They must be skilled in data preprocessing, feature engineering, and model evaluation and possess strong problem-solving and critical thinking abilities.

- **AI Developer:** The AI developer is responsible for implementing the AI solution and writing the code and algorithms necessary to bring the AI architect's vision to life. They must be proficient in various programming languages, such as Python or Java, and have experience working with AI frameworks and libraries, such as TensorFlow or PyTorch.

- **AI Ethicist:** The AI ethicist ensures that the AI solution adheres to ethical guidelines and principles, addressing potential biases and unintended consequences that may arise during development and deployment. They must have a strong understanding of ethical considerations in AI and the ability to communicate these concerns effectively to the rest of the team.

Strategies for Assembling a Strong AI Project Team

Assess Your Organization's Needs: Before assembling your AI project team, you must clearly understand your organization's goals and objectives and the specific AI solutions that will best address these needs. This will help you identify the skills and expertise required for your team and guide your recruitment efforts.

- **Prioritize Diversity and Inclusivity:** A diverse and inclusive AI project team is more likely to generate innovative ideas and solutions and avoid potential biases in AI development. Seek out team members with diverse backgrounds, experiences, and perspectives, and foster an inclusive environment where all voices are valued and respected.

- **Invest in Training and Development:** As AI technology evolves, your team members must stay up-to-date with the latest advancements and best practices. Encourage ongoing learning and professional development, and allow team members to expand their skills and knowledge in AI-related fields.

- **Foster a Collaborative Culture:** Effective collaboration is essential for the success of any AI project, as it allows team members to share ideas, knowledge, and expertise. Encourage open communication and teamwork, and provide the necessary tools and resources to facilitate collaboration, such as project management software and shared workspaces.

- **Emphasize Adaptability and Resilience:** AI projects can be unpredictable, with unexpected challenges and setbacks often arising throughout development. Look for team members who demonstrate adaptability and resilience and can navigate these challenges with a positive attitude and a willingness to learn from their experiences.

In conclusion, building a strong AI project team is critical to successful AI project management. By assembling a diverse and skilled team, investing in ongoing training and development, and fostering a collaborative and adaptable culture, your organization will be well-positioned to harness the power of AI and drive meaningful change within your industry.

Implementing AI Projects: A Step-by-Step Guide

As the world of technology continues to evolve rapidly, integrating artificial intelligence (AI) into project management has become increasingly essential for organizations seeking to maintain a competitive edge. Implementing AI projects, however, can be a complex and daunting task for managers who may need to become more familiar with the intricacies of this cutting-edge technology. To help navigate this process, we have compiled a step-by-step guide that outlines the key stages of implementing AI projects, ensuring a smooth and successful integration.

Define the project scope and objectives: Before diving into the implementation process, it is crucial to understand the project's scope and objectives clearly. This involves identifying the specific AI solutions that will be utilized and the desired outcomes and benefits for the organization. Establishing these parameters early on will provide a solid foundation for the project and help to maintain focus throughout its duration.

Develop a detailed project plan: With the project scope and objectives in place, the next step is to create a comprehensive project plan. This should include a timeline for each phase of the project and the resources and personnel required to execute it. Additionally, the plan should outline the key milestones and deliverables, ensuring that all stakeholders are aligned and working towards the same goals.

Assemble a skilled project team: The success of any AI project hinges on the expertise and capabilities of the team responsible for its implementation. As such, assembling a diverse group of individuals with the necessary skills and experience in AI, data science, and project management is essential. This team should collaborate effectively, adapt to new challenges, and drive the project forward.

Establish a strong communication plan: Effective communication is critical to any successful project, particularly regarding AI implementation. Establishing a robust communication plan will ensure that all team members are informed of project updates, progress, and any potential issues. This plan should include regular meetings, status reports, and a clear escalation process for addressing concerns or roadblocks.

Execute the project plan: With a solid project plan and team in place, it's time to begin executing the various tasks and activities outlined in the plan. This will involve developing the AI algorithms, training the models, and integrating the AI solutions into the organization's existing systems and processes. Throughout this phase, it is essential to monitor progress closely and make any necessary adjustments to the plan as needed.

Monitor and evaluate project performance: As the AI project progresses, it is crucial to assess its performance against the established objectives and milestones continually. This will help identify any areas where improvements can be made and ensure that the project remains on track and within budget. Regular evaluations will also provide valuable insights into the effectiveness of the AI solutions and their impact on the organization's overall performance.

Review and refine the AI solutions: Once the AI project has been successfully implemented, it is important to review and refine the solutions as needed. This may involve fine-tuning the algorithms, updating the training data, or adjusting the integration process. By continually refining AI solutions, organizations can ensure that they remain effective and relevant in the ever-evolving world of technology.

In conclusion, implementing AI projects can be a complex and challenging endeavor. Still, with the right approach and a clear step-by-step guide, managers can successfully navigate this process and unlock the full potential of AI in project management. By following these best practices and strategies, organizations can enhance their project management capabilities and drive innovation and growth in today's competitive business landscape.

Overcoming Challenges and Mitigating Risks in AI Project Management

As organizations increasingly embrace AI in project management, it is crucial to recognize and address the potential challenges and risks that may arise during implementation. By proactively identifying these obstacles and developing strategies to mitigate them, managers can ensure the successful integration of AI solutions and maximize their benefits. This section will explore some common challenges and risks associated with AI project management and provide practical advice on overcoming them.

- **Data Quality and Availability:** AI systems rely heavily on data to learn and make decisions. Ensuring the quality and availability of data is essential for the success of any AI project. To overcome this challenge, managers should establish a robust data governance framework that includes data validation, cleansing, and enrichment processes. Additionally, they should collaborate with data providers and stakeholders to ensure data is accurate, complete, and up-to-date.
- **Ethical and Legal Considerations:** AI projects can raise ethical and legal concerns, such as data privacy, security, and bias. Managers must be aware of these issues and develop strategies to address them. This may involve conducting thorough risk assessments, implementing privacy-by-design principles, and establishing ethical guidelines for AI usage. Furthermore, managers should stay informed about relevant laws and regulations and ensure their AI projects comply.
- **Resistance to Change:** The introduction of AI solutions can be met with resistance from employees who may fear job displacement or struggle to adapt to new technologies. To overcome this challenge, managers should communicate the benefits of AI clearly and

transparently, emphasizing how it can enhance productivity and decision-making rather than replace human workers. Additionally, they should provide training and support to help employees develop the necessary skills to work effectively with AI systems.

- **Integration with Existing Systems:** Integrating AI solutions with existing systems and processes can be complex and time-consuming. To mitigate this risk, managers should thoroughly assess their current systems and identify potential compatibility issues. They should also collaborate with IT teams and vendors to develop integration plans that minimize disruptions and ensure seamless transitions.
- **Unrealistic Expectations:** AI projects can sometimes be hindered by unrealistic expectations regarding their capabilities and outcomes. To avoid disappointment and ensure project success, managers should set achievable goals and manage stakeholder expectations accordingly. This may involve educating stakeholders about the limitations of AI and establishing realistic timelines for project milestones.

In conclusion, overcoming challenges and mitigating risks in AI project management requires a proactive approach, effective communication, and a commitment to continuous improvement. By addressing these issues head-on and implementing best practices, managers can ensure the successful integration of AI solutions and drive long-term success in their organizations.

Ensuring Long-term Success with AI in Project Management

As we conclude this enlightening journey through AI project management, reflecting on the key takeaways and best practices discussed throughout this chapter is essential. Integrating artificial intelligence into project management is no longer a distant dream

but rather a present reality transforming how organizations operate. By embracing AI and leveraging its potential, managers can
unlock unprecedented efficiency, productivity, and innovation
levels.

To ensure long-term success with AI in project management, it
is crucial to keep the following principles in mind:

- **Stay informed and adaptable:** The landscape of AI is
  constantly evolving, with new technologies and
  applications emerging rapidly. As a manager, you are
  responsible for staying informed about the latest
  developments and being prepared to adapt your
  strategies accordingly. This will enable you to make
  informed decisions and maintain a competitive edge in
  the ever-changing world of AI.
- **Foster a culture of collaboration and learning:**
  Successfully implementing AI projects requires a strong
  team with diverse skill sets and expertise. Encourage
  collaboration and knowledge sharing among team
  members, and invest in continuous learning and
  development opportunities to ensure your team stays
  up-to-date with the latest AI trends and technologies.
- **Prioritize ethical considerations:** As AI increasingly
  integrates into project management, ethical concerns
  surrounding data privacy, security, and fairness must be
  addressed. Ensure that your organization adheres to
  ethical guidelines and best practices, and be transparent
  with stakeholders about how AI is being used and its
  potential implications.
- **Measure and track progress:** Establish clear goals and
  metrics for your AI projects and regularly monitor and
  evaluate their progress. This will enable you to identify
  areas for improvement, make data-driven decisions, and
  demonstrate the value of AI to stakeholders.

- **Embrace a growth mindset:** The successful integration of AI into project management requires a willingness to experiment, learn from mistakes, and iterate on your strategies. Cultivate a growth mindset within your team and organization, and view setbacks as opportunities for growth and learning.

In conclusion, implementing AI in project management hinges on strategic planning, effective team building, and a commitment to continuous learning and improvement. By keeping these principles in mind and staying informed about the latest developments in AI, managers can harness the power of artificial intelligence to drive their organizations towards new heights of success.

Chapter Summary

- AI has the potential to revolutionize project management by streamlining processes, enhancing decision-making, and driving innovation within organizations.
- Identifying the right AI solution involves defining objectives, assessing organizational readiness, researching and evaluating AI technologies, consulting with experts, and conducting pilot projects.
- Building a strong AI project team requires assembling a diverse group of individuals with the necessary skills and experience in AI, data science, and project management and fostering a collaborative and adaptable culture.
- Implementing AI projects involves defining project scope and objectives, developing a detailed project plan, assembling a skilled project team, establishing a strong communication plan, executing the project plan,

monitoring and evaluating project performance, and refining AI solutions as needed.

- Overcoming challenges and mitigating risks in AI project management requires addressing data quality and availability, ethical and legal considerations, resistance to change, integration with existing systems, and unrealistic expectations.
- Ensuring long-term success with AI in project management involves staying informed and adaptable, fostering a culture of collaboration and learning, prioritizing ethical considerations, measuring and tracking progress, and embracing a growth mindset.
- The successful integration of AI into project management requires strategic planning, effective team building, and a commitment to continuous learning and improvement.
- By harnessing the power of AI and following best practices, managers can drive their organizations toward greater efficiency, productivity, and innovation in the competitive business landscape.

9

MEASURING AI PERFORMANCE: KEY METRICS AND EVALUATION TECHNIQUES

A futuristic AI performance meter with neon blue indicators and digital readouts on a light background.

I n today's swiftly changing business environment, artificial intelligence (AI) has surfaced as a potent instrument that can propel innovation, simplify operations, and improve decision-making processes. As a manager, grasping the fundamentals of AI and its potential influence on your organization is vital to remain at the forefront and fully utilize this transformative technology. A crucial aspect of AI implementation that managers need to understand is the evaluation of AI performance. This chapter will explore the significance of measuring AI performance, the essential metrics and assessment techniques, and how to synchronize these metrics with your organization's objectives.

Evaluating AI performance is essential for several reasons. First and foremost, it allows managers to assess the effectiveness of AI systems and ensure that they deliver the desired results. By measuring performance, you can identify areas where the AI system may be underperforming or failing to meet expectations, enabling you to make informed decisions about investing in improvements or exploring alternative solutions.

Second, evaluating AI performance helps managers demonstrate AI investments' value to stakeholders, including senior management and investors. By showcasing the tangible benefits of AI systems, such as increased efficiency, cost savings, or improved customer satisfaction, you can build a strong case for continued investment in AI technologies and secure the necessary resources to drive your organization's AI initiatives forward.

Third, performance measurement is crucial in fostering a culture of continuous improvement within your organization. By regularly assessing AI performance and identifying areas for enhancement, you can encourage your team to strive for excellence and embrace a mindset of constant learning and growth. This, in turn, can lead to the development of more advanced and effective AI solutions that drive even greater value for your organization.

This chapter will explore the key metrics and evaluation techniques managers can use to measure AI performance, including accuracy, precision, recall, and F1 score. We will also discuss various evaluation methods, such as cross-validation, confusion matrix, and ROC curves, which can provide valuable insights into the performance of AI systems. Additionally, we will examine how to align AI performance metrics with your organization's goals and share real-world case studies demonstrating these measurement techniques' successful application.

By gaining a solid understanding of AI performance measurement, managers can play a pivotal role in ensuring the success of AI initiatives within their organizations. Armed with this knowledge, you will be better equipped to make data-driven decisions, optimize AI systems, and, ultimately, unlock the full potential of artificial intelligence to drive growth and innovation in your organization.

Understanding Key Metrics: Accuracy, Precision, Recall, and F1 Score

As a manager, it is crucial to have a firm grasp of the key metrics used to evaluate AI performance. These metrics provide a quantitative measure of how well an AI system performs, allowing you to make informed decisions about its deployment, improvement, and overall value to your organization. This section will delve into four essential metrics: accuracy, precision, recall, and F1 score.

Accuracy is the most straightforward metric for evaluating AI performance. It is the ratio of correct predictions the AI system makes to the total number of predictions. In other words, it tells you how often the AI system is right. While accuracy is a useful starting point, it may not always provide a complete picture of an AI system's performance, especially when dealing with imbalanced datasets. Other metrics like precision, recall and F1 score become more relevant in such cases.

Precision is the ratio of true positive predictions (correctly identified instances) to the sum of true positive and false positive predictions (instances incorrectly identified as positive). This metric is critical when the cost of false positives is high. For example, high precision in a fraud detection system means that the AI system is good at identifying actual fraud cases without raising too many false alarms.

Recall, also known as sensitivity or true positive rate, is the ratio of true positive predictions to the sum of true positive and false negative predictions (instances incorrectly identified as negative). Recall is a crucial metric when the cost of false negatives is high. For instance, in a medical diagnosis system, a high recall ensures that the AI system identifies as many patients with a particular condition as possible, minimizing the risk of missed diagnoses.

The **F1 score** is the harmonic mean of precision and recall, providing a single metric that balances both aspects of AI performance. It ranges from 0 to 1, with 1 being the best possible score. The F1 score is instrumental when comparing AI systems with different precision and recall values, as it helps you identify the system with the best trade-off between these two metrics.

In conclusion, understanding the key metrics of accuracy, precision, recall, and F1 score is essential for managers to evaluate AI performance effectively. By considering these metrics in the context of your organization's specific needs and goals, you can make informed decisions about AI deployment and improvement, ultimately driving success in your AI initiatives.

Evaluation Techniques: Cross-Validation, Confusion Matrix, and ROC Curves

As a manager, understanding the various evaluation techniques used to measure AI performance is crucial in making informed decisions about deploying and improving AI systems. This section will delve into three widely-used evaluation techniques: cross-validation, confusion matrix, and ROC curves. By the end of this section, you will have a solid grasp of these techniques and their significance in the context of AI performance measurement.

Cross-validation is a robust evaluation technique that helps ensure AI models' accuracy and reliability. It involves partitioning the available data into multiple subsets, training the AI model on a combination, and testing the model on the remaining subset. This process is repeated multiple times, with each subset being used for testing exactly once. The average performance across all iterations is then calculated to provide a more reliable estimate of the AI model's performance.

Cross-validation is particularly useful for managers because it helps identify potential overfitting issues in AI models. Overfitting occurs when a model performs exceptionally well on the training data but fails to generalize to new, unseen data. By using cross-validation, managers can ensure that their AI models are accurate and capable of making reliable predictions on new data.

A **confusion matrix** is a visual representation of an AI model's performance, providing a comprehensive view of the true positives, true negatives, false positives, and false negatives generated by the model. In simpler terms, it shows how well the model has classified the data into its respective categories.

For managers, the confusion matrix is an invaluable tool for understanding the strengths and weaknesses of their AI models. By analyzing the matrix, managers can identify areas where the model is performing well and where improvements are needed. This information can then guide further development and optimization of the AI system.

Receiver Operating Characteristic (ROC) curves are graphical representations that illustrate the performance of AI models at various classification thresholds. They plot the true positive rate (sensitivity) against the false positive rate (1-specificity) for different threshold values. The area under the ROC curve (AUC) is a single value that summarizes the model's performance across all thresholds.

ROC curves are particularly useful for managers because they clearly represent the trade-off between sensitivity and specificity. By analyzing the ROC curve, managers can determine the optimal threshold for their AI model, balancing the need for accurate predictions with the risk of generating false positives or negatives. This information can then be used to fine-tune the AI system and ensure that it meets the organization's performance goals.

In conclusion, cross-validation, confusion matrix, and ROC curves are essential evaluation techniques that managers should be familiar with to measure AI performance effectively. By understanding these techniques and their implications, managers can make informed decisions about deploying and improving AI systems, ultimately driving better results for their organizations.

AI Performance in Business Context: Aligning Metrics with Organizational Goals

In today's rapidly evolving business landscape, artificial intelligence (AI) has become an indispensable tool for managers seeking to drive innovation, efficiency, and growth. As AI systems continue to permeate various aspects of organizational operations, managers must understand how to measure their performance effectively. This section will delve into the importance of aligning AI performance metrics with organizational goals, ensuring that AI initiatives contribute to the business's overall success.

To begin, managers need to recognize that AI performance metrics should not be viewed in isolation. Instead, they must be considered within the broader context of the organization's strategic objectives. This alignment ensures that AI systems are designed and deployed to support the achievement of key business goals, such as increasing revenue, improving customer satisfaction, or enhancing operational efficiency.

One of the first steps in aligning AI performance metrics with organizational goals is to identify the specific objectives the AI system intends to support. For example, if the goal is to improve customer satisfaction, the AI system might be designed to analyze customer feedback and provide personalized recommendations for service improvements. In this case, the relevant performance metrics might include the accuracy and recall of the AI system's recommendations and the overall impact on customer satisfaction ratings.

Once the relevant objectives have been identified, managers should work closely with their AI development teams to establish clear, measurable performance targets. These targets should be directly linked to the organization's strategic goals and regularly reviewed and updated. By setting clear performance targets, managers can ensure that AI systems are held accountable for delivering tangible business results.

In addition to setting performance targets, managers should consider the potential trade-offs between AI performance metrics. For example, in some cases, optimizing for accuracy might come at the expense of recall or vice versa. Managers must carefully weigh these trade-offs to determine the optimal balance for their specific business context. This may involve conducting sensitivity analyses or scenario planning exercises to assess the potential impact of different performance metric combinations on the organization's overall goals.

Finally, managers need to foster a culture of continuous improvement in AI performance measurement. This includes regularly reviewing and refining performance metrics and encouraging open communication and collaboration between AI development teams and other stakeholders within the organization. By fostering a culture of continuous improvement, managers can ensure that AI systems consistently deliver value and contribute to achieving key business objectives.

In conclusion, aligning AI performance metrics with organizational goals is critical to ensuring AI success in a business context. Managers can effectively measure AI performance and drive meaningful business results by identifying relevant objectives, setting clear performance targets, considering trade-offs, and fostering a culture of continuous improvement. As AI continues to transform the way organizations operate, managers who embrace these principles will be well-positioned to harness the full potential of AI and secure a competitive advantage for their organizations.

Case Studies: Successful AI Performance Measurement in Real-World Scenarios

In this section, we will delve into three real-world case studies demonstrating the successful implementation of AI performance measurement. These examples will provide valuable insights into how managers can effectively evaluate AI systems and align them with organizational goals.

AI-Powered Customer Support Chatbot

A leading e-commerce company sought to improve its customer support services by implementing an AI-powered chatbot. The primary goal was to reduce response time and increase customer satisfaction. The company's management team identified key performance metrics, such as accuracy, precision, recall, and F1 score, to evaluate the chatbot's effectiveness.

The team could fine-tune the chatbot's algorithms and improve its performance by using cross-validation and confusion matrix techniques. As a result, the chatbot's accuracy increased by 20%, leading to a significant reduction in response time and a 15% increase in customer satisfaction ratings.

AI-Driven Fraud Detection System

A global financial institution aimed to enhance its fraud detection capabilities by implementing an AI-driven system. The primary objective was to minimize false positives and false negatives, ensuring that genuine transactions were not flagged as fraudulent and vice versa.

The management team aligned the AI system's performance metrics with the organization's goals, focusing on precision and recall. By employing ROC curves and cross-validation techniques, the team was able to optimize the system's performance. Consequently, the financial institution experienced a 30% reduction in false positives and a 25% decrease in false negatives, resulting in substantial cost savings and improved customer trust.

AI-Enabled Predictive Maintenance for Manufacturing

A large manufacturing company aimed to reduce equipment downtime and maintenance costs by implementing an AI-enabled predictive maintenance system. The primary goal was to predict equipment failures and schedule maintenance proactively and accurately.

The management team identified key performance metrics, such as accuracy and F_1 score, to evaluate the AI system's effectiveness. By using cross-validation and confusion matrix techniques, the team was able to refine the system's algorithms and improve its performance. As a result, the company experienced a 35% reduction in equipment downtime and a 20% decrease in maintenance costs.

In conclusion, these case studies demonstrate the importance of measuring AI performance using appropriate metrics and evaluation techniques. By aligning AI systems with organizational goals and continuously monitoring their performance, managers can ensure the successful implementation and optimization of AI solutions in various business contexts.

The Role of Managers in Ensuring AI Success Through Performance Measurement

In conclusion, the role of managers in ensuring AI success through performance measurement is paramount. As we have explored throughout this chapter, understanding and applying key metrics and evaluation techniques are crucial in determining the effectiveness of AI systems. By actively measuring AI performance, managers can make informed decisions that drive their organizations toward achieving their goals.

First and foremost, managers must be well-versed in the key

metrics of AI performance, such as accuracy, precision, recall, and F1 score. These metrics provide a comprehensive understanding of how well an AI system is performing, allowing managers to identify areas of improvement and make necessary adjustments. By staying up-to-date with the latest developments in AI performance measurement, managers can ensure that their organizations remain competitive in the rapidly evolving world of artificial intelligence.

In addition to understanding key metrics, managers must be proficient in various evaluation techniques, such as cross-validation, confusion matrix, and ROC curves. These techniques offer valuable insights into the performance of AI systems, enabling managers to make data-driven decisions that optimize the effectiveness of their AI initiatives. By incorporating these evaluation techniques into their performance measurement strategies, managers can ensure that their organizations make the most of their AI investments.

Furthermore, managers must recognize the importance of aligning AI performance metrics with organizational goals. By doing so, they can ensure that AI systems are contributing to the organization's overall success rather than simply achieving high performance in isolation. This alignment is crucial in demonstrating the value of AI initiatives to stakeholders and justifying continued investment in AI technologies.

The case studies presented in this chapter are powerful examples of how successful AI performance measurement can lead to real-world success. These examples allow managers to gain valuable insights into the best practices for measuring AI performance and apply these lessons to their organizations.

Ultimately, the role of managers in ensuring AI success through performance measurement is multifaceted. Managers can drive their organizations towards AI success by mastering key metrics and evaluation techniques and aligning AI performance with organizational goals. As artificial intelligence continues to reshape the business landscape, effectively measuring AI performance will become an increasingly vital skill for managers. By embracing this responsibility, managers can position their organizations for long-term success in the age of AI.

Chapter Summary

- Evaluating AI performance is essential for assessing effectiveness, demonstrating value to stakeholders, and fostering a culture of continuous improvement within an organization.
- Key metrics for evaluating AI performance include accuracy, precision, recall, and F1 score, which provide a comprehensive understanding of how well an AI system is performing.
- Cross-validation, confusion matrix, and ROC curves are widely-used evaluation techniques that help managers make informed decisions about AI deployment and improvement.
- Aligning AI performance metrics with organizational goals ensures that AI systems contribute to the business's overall success and demonstrate their value to stakeholders.
- Setting clear performance targets and considering trade-offs between metrics helps managers optimize AI systems to meet their organization's specific needs and goals.
- Fostering a culture of continuous improvement in AI performance measurement encourages teams to strive for excellence and embrace a mindset of constant learning and growth.
- Real-world case studies demonstrate the importance of measuring AI performance using appropriate metrics and evaluation techniques, leading to tangible business results and success.

- Managers play a pivotal role in ensuring AI success through performance measurement, and by mastering key metrics and evaluation techniques and aligning AI performance with organizational goals, they can drive their organizations toward long-term success in the age of AI.

10

THE FUTURE OF AI IN BUSINESS: TRENDS, OPPORTUNITIES, AND THREATS

A futuristic cityscape at sunset with AI robots interacting with humans, showcasing harmony and advanced technology.

In today's swiftly advancing tech world, artificial intelligence (AI) has risen as a critical catalyst in the metamorphosis of diverse industries. As a manager, grasping the fundamentals of AI and its potential influence on your organization is essential. This chapter seeks to equip you with a thorough understanding of AI's future in business, underlining the trends, opportunities, and challenges you should be aware of as you traverse this thrilling new territory.

The AI revolution is no longer a distant dream; it is happening right now, and businesses across the globe are harnessing the power of AI to streamline operations, enhance customer experiences, and drive innovation. From automating mundane tasks to making data-driven decisions, AI is reshaping how we conduct business and manage our organizations.

As a manager, embracing the AI revolution means recognizing the potential of this transformative technology and taking proactive steps to integrate it into your business strategy. This involves staying informed about the latest developments in AI, understanding the opportunities and challenges it presents, and fostering a culture of innovation and adaptability within your organization.

This chapter will delve into the emerging trends in AI for business applications, exploring how AI can transform your business landscape and help you stay ahead of the competition. We will also discuss the potential threats of AI integration, offering insights on navigating these challenges and mitigating risks. Finally, we will examine the role of managers in shaping the AI-driven business environment, guiding how to prepare for a future defined by AI in business management.

By gaining a solid understanding of the future of AI in business, you will be better equipped to lead your organization into this new era of innovation and growth. So, let us embark on this journey together and embrace the AI revolution in business management.

Unveiling the Emerging Trends in AI for Business Applications

As we embark on this exciting journey into artificial intelligence, managers must stay informed about the latest trends and developments in AI for business applications. By understanding these trends, you can better position your organization to capitalize on the opportunities and mitigate the risks associated with AI integration. In this section, we will explore some of the most significant emerging trends in AI for business applications, providing you with a comprehensive overview of the current AI landscape.

Enhanced Automation and Efficiency

One of the most prominent trends in AI for business applications is the increasing use of automation to streamline processes and improve efficiency. From automating routine tasks to optimizing complex workflows, AI-powered tools enable businesses to save time, reduce costs, and enhance productivity. For example, AI-driven chatbots are revolutionizing customer service by providing instant, personalized support, while machine learning algorithms are helping organizations make data-driven decisions with unprecedented speed and accuracy.

Predictive Analytics and Forecasting

Another key trend in AI for business applications is the growing use of predictive analytics and forecasting tools. By leveraging vast amounts of data and sophisticated algorithms, these tools can help organizations anticipate future trends, identify potential risks, and uncover new opportunities. This can be particularly valuable in areas such as sales forecasting, inventory management, and financial planning, where accurate predictions can significantly impact a company's bottom line.

Personalization and Customization

In today's competitive business environment, personalization and customization are becoming increasingly important for organizations looking to differentiate themselves from their rivals. AI plays a crucial role in this trend, enabling businesses to tailor their products, services, and marketing efforts to individual customers' unique preferences and needs. By harnessing the power of AI, companies can create more engaging and relevant experiences for their customers, ultimately driving loyalty and growth.

Enhanced Decision-Making and Problem-Solving

AI is also transforming the way businesses approach decision-making and problem-solving. By analyzing vast amounts of data and identifying patterns and relationships, AI-powered tools can provide managers with valuable insights and recommendations that would be difficult, if not impossible, to uncover using traditional methods. This can lead to more informed, data-driven decisions and, ultimately, better outcomes for the organization.

Ethical and Responsible AI

As AI becomes more integrated into our daily lives, concerns about the ethical implications of AI are growing. This has led to a trend toward developing and implementing ethical and responsible AI practices. Businesses increasingly focus on ensuring that their AI applications are transparent, fair, and accountable and adhere to established ethical guidelines and principles. This trend will likely continue as organizations recognize the importance of building trust and maintaining a positive reputation in the age of AI.

In conclusion, the emerging trends in AI for business applications are shaping the future of how organizations operate and compete. By staying informed about these trends and understanding their implications, managers can better position their organizations to seize the opportunities and navigate the challenges AI integration presents. The next section will delve deeper into how AI can transform your business landscape, providing actionable insights and strategies for leveraging AI to drive growth and success.

Seizing the Opportunities: How AI Can Transform Your Business Landscape

As the world continues to embrace the AI revolution, businesses must recognize the potential opportunities artificial intelligence can bring to their operations. By understanding the transformative power of AI, managers can make informed decisions and strategically position their organizations for success in the ever-evolving business landscape. This section will explore the various ways AI can revolutionize your business, from enhancing customer experiences to streamlining internal processes.

Personalizing Customer Experiences

One of AI's most significant opportunities is the ability to personalize customer experiences. By leveraging AI-powered tools, businesses can analyze vast amounts of data to gain insights into customer preferences, behaviors, and needs. This information can then be used to tailor marketing campaigns, product offerings, and customer service interactions, ultimately increasing customer satisfaction and loyalty.

Streamlining Operations and Reducing Costs

AI can also help businesses optimize their operations and reduce costs. By automating repetitive tasks and processes, AI can free up valuable time and resources, allowing employees to focus on more strategic and creative endeavors. Additionally, AI-powered analytics can identify inefficiencies and areas for improvement, enabling businesses to make data-driven decisions that enhance productivity and profitability.

Enhancing Decision-Making and Forecasting

Making informed decisions is crucial for any business, and AI can significantly improve this process. By analyzing historical data and identifying patterns, AI can provide managers with valuable insights and recommendations, leading to better decision-making. Furthermore, AI can enhance forecasting capabilities by predicting future trends and market fluctuations, allowing businesses to stay ahead of the curve and adapt to changing conditions.

Fostering Innovation and New Business Models

AI has the potential to drive innovation and create new business models. By harnessing the power of AI, businesses can develop cutting-edge products and services that cater to evolving customer needs. Additionally, AI can help organizations identify new market opportunities and revenue streams, ensuring long-term growth and success.

Addressing Talent and Skill Gaps

As the demand for AI expertise grows, businesses must address the talent and skill gaps that may arise. By investing in AI training and development programs, organizations can equip their workforce with the necessary skills to navigate the AI-driven business environment. Furthermore, AI can enhance recruitment processes, ensuring businesses attract and retain top talent.

In conclusion, the opportunities presented by AI are vast and varied, offering businesses the chance to revolutionize their operations and stay competitive in the rapidly changing landscape. By seizing these opportunities, managers can ensure that their organizations are well-prepared for the future of AI in business management.

Navigating the Challenges: Addressing the Potential Threats of AI Integration

As we delve into the world of AI and its potential to revolutionize business management, it is crucial to acknowledge the challenges and potential threats of AI integration. While the benefits of AI are immense, managers need to be aware of the potential pitfalls and take proactive measures to mitigate them. This section will explore the key challenges and threats associated with AI integration and guide how managers can navigate these issues effectively.

Data Privacy and Security

Data privacy and security are among the most pressing concerns in the age of AI. As AI systems rely on vast amounts of data to function effectively, businesses must handle sensitive information responsibly. Managers must be vigilant in implementing robust data protection measures and staying up-to-date with evolving data privacy regulations. This includes investing in secure data storage solutions, implementing strong encryption protocols, and ensuring that employees are trained in data protection best practices.

Ethical Considerations

AI systems can perpetuate and amplify existing biases, leading to unfair and discriminatory outcomes. Managers must proactively address these ethical concerns by ensuring that AI algorithms are transparent, fair, and unbiased. This involves working closely with AI developers to scrutinize the data used to train AI models and regularly auditing AI systems to identify and rectify any instances of bias or discrimination.

Workforce Disruption

Integrating AI in business management could disrupt the workforce as certain tasks and roles become automated. Managers must be prepared to navigate this transition by investing in employee training and development programs focusing on upskilling and reskilling. This will enable employees to adapt to the changing business landscape and remain valuable contributors in an AI-driven environment.

Legal and Regulatory Compliance

As AI continues to evolve, so will the legal and regulatory landscape surrounding its use. Managers must stay informed about the latest developments in AI-related legislation and ensure that their organizations remain compliant. This may involve working closely with legal and compliance teams to develop policies and procedures addressing AI integration's unique challenges.

Managing Expectations

Finally, managers need to manage expectations surrounding AI integration. While AI can potentially deliver significant benefits, it is only a panacea for some business challenges. Managers must be realistic about the capabilities and limitations of AI and communicate these clearly to stakeholders. By setting realistic expectations, managers can help to ensure that AI is integrated effectively and delivers tangible value to the organization.

In conclusion, navigating the challenges and potential threats of AI integration requires a proactive and informed approach from managers. By addressing data privacy and security, ethical considerations, workforce disruption, legal and regulatory compliance, and managing expectations, managers can successfully steer their organizations through the complexities of AI integration and unlock the full potential of this transformative technology.

The Role of Managers in Shaping the AI-Driven Business Environment

As the business world continues to evolve, integrating artificial intelligence (AI) into various aspects of management has become increasingly prevalent. This shift towards an AI-driven business environment presents opportunities and challenges for managers, who must effectively adapt their roles and responsibilities to harness AI's power. In this section, we will explore managers' crucial role in shaping the AI-driven business environment and how they can successfully navigate this new landscape.

Embracing the AI Mindset

The first step for managers in shaping the AI-driven business environment is to embrace the AI mindset. This means recognizing the potential of AI to transform business operations and being open to incorporating AI technologies into their management strategies. By adopting an AI mindset, managers can foster a culture of innovation and continuous improvement within their organizations, which is essential for staying competitive in today's rapidly changing business landscape.

Identifying AI Opportunities

Managers play a pivotal role in identifying opportunities for AI integration within their organizations. This involves staying informed about the latest AI trends and developments and understanding how these technologies can be applied to improve various aspects of business operations. By actively seeking AI opportunities, managers can ensure that their organizations are at the forefront of technological advancements and are well-positioned to capitalize on the benefits of AI.

Overcoming AI Challenges

While AI presents numerous business opportunities, it has its fair share of challenges. Managers must be prepared to address these challenges head-on by developing strategies to mitigate potential risks and overcome obstacles associated with AI integration. This may involve addressing ethical concerns, ensuring data privacy and security, and managing the potential displacement of human workers. By proactively addressing these challenges, managers can help to create a more seamless transition towards an AI-driven business environment.

Developing AI Skills and Expertise

As AI becomes increasingly integrated into business operations, managers must also invest in developing their AI skills and expertise. This may involve participating in training programs, attending industry conferences, or collaborating with AI experts to understand the technology better. By enhancing their AI knowledge, managers can make more informed decisions about AI integration and better support their teams in navigating the AI-driven business environment.

Fostering Collaboration and Communication

Finally, managers play a crucial role in fostering collaboration and communication within their organizations, particularly regarding AI integration. This involves creating an open dialogue about AI, encouraging employees to share their ideas and concerns, and promoting a culture of collaboration between human workers and AI systems. By facilitating effective communication and collaboration, managers can help ensure that AI is integrated to benefit the entire organization and drive overall business success.

In conclusion, the role of managers in shaping the AI-driven business environment is multifaceted and complex. By embracing the AI mindset, identifying AI opportunities, overcoming challenges, developing AI skills and expertise, and fostering collaboration and communication, managers can successfully navigate this new landscape and position their organizations for long-term success in the age of AI.

Preparing for a Future Defined by AI in Business Management

As we have explored throughout this chapter, the future of AI in business is both promising and challenging. Rapid advancements in AI technology can potentially revolutionize how businesses operate, offering unprecedented opportunities for growth, efficiency, and innovation. However, these advancements also bring a host of potential threats and challenges that managers must be prepared to navigate.

In this concluding section, we will synthesize the key insights gleaned from our exploration of AI in business management and offer practical guidance for managers seeking to embrace the AI revolution.

First and foremost, managers need to stay informed about the latest developments in AI technology and its applications in the business world. This requires a commitment to continuous learning and a willingness to adapt to the ever-evolving landscape of AI. By staying abreast of emerging trends and best practices, managers can make informed decisions about integrating AI into their organizations to maximize its benefits while minimizing potential risks.

Second, managers must be proactive in identifying and seizing the opportunities presented by AI. This may involve rethinking traditional business models, processes, and strategies to capitalize on the unique capabilities of AI-driven technologies. By fostering a culture of innovation and experimentation, managers can encourage their teams to explore new ways of leveraging AI to drive growth and create a competitive advantage.

At the same time, managers must be prepared to address AI integration's potential threats and challenges. This includes grappling with ethical considerations, ensuring data privacy and security, and managing the potential displacement of human workers. By engaging in open and honest dialogue with stakeholders, managers can work to develop strategies that balance the benefits of AI with the need to protect the interests of employees, customers, and society at large.

Moreover, managers play a critical role in shaping the AI-driven business environment by cultivating the necessary organizational skills and competencies. This includes technical expertise in AI and related fields and the soft skills needed to navigate the complex and often ambiguous challenges posed by AI integration. By investing in the development of their teams, managers can ensure that their organizations are well-equipped to thrive in the AI-driven future.

In conclusion, the future of AI in business management is exciting and uncertain. By staying informed, embracing innovation, addressing potential threats, and cultivating the necessary skills and competencies, managers can position their organizations for success in the rapidly evolving world of AI. As we move forward into this brave new world, it is up to managers to lead the charge, harnessing AI's power to shape a prosperous and sustainable future for all.

Chapter Summary

- AI is revolutionizing business management, offering opportunities for growth, efficiency, and innovation while presenting potential threats and challenges.
- Managers must stay informed about the latest AI trends and developments to make informed decisions about AI integration in their organizations.
- AI can transform businesses by personalizing customer experiences, streamlining operations, enhancing

decision-making, fostering innovation, and addressing talent gaps.

- Managers must address potential threats and challenges associated with AI integration, such as data privacy and security, ethical considerations, workforce disruption, and legal and regulatory compliance.
- Embracing the AI mindset and fostering a culture of innovation is crucial for managers to navigate the AI-driven business environment successfully.
- Identifying AI opportunities and proactively addressing challenges is essential for managers to maximize the benefits of AI while minimizing potential risks.
- Managers play a critical role in shaping the AI-driven business environment by cultivating the necessary organizational skills and competencies.
- By staying informed, embracing innovation, addressing potential threats, and cultivating the necessary skills and competencies, managers can position their organizations for success in the rapidly evolving world of AI.

EMBRACING AI FOR EFFECTIVE MANAGEMENT AND BUSINESS GROWTH

A s the sun rises on a new day, so does it herald the dawn of a new era in management. This era is marked by the rapid and transformative integration of artificial intelligence (AI) into business operations. AI's potential to revolutionize how we work, think, and interact is no longer a distant dream but a tangible reality that is reshaping the managerial landscape.

In this age of digital disruption, AI has emerged as a powerful force driving innovation, efficiency, and growth across industries. From automating mundane tasks to making data-driven decisions, AI empowers managers to unlock new levels of productivity and performance. As a result, businesses that embrace AI are poised to thrive in the competitive global market, while those that resist risk being left behind.

This chapter aims to provide a comprehensive overview of the role of AI in modern management and its implications for business growth. We will delve into the major themes and findings that have emerged from the study of AI in business, exploring the myriad ways this technology is transforming how managers operate. We will also address the limitations and critiques that have arisen in response to the rapid adoption of AI and offer recommendations for navigating the challenges and opportunities that lie ahead.

As we embark on this journey, it is essential to recognize that integrating AI into management is not a threat to be feared but an opportunity to be seized. By embracing AI and harnessing its potential, managers can unlock unprecedented levels of success and drive their businesses toward a brighter, more prosperous future. So, let us step boldly into this new era and explore the exciting possibilities in AI-driven management.

Unveiling the Power of AI in Business

As we delve into the heart of this chapter, it is crucial to understand the major themes and findings that have emerged from our exploration of AI in management and business growth. By shedding light on these key aspects, we aim to provide a comprehensive understanding of the transformative potential of AI and its far-reaching implications for managers and organizations alike.

One of the most significant themes that have emerged from our investigation is the unparalleled ability of AI to enhance decision-making and strategic planning processes. By harnessing the power of advanced algorithms, machine learning, and data analytics, AI systems can process vast amounts of information at lightning speed, identify patterns and trends, and generate valuable insights that would be impossible for humans to discern. This empowers managers to make more informed, data-driven decisions, optimize resource allocation, and devise innovative strategies that drive business growth and success.

Another major finding is AI's potential to revolutionize how businesses operate by automating routine tasks, streamlining workflows, and optimizing processes. Managers can free up valuable time and resources by delegating mundane, repetitive tasks to AI-powered tools and software, allowing them to focus on more strategic, high-level responsibilities. This boosts overall efficiency and productivity and fosters a more agile, adaptable, and resilient organization that can thrive in today's fast-paced, ever-evolving business landscape.

In today's highly competitive market, delivering exceptional customer experiences is more important than ever. Our research has revealed that AI can play a pivotal role in helping businesses achieve this goal by enabling them to offer personalized, tailored experiences that cater to individual preferences, needs, and expectations. By leveraging AI-driven technologies such as natural language processing, sentiment analysis, and recommendation engines, managers can better understand their customers, anticipate their desires, and deliver customized solutions that foster loyalty, satisfaction, and long-term relationships.

The power of AI extends beyond the realm of customer experiences and operational efficiency; it also has the potential to transform how businesses manage their most valuable asset – their workforce. By utilizing AI-powered tools and platforms, managers can streamline recruitment processes, identify top talent, and make data-driven hiring, training, and development decisions. Furthermore, AI can help create a more engaged, motivated, and empowered workforce by providing personalized learning opportunities, real-time feedback, and performance analytics that drive continuous improvement and professional growth.

Lastly, our exploration of AI in management and business growth would be incomplete without addressing the critical theme of ethics and responsible AI. As AI systems become increasingly sophisticated and autonomous, managers must consider the ethical implications of their AI-driven decisions and actions. This includes ensuring transparency, fairness, and accountability in AI applications and safeguarding privacy, security, and human rights. By embracing a responsible, ethical approach to AI, managers can not only mitigate potential risks and challenges but also foster trust, credibility, and long-term success in the age of AI.

In conclusion, examining the major themes and findings

surrounding AI in management and business growth has unveiled a world of possibilities and opportunities for organizations willing to embrace this cutting-edge technology. By leveraging the power of AI to enhance decision-making, improve efficiency, personalize customer experiences, empower their workforce, and uphold ethical standards, managers can unlock unprecedented levels of success and drive their businesses toward a prosperous, AI-driven future.

Transforming the Managerial Landscape

As we delve deeper into the age of artificial intelligence, managers must understand the implications and significance of AI in transforming the managerial landscape. This section will explore how AI is revolutionizing business operations, decision-making processes, and overall organizational growth.

First and foremost, AI has the potential to enhance the efficiency and effectiveness of managerial tasks significantly. By automating routine and repetitive tasks, AI allows managers to focus on more strategic and value-adding activities. This leads to increased productivity and enables managers to make better use of their time and resources.

Moreover, AI-driven analytics and data processing capabilities can provide managers with valuable insights and information previously inaccessible or difficult to obtain. This empowers managers to make more informed decisions, identify trends and patterns, and anticipate future challenges and opportunities. Consequently, organizations can become more agile and responsive to market changes, ensuring long-term success and competitiveness.

Another significant implication of AI in management is its ability to facilitate collaboration and communication within teams and across departments. AI-powered tools can streamline workflows, manage projects, and foster creativity and innovation by connecting individuals with diverse skill sets and expertise. This not only enhances teams' overall performance but also promotes a culture of continuous learning and improvement.

Furthermore, AI can be pivotal in talent management and human resources. From recruitment and onboarding to performance evaluation and employee engagement, AI can help managers make data-driven decisions that optimize the workforce and align with organizational goals. This can improve employee satisfaction, retention, and a more skilled and motivated workforce.

However, the transformative power of AI in management has its challenges and concerns. As AI becomes more integrated into business operations, managers must be prepared to address issues related to privacy, security, and ethical considerations. Additionally, the rapid pace of technological advancements may require managers to continuously update their skills and knowledge to stay relevant in the ever-evolving AI landscape.

In conclusion, embracing AI in management has the potential to significantly transform the way organizations operate, make decisions, and grow. By understanding the implications and significance of AI, managers can harness its power to drive efficiency, innovation, and success in their businesses. As we move forward in this new era, managers must remain adaptable, open-minded, and proactive in leveraging AI to its fullest potential.

Addressing the Concerns and Misconceptions

As we delve into artificial intelligence and its potential to revolutionize management and business growth, it is crucial to address the limitations and critiques often arising in AI discussions. By acknowledging these concerns and misconceptions, we can better understand the challenges ahead and work towards creating a more balanced and informed perspective on AI's role in the business world.

One of the most common concerns associated with AI is the **fear of job loss** and displacement. Many worry that AI systems will replace human workers as they become more advanced and capable, leading to widespread unemployment. While it is true that AI has the potential to automate certain tasks and roles, it is essential to recognize that AI can also create new job opportunities and enhance existing ones. By focusing on developing AI systems that complement human skills and expertise, we can foster a collaborative environment where both humans and AI can thrive.

Another critique of AI is the potential for **ethical issues and biases** to arise. As AI systems are trained on data sets that may contain inherent biases, there is a risk that these biases will be perpetuated and even amplified by AI algorithms. To address this concern, businesses must prioritize transparency and fairness in their AI systems. This can be achieved by carefully selecting and curating data sets, as well as by implementing robust auditing processes to ensure that AI systems are operating in an ethical and unbiased manner.

The **"black box" problem** refers to the difficulty in understanding and interpreting the decision-making processes of AI systems. This lack of transparency can lead to concerns about accountability and trust, particularly in high-stakes business decisions. Researchers and developers are working on explainable AI (XAI) techniques to mitigate this issue to make AI systems more transparent and understandable. By embracing these advancements, businesses can build trust in AI systems and ensure they make well-informed decisions.

While AI has the potential to enhance management and business growth greatly, it is important not to become **overly reliant** on AI systems. AI cannot replicate human intuition, creativity, and empathy; these traits remain essential in effective management. Striking the right balance between leveraging AI's capabilities and maintaining human involvement is key to harnessing the full potential of AI in the business world.

In conclusion, while there are valid concerns and critiques surrounding the implementation of AI in management and business growth, these challenges can be addressed through thoughtful planning, ethical considerations, and a balanced approach to AI integration. By acknowledging and addressing these limitations, we can work towards a future where AI and human intelligence work together to drive success and innovation in the business world.

Charting the Path to AI-Driven Success

As we conclude our exploration into artificial intelligence and its impact on management and business growth, reflecting on the key insights gleaned from this journey is essential. The transformative power of AI is undeniable, and its potential to revolutionize how we conduct business is immense. However, harnessing this potential requires a strategic and thoughtful approach and a willingness to embrace change and adapt to new paradigms.

In this final section, we offer a set of recommendations to guide managers and business leaders in their quest to leverage AI for effective management and business growth. These recommendations provide a roadmap for navigating the challenges and opportunities in the rapidly evolving landscape of AI-driven management.

- **Develop a clear AI strategy:** The first step towards embracing AI is to develop a comprehensive and well-defined strategy that outlines the organization's goals, objectives, and desired outcomes. This strategy should align with the overall business vision and serve as a guiding framework for all AI-related initiatives and investments.
- **Invest in AI education and training:** To fully capitalize on the benefits of AI, managers, and employees must possess a solid understanding of the technology and its applications. Investing in AI education and training programs will help build a well-equipped workforce to navigate the complexities of AI-driven management and contribute to the organization's success.

- **Foster a culture of innovation and experimentation:** Embracing AI requires a willingness to take risks and explore new ideas. Encourage a culture of innovation and experimentation within your organization by providing employees with the resources, support, and autonomy they need to test new approaches and learn from their experiences.
- **Collaborate with AI experts and partners:** AI technology's rapidly evolving nature means that no organization can possess all the necessary expertise and resources. Forge strategic partnerships with AI experts, research institutions, and technology providers to access cutting-edge knowledge and tools that can help drive your AI initiatives forward.
- **Address ethical and social considerations:** As AI becomes increasingly integrated into our daily lives, it is crucial to consider its use's ethical and social implications. Develop policies and guidelines that promote responsible AI practices, and engage in open dialogue with stakeholders to address concerns and foster trust.
- **Monitor and evaluate AI performance:** Regularly assess your AI initiatives' performance to ensure they deliver the desired outcomes and provide value to your organization. Use data-driven insights to inform decision-making and drive continuous improvement.
- **Be agile and adaptable:** The world of AI is constantly changing, and organizations must be prepared to adapt their strategies and approaches accordingly. Stay informed about the latest developments in AI technology, and be prepared to pivot your AI initiatives as needed to stay ahead of the curve.

In conclusion, the dawn of AI-driven management presents both challenges and opportunities for businesses across all industries. By embracing AI and adopting a strategic, informed approach, managers can harness the power of this transformative technology to drive effective management and business growth. The journey may be complex and filled with uncertainties, but the potential rewards are immense, and the future of AI-driven management is undoubtedly bright.

ESSENTIAL MATH FOR AI

EXPLORING LINEAR ALGEBRA,
PROBABILITY AND STATISTICS,
CALCULUS, GRAPH THEORY, DISCRETE
MATHEMATICS, NUMERICAL METHODS,
OPTIMIZATION TECHNIQUES, AND MORE

THE ROLE OF MATHEMATICS IN ARTIFICIAL INTELLIGENCE

In the rapidly evolving world of artificial intelligence (AI), one might be tempted to think that the key to success lies solely in mastering the latest programming languages, algorithms, and software tools. While these skills are undoubtedly necessary, there is a foundational element that underpins the entire field of AI: mathematics. The inextricable link between mathematics and AI is a testament to the fact that, at its core, AI is a discipline rooted in mathematical principles and concepts. This connection is not a mere coincidence but rather a reflection of mathematics's fundamental role in shaping the development and application of AI technologies.

Mathematics provides the language and framework to understand, analyze, and manipulate the complex data structures and algorithms that drive AI systems. From the basic building blocks of linear algebra and calculus to the more advanced realms of probability theory, optimization, and graph theory, mathematics is the backbone of AI, enabling researchers and practitioners to push the boundaries of what is possible in this exciting field.

As AI continues to permeate every aspect of our lives, from self-driving cars and virtual personal assistants to advanced medical diagnostics and financial forecasting, understanding the underlying mathematical principles cannot be overstated. By delving into the essential math for AI, we not only equip ourselves with the tools necessary to navigate this complex landscape but also gain a deeper appreciation for the intricate interplay between mathematics and AI that has given rise to some of the most groundbreaking innovations of our time.

In this book, we will embark on a journey to explore the fascinating world of AI mathematics, shedding light on the key concepts and techniques that form the foundation of this rapidly growing field. Through a unique blend of theory and practical applications, we will empower AI enthusiasts with the essential mathematical knowledge needed to excel in their pursuits and contribute to the ongoing development of AI technologies.

As we prepare to delve into the multifaceted world of AI mathematics, let us remember that the challenges we face today are merely stepping stones to the incredible innovations that await us. By embracing the power of mathematics and harnessing its potential, we can unlock the door to a new era of AI-driven advancements that will undoubtedly reshape the world as we know it.

A Brief History of Mathematical Foundations in AI

The story of artificial intelligence (AI) is deeply intertwined with the history of mathematics. From the earliest days of AI research, mathematical concepts and techniques have shaped the field's development. In this section, we will briefly journey through the annals of AI history, highlighting the key mathematical milestones that have contributed to the field's growth and evolution.

The roots of AI can be traced back to the ancient world, where philosophers and mathematicians like Aristotle and Euclid laid the groundwork for logic and geometry. These early thinkers grappled with questions about the nature of intelligence and the possibility of creating machines that could think and reason like humans. Their ideas would later inspire the pioneers of AI, who sought to build on these foundations and develop mathematical intelligence models.

In the 20th century, AI began to take shape, driven by the work of mathematicians and computer scientists such as Alan Turing, John von Neumann, and Claude Shannon. Turing's ground-breaking work on computability theory and the Turing machine provided a formal framework for understanding the limits of computation, while von Neumann's contributions to game theory and cellular automata laid the groundwork for the study of complex systems and decision-making in AI. Shannon's information theory, meanwhile, offered a mathematical basis for understanding the transmission and processing of information, which would become central to AI research.

As AI research progressed, new mathematical tools and techniques were developed to tackle the challenges of modeling and simulating intelligent behavior. Probability theory and statistics emerged as essential tools for dealing with uncertainty and making inferences from data, while optimization techniques provided a means of finding the best solutions to complex problems. Graph theory and combinatorics played a crucial role in understanding the structure and properties of networks, which are fundamental to many AI applications.

In the latter half of the 20th century, the advent of machine learning and neural networks brought new mathematical challenges to the forefront of AI research. Researchers drew on concepts from linear algebra, calculus, and numerical analysis to develop algorithms that could learn from data and adapt their behavior over time. These advances paved the way for developing robust AI systems tackling various tasks, from image recognition to natural language processing.

Today, the field of AI continues to evolve at a rapid pace, driven by ongoing advances in mathematics and computer science. As we explore the essential math for AI in this book, we will delve into the rich tapestry of mathematical ideas that underpin the field, from the foundational concepts of logic and probability to the cutting-edge techniques of deep learning and reinforcement learning. By understanding the mathematical foundations of AI, we can better appreciate the intricate interplay between theory and practice that defines this exciting and ever-changing discipline.

Empowering AI Enthusiasts with Essential Mathematical Knowledge

The primary purpose of this book is to empower AI enthusiasts, be they students, researchers, or professionals, with the essential mathematical knowledge required to excel in the field of artificial intelligence. As the world increasingly relies on AI-driven technologies, it is crucial for those involved in developing and implementing these systems to possess a strong foundation in the mathematical concepts underpinning their functionality.

This book aims to provide a comprehensive yet accessible guide to the mathematical principles that form the backbone of AI. By presenting these concepts clearly and concisely, we aim to make the subject matter approachable for readers of all levels of expertise, from those just beginning their journey into AI to seasoned professionals seeking to deepen their understanding.

Throughout the chapters, we will explore a wide range of topics, including linear algebra, probability theory, optimization, and more, all of which play a crucial role in designing and operating AI systems. By providing a thorough grounding in these areas, we aim to equip our readers with the tools they need to tackle the complex challenges that arise in the development of AI technologies.

Moreover, this book is designed to balance theory and practical applications. While it is essential to understand the underlying mathematical principles, it is equally important to see how these concepts can be applied in real-world situations. To this end, we will include numerous examples and case studies that demonstrate the relevance of the mathematical concepts discussed in the context of AI.

In conclusion, this book aims to empower AI enthusiasts with the essential mathematical knowledge needed to excel in the field of artificial intelligence. By providing a comprehensive and accessible guide to the mathematical foundations of AI, we hope to prepare our readers for the challenges and opportunities in the exciting world of AI innovation.

Preparing for the Mathematical Challenges of Tomorrow's AI Innovations

As we stand on the precipice of a new era in artificial intelligence, it is crucial to recognize mathematics's indispensable role in shaping the future of this rapidly evolving field. The innovations of tomorrow will undoubtedly present a myriad of mathematical challenges, and it is our responsibility as AI enthusiasts, researchers, and practitioners to be well-equipped with the essential mathematical knowledge to tackle these obstacles head-on.

Throughout this book, we have embarked on a journey to explore the multifaceted world of AI mathematics, delving into the theoretical underpinnings and practical applications that form the backbone of artificial intelligence. By providing a comprehensive understanding of the mathematical foundations that govern AI, we aim to empower our readers with the tools and confidence necessary to contribute to this exciting field's ongoing development and advancement.

As we look ahead to the future of artificial intelligence, it is important to remember that the innovations of tomorrow will be built upon the mathematical foundations of today. By fostering a deep understanding of the essential mathematical concepts underlying AI, we can ensure that we are prepared to navigate this dynamic field's complex and ever-changing landscape.

In conclusion, the role of mathematics in artificial intelligence cannot be overstated. As we continue to push the boundaries of what is possible with AI, we must remain steadfast in our commitment to mastering the mathematical principles that drive these innovations. By doing so, we can unlock the full potential of artificial intelligence and usher in a new era of technological breakthroughs that will undoubtedly reshape the world as we know it.

So, as you turn the pages of this book and immerse yourself in the fascinating world of AI mathematics, remember that you are not only gaining valuable knowledge but also preparing yourself for the mathematical challenges that lie ahead in the ever-evolving realm of artificial intelligence. Embrace the journey, and let the power of mathematics guide you toward a brighter, AI-driven future.

1

LINEAR ALGEBRA: THE FOUNDATION OF MACHINE LEARNING

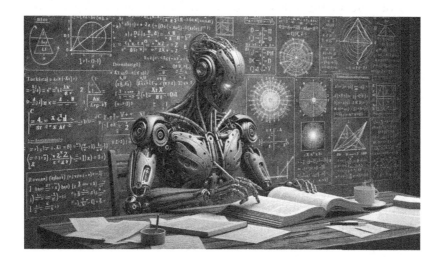

I n the world of artificial intelligence (AI), one might wonder what role mathematics, specifically linear algebra, plays in developing and advancing this cutting-edge technology. As it turns out, linear algebra is not only a crucial component of AI but also the foundation upon which machine learning algorithms are built. In this chapter, we will delve into the fascinating world of linear algebra and explore its significance in AI, providing you with the essential knowledge to understand and master this critical mathematical discipline.

Linear algebra, at its core, is the study of vector spaces and the linear relationships between them. It is a branch of mathematics that deals with vectors, matrices, and systems of linear equations, all fundamental concepts in AI. As we progress through this chapter, we will uncover the reasons behind the importance of linear algebra in AI and how it enables machines to learn, adapt, and make intelligent decisions.

One of the primary reasons linear algebra is essential to AI is its ability to represent and manipulate large amounts of data efficiently. In the world of AI, data is king. The more data an algorithm can process, the better it can learn and make accurate predictions. Linear algebra provides the tools necessary to handle vast quantities of data in the form of vectors and matrices, which are the building blocks of this mathematical field. By understanding how to work with these structures, we can create powerful machine-learning algorithms that can process and analyze data at an incredible scale.

Another reason linear algebra is vital to AI is its role in transforming and manipulating data. Machine learning algorithms often require data to be transformed or manipulated in specific ways to extract valuable insights and patterns. Linear algebra provides a set of operations and transformations, such as matrix multiplication and inversion, that allow us to modify data in a structured and efficient manner. By mastering these techniques, we can preprocess and transform data to be more suitable for machine learning algorithms, ultimately improving their performance and accuracy.

Eigenvalues and eigenvectors, two essential concepts in linear algebra, also play a significant role in AI. They uncover hidden patterns and structures within data, which can be invaluable in machine learning applications. By understanding the principles behind eigenvalues and eigenvectors, we can develop algorithms to identify and exploit these patterns, leading to more effective and intelligent AI systems.

In conclusion, linear algebra is the foundation for building machine learning and AI. By understanding and mastering the concepts of vectors, matrices, and the various operations and transformations associated with them, we can develop powerful AI algorithms capable of learning from vast amounts of data and making intelligent decisions. As we progress through this chapter, we will explore these concepts in greater detail, providing you with the essential mathematical knowledge to excel in AI.

Understanding Vectors and Matrices: The Building Blocks of Linear Algebra

This section will delve into the fascinating world of vectors and matrices, the fundamental building blocks of linear algebra. These mathematical entities play a crucial role in developing and implementing artificial intelligence (AI) and machine learning algorithms. By the end of this section, you will have a solid understanding of vectors and matrices and be well-equipped to appreciate their significance in the realm of AI.

Vectors: The Backbone of Data Representation

A vector is a mathematical object that represents both magnitude and direction. In the context of AI, vectors are used to represent data points in a multi-dimensional space. For instance, consider a simple example of a movie rating system. Each movie can be represented by a vector containing ratings in various categories, such as action, romance, and comedy. By representing data in this manner, we can easily compare and analyze different movies based on their ratings.

Vectors are typically represented as an ordered list of numbers enclosed in square brackets. For example, a 3-dimensional vector can be represented as [x, y, z], where x, y, and z are the magnitudes of the vector in the respective dimensions. The number of dimensions in a vector is called its size or dimensionality.

Matrices: Organizing Data for Efficient Processing

A matrix is a rectangular array of numbers, symbols, or expressions arranged in rows and columns. In AI, matrices organize and manipulate large amounts of data efficiently. They are instrumental in representing and processing data through images, graphs, and networks.

A matrix is a collection of vectors where each row or column represents a vector. The size of a matrix is defined by the number of rows (m) and columns (n) and is denoted as an m × n matrix. For example, a 3 × 2 matrix has 3 rows and 2 columns.

The Connection Between Vectors and Matrices

Vectors and matrices are intrinsically connected, as a matrix can be considered a collection of vectors. This connection is vital in AI, as it allows us to manipulate and transform data in a structured and efficient manner. We can perform complex operations and transformations essential for machine learning algorithms by representing data as vectors and matrices.

In the following sections, we will explore various matrix operations and transformations, as well as the concepts of eigenvalues and eigenvectors, which play a pivotal role in uncovering hidden patterns in data. By mastering these concepts, you will be well on your way to building a solid foundation in linear algebra, which is essential for success in AI.

Matrix Operations and Transformations: Manipulating Data for Machine Learning

In the fascinating world of artificial intelligence, linear algebra plays a pivotal role in shaping the foundation of machine learning algorithms. As we delve deeper into this realm, we come across matrix operations and transformations, which are crucial in manipulating data for machine learning. In this section, we will explore the various matrix operations, their significance, and how they contribute to the development of AI.

Matrix operations are mathematical procedures that involve the manipulation of matrices, which are essentially rectangular arrays of numbers, symbols, or expressions. These operations are vital in machine learning, enabling us to efficiently perform complex calculations and transformations on large datasets. Let's examine some of the most common matrix operations and their significance in AI.

- **Matrix Addition and Subtraction:** These are the most basic operations that involve adding or subtracting corresponding elements of two matrices. This operation is particularly useful in machine learning when we combine or compare datasets, update weights in neural networks, or calculate the error between predicted and actual values.
- **Matrix Multiplication:** This operation involves multiplying two matrices in a specific order, resulting in a new matrix. Matrix multiplication is essential in machine learning, as it allows us to apply transformations to our data, such as scaling, rotation, and translation. Furthermore, it significantly implements various algorithms, such as linear regression and neural networks.
- **Matrix Transpose:** The transpose of a matrix is obtained by interchanging its rows and columns. This operation is particularly useful in machine learning when we need to rearrange data for specific calculations or when working with algorithms requiring input data to be in a particular format.

- **Matrix Inversion:** The inverse of a square matrix is a matrix that, when multiplied with the original matrix, results in the identity matrix. Matrix inversion is a crucial operation in machine learning, as it helps solve systems of linear equations, which are often encountered in various algorithms, such as linear regression and support vector machines.

Now that we have a basic understanding of matrix operations let's discuss matrix transformations. In machine learning, transformations are essential in preprocessing data, reducing dimensions, and extracting features. Some common matrix transformations include:

- **Scaling:** This transformation involves multiplying the elements of a matrix by a scalar value, effectively changing the size of the data. Scaling is often used in machine learning to normalize data, ensuring that all features have the same range of values, which helps improve the performance of algorithms.
- **Rotation:** This transformation involves rotating the data in a multi-dimensional space, which can be achieved by multiplying the data matrix with a rotation matrix. Rotation is useful in machine learning for data visualization, dimensionality reduction, and improving the performance of certain algorithms.
- **Translation:** This transformation involves adding or subtracting a constant value to the elements of a matrix, effectively shifting the data in a multi-dimensional space. Translation is often used in machine learning to center the data around the origin, which can improve the performance of various algorithms.

In conclusion, matrix operations and transformations are indispensable tools in machine learning. They enable us to manipulate and preprocess data efficiently, paving the way for developing robust AI algorithms. Mastering these concepts can build a strong foundation in AI and contribute to the ever-evolving landscape of artificial intelligence.

Eigenvalues and Eigenvectors: Uncovering Hidden Patterns in Data

In artificial intelligence, the ability to identify patterns and extract valuable information from vast amounts of data is crucial. One of the most powerful tools for achieving this is the concept of eigenvalues and eigenvectors. In this section, we will delve into the world of these mathematical entities, exploring their significance and applications in machine learning.

The Essence of Eigenvalues and Eigenvectors

Before we dive into the intricacies of eigenvalues and eigenvectors, let's first establish a fundamental understanding of these terms. In linear algebra, an eigenvector is a non-zero vector that, when multiplied by a matrix, results in a scalar multiple of itself. This scalar multiple is known as the eigenvalue. Mathematically, this relationship can be expressed as:

$$A * v = \lambda * v$$

Here, A represents the matrix, v is the eigenvector, and λ is the eigenvalue.

The Intuition Behind Eigenvalues and Eigenvectors

Let's consider a real-world analogy to grasp the concept of eigenvalues and eigenvectors better. Imagine a group of people standing on a platform that can rotate around a central axis. Each person's position changes as the platform rotates, but the central axis remains fixed. In this scenario, the central axis represents the eigenvector, and the rotation angle corresponds to the eigenvalue.

In the context of data analysis, eigenvalues, and eigenvectors can be thought of as the "central axes" around which the data points are organized. By identifying these axes, we can uncover hidden patterns and relationships within the data, enabling us to make more informed decisions and predictions.

Applications of Eigenvalues and Eigenvectors in Machine Learning

Eigenvalues and eigenvectors are pivotal in various machine learning algorithms, particularly in dimensionality reduction and data compression. Some notable applications include:

Principal Component Analysis (PCA): PCA is a widely-used technique for reducing the dimensionality of large datasets while preserving as much information as possible. By calculating the eigenvectors and eigenvalues of the data's covariance matrix, PCA identifies the directions (principal components) along which the variance of the data is maximized.

Singular Value Decomposition (SVD): SVD is a matrix factorization technique that decomposes a given matrix into three matrices, one containing the eigenvectors. SVD is used in numerous machine learning applications, such as image compression, natural language processing, and recommender systems.

Spectral Clustering: In spectral clustering, eigenvalues and eigenvectors are employed to partition data points into distinct clusters based on similarity. This technique is handy for identifying non-linear structures within the data.

Mastering Eigenvalues and Eigenvectors for a Strong AI Foundation

In conclusion, eigenvalues and eigenvectors are indispensable tools in artificial intelligence and machine learning. Understanding their underlying principles and applications, you will be better equipped to tackle complex data analysis tasks and develop more effective machine learning models. As you continue to explore the fascinating world of linear algebra, remember that the key to success lies in building a solid foundation and continually expanding your knowledge.

Applications of Linear Algebra in Machine Learning Algorithms

In this section, we will delve into the fascinating world of machine learning and explore how linear algebra plays a crucial role in developing and optimizing various algorithms. By understanding the applications of linear algebra in machine learning, we can appreciate its significance and harness its power to create more efficient and accurate models.

Image Recognition and Computer Vision

One of the most popular applications of machine learning is image recognition, where computers are trained to identify and classify objects within images. Linear algebra is at the heart of this process, as images can be represented as matrices of pixel values. By applying matrix operations and transformations, we can manipulate these images, extract features, and reduce dimensions for more efficient processing. Furthermore, eigenvectors and eigenvalues can be used to identify principal components essential in techniques like Principal Component Analysis (PCA) for dimensionality reduction and data compression.

Natural Language Processing

Linear algebra is also a key component in natural language processing (NLP), which involves computer computers' analysis and generation of human language. In NLP, text data is often represented as vectors in high-dimensional spaces, where each dimension corresponds to a unique word or feature. By applying linear algebra techniques, we can measure the similarity between texts, perform sentiment analysis, and even generate new text based on existing patterns. Techniques such as Word2Vec and Latent Semantic Analysis (LSA) rely heavily on linear algebra concepts to create meaningful representations of text data.

Recommender Systems

Recommender systems are widely used in e-commerce, content platforms, and social media to suggest products, articles, or connections based on user preferences and behavior. Linear algebra plays a vital role in developing these systems, as it allows us to represent user preferences and item features as vectors and matrices. By applying matrix factorization techniques, we can uncover latent factors that explain observed user-item interactions and make personalized recommendations. Singular Value Decomposition (SVD) and collaborative filtering are popular linear algebra-based techniques used in recommender systems.

Deep Learning and Neural Networks

Deep learning, a subset of machine learning, involves using artificial neural networks to model complex patterns and make predictions. Linear algebra is fundamental to the structure and functioning of these networks, as they consist of layers of interconnected nodes, each performing linear transformations on input data. By adjusting the weights and biases of these connections through backpropagation, the network can learn to make accurate predictions. Convolutional Neural Networks (CNNs), a popular type of deep learning architecture for image recognition, rely heavily on linear algebra operations such as convolution and pooling to process and analyze input data.

In conclusion, linear algebra is a powerful and versatile tool that underpins many machine learning algorithms. By mastering the concepts and techniques of linear algebra, we can build a strong foundation for understanding and developing advanced AI models. As AI continues to evolve, linear algebra will undoubtedly remain essential in the quest for more intelligent and efficient machines.

Mastering Linear Algebra for a Strong AI Foundation

In conclusion, linear algebra plays a pivotal role in artificial intelligence. As we have explored throughout this chapter, the concepts and techniques of linear algebra are deeply intertwined with the foundations of machine learning, providing the necessary tools to manipulate, analyze, and interpret vast amounts of data. By mastering linear algebra, one can unlock the true potential of AI and contribute to the development of innovative solutions that can revolutionize various aspects of our lives.

The journey through linear algebra began with understanding the basic building blocks: vectors and matrices. These fundamental elements serve as the backbone of linear algebra, allowing us to represent complex data structures and perform intricate calculations. As we delved deeper into the subject, we discovered the power of matrix operations and transformations, which enable us to manipulate data in ways that facilitate machine learning processes.

One of the most intriguing aspects of linear algebra is the concept of eigenvalues and eigenvectors. These unique properties of matrices allow us to uncover hidden patterns and structures within data, providing valuable insights that machine learning algorithms can harness. By understanding the significance of eigenvalues and eigenvectors, we can develop more efficient and accurate models that tackle various AI challenges.

Throughout this chapter, we have also highlighted various linear algebra applications in machine learning algorithms. From linear regression to neural networks, the influence of linear algebra is omnipresent, showcasing its importance in the field of AI. By mastering these techniques, aspiring AI professionals can equip themselves with the knowledge and skills to excel in this rapidly evolving domain.

In summary, linear algebra is an indispensable component of artificial intelligence, serving as the foundation upon which machine learning algorithms are built. Mastering the concepts and techniques presented in this chapter can establish a strong foundation in AI and contribute to advancing this transformative technology. As we continue to explore the vast landscape of artificial intelligence, let us remember the significance of linear algebra and its power in shaping AI's future.

Chapter Summary

- Linear algebra is the foundation of artificial intelligence and machine learning, providing the necessary tools to manipulate, analyze, and interpret vast amounts of data.
- Vectors and matrices are the fundamental building blocks of linear algebra, allowing for the representation of complex data structures and the performance of intricate calculations.
- Matrix operations and transformations, such as addition, subtraction, multiplication, inversion, and transpose, are crucial for manipulating data to facilitate machine learning processes.
- Eigenvalues and eigenvectors are unique properties of matrices that uncover hidden patterns and structures within data, providing valuable insights for machine learning algorithms.
- Linear algebra plays a significant role in various machine learning applications, including image recognition, natural language processing, recommender systems, and deep learning.

- Principal Component Analysis (PCA) and Singular Value Decomposition (SVD) are popular linear algebra-based techniques used for dimensionality reduction and data compression in machine learning.
- Convolutional Neural Networks (CNNs), a popular deep learning architecture for image recognition, rely heavily on linear algebra operations such as convolution and pooling to process and analyze input data.
- Mastering linear algebra concepts and techniques is essential for building a solid foundation in artificial intelligence and contributing to developing innovative AI solutions.

PROBABILITY AND STATISTICS: UNDERSTANDING DATA AND UNCERTAINTY

When working with artificial intelligence (AI), making informed decisions and predictions based on data is crucial. As AI systems continue to permeate various aspects of our lives, from healthcare to finance, understanding the underlying mathematical concepts becomes increasingly important. One such area of mathematics that plays a pivotal role in AI is probability and statistics. This chapter will delve into the fascinating world of probability and statistics, exploring their significance in AI and how they help us make sense of the vast amounts of data we encounter daily.

Probability and statistics are two interconnected branches of mathematics that deal with the analysis and interpretation of data. While probability theory focuses on the likelihood of events occurring, statistics is concerned with data collection, organization, analysis, interpretation, and presentation. Together, they provide a powerful toolkit for understanding and managing uncertainty, a fundamental aspect of AI.

In AI, probability and statistics are used to model and predict various phenomena, such as the behavior of users, the performance of algorithms, and the outcomes of experiments. By quantifying uncertainty and extracting meaningful insights from data, AI developers can create more robust and reliable systems that can adapt to new information and make better decisions.

The chapter will begin with an overview of the fundamentals of probability theory, including the basic concepts and principles that underpin this fascinating area of mathematics. We will then move on to descriptive statistics, where we will learn how to summarize and visualize data meaningfully. This will be followed by a discussion of inferential statistics, which involves drawing conclusions from data and predicting future events.

Next, we will explore the concept of Bayesian inference, a powerful statistical technique that allows us to update our beliefs about the world as new data becomes available. This approach is particularly relevant in AI, enabling machines to learn from experience and improve their performance over time.

Finally, we will conclude the chapter by reflecting on the role of probability and statistics in AI development, highlighting their importance in building intelligent systems that can navigate the complexities of the real world.

As we embark on this journey through the realm of probability and statistics, we invite you to join us in discovering the beauty and power of these mathematical tools and how they can help us unlock the full potential of AI. With a blend of expository, descriptive, narrative, and persuasive writing, this chapter aims to provide a comprehensive and engaging introduction to the essential math for AI. So, let's dive in and explore the fascinating world of probability and statistics in AI!

Fundamentals of Probability Theory

In artificial intelligence (AI), making informed data-based decisions is crucial. Probability theory is the backbone of this decision-making process, providing a mathematical framework to quantify uncertainty and make predictions. In this section, we will delve into the fundamentals of probability theory, exploring its core concepts and their applications in AI.

Basic Concepts of Probability

- **Sample Space and Events:** The sample space (S) represents the set of all possible outcomes of a random experiment. An event is a subset of the sample space of one or more outcomes. For example, when rolling a six-sided die, the sample space is S = {1, 2, 3, 4, 5, 6}, and an event could be rolling an even number, represented as E = {2, 4, 6}.
- **Probability Measure:** A probability measure (denoted as P) is a function that assigns a value between 0 and 1 to each event, indicating the likelihood of that event occurring. The sum of probabilities for all events in the sample space must equal 1. In our die-rolling example, the probability of rolling an even number is P(E) = 3/6 = 1/2.
- **Conditional Probability:** Conditional probability (P(A|B)) represents the probability of event A occurring,

given that event B has occurred. This concept is essential in AI, allowing us to update our beliefs based on new information. For instance, if we know that a rolled die shows an even number, the probability of it being a 4 is $P(4|\text{even}) = 1/3$.

Probability Rules and Theorems

- **Addition Rule:** The addition rule states that the probability of either event A or event B occurring equals the sum of their individual probabilities minus the probability of both events occurring simultaneously. Mathematically, $P(A \cup B) = P(A) + P(B) - P(A \cap B)$.
- **Multiplication Rule:** The multiplication rule is used to calculate the probability of two events occurring simultaneously. If events A and B are independent (i.e., the occurrence of one does not affect the other), then $P(A \cap B) = P(A) \times P(B)$. If they are dependent, $P(A \cap B) = P(A) \times P(B|A)$.
- **Bayes' Theorem:** Bayes' theorem is a cornerstone of probability theory, allowing us to update our beliefs based on new evidence. It states that $P(A|B) = P(B|A) \times P(A) / P(B)$. This theorem is often used in AI to refine predictions as more data becomes available.

Applications of Probability Theory in AI

- **Decision-making:** AI systems often need to make decisions based on uncertain information. Probability theory provides a framework for weighing the likelihood of different outcomes and choosing the most favorable option.
- **Machine Learning:** Probability theory plays a significant role in machine learning algorithms, particularly in the training and evaluation of models.

For example, in supervised learning, probability distributions estimate the relationship between input features and output labels.

- **Natural Language Processing:** In natural language processing, probability theory models the likelihood of different word sequences, enabling AI systems to generate coherent sentences and understand the meaning behind human language.

In conclusion, understanding the fundamentals of probability theory is essential for anyone working in AI. Probability theory enables AI systems to make informed decisions, learn from data, and process human language by providing a mathematical framework to quantify uncertainty. As we continue to explore the vast landscape of AI, the importance of probability theory will only grow, making it an indispensable tool for developers and researchers alike.

Descriptive Statistics: Summarizing and Visualizing Data

In artificial intelligence, data is the lifeblood that fuels the development and growth of intelligent systems. AI practitioners must understand the underlying patterns and structures within the data to make informed decisions and build effective models. This is where descriptive statistics come into play, providing us with the tools to summarize and visualize data meaningfully.

Measures of Central Tendency

The first step in understanding data is to identify its central tendency, a single value representing the center or the "typical" value of a dataset. There are three primary measures of central tendency: the mean, the median, and the mode.

- The **mean**, often called the average, is calculated by adding up all the values in a dataset and dividing the sum by the total number of values. The mean is highly susceptible to the influence of outliers, which can skew the result.
- The **median** is the middle value in a dataset when the values are arranged in ascending or descending order. If there is an even number of values, the median is the average of the two middle values. The median is less affected by outliers and more accurately represents the central tendency in such cases.
- The **mode** is the value that occurs most frequently in a dataset. A dataset can have multiple modes or no modes at all. The mode is handy when dealing with categorical data, where the mean and median may not be applicable.

Measures of Dispersion

While central tendency provides a snapshot of the data's center, it is equally important to understand the spread or dispersion of the data. Measures of dispersion help us quantify the variability within a dataset.

- The **range** is the simplest measure of dispersion, calculated as the difference between a dataset's maximum and minimum values. While easy to compute, the range is highly sensitive to outliers.
- **Variance** is the average of the squared differences between each value and the mean. The standard deviation, the square root of the variance, is a more interpretable measure of dispersion expressed in the same units as the data. A larger standard deviation indicates greater variability in the data.

- The **Interquartile Range (IQR)** is the range within which the central 50% of the data lies. It is calculated as the difference between the first quartile (25th percentile) and the third quartile (75th percentile). The IQR is less sensitive to outliers and provides a more robust measure of dispersion.

Visualizing Data

Visual data representations can provide valuable insights and help identify patterns, trends, and outliers. Some standard data visualization techniques include:

- **Histograms:** A histogram is a graphical representation of the distribution of a dataset, where data is divided into bins or intervals, and the height of each bar represents the frequency of values within that bin.
- **Box Plots:** A box plot is a standardized way of displaying the distribution of a dataset based on the five-number summary (minimum, first quartile, median, third quartile, and maximum). It provides a visual representation of the data's central tendency, dispersion, and potential outliers.
- **Scatter Plots:** Scatter plots visualize the relationship between two continuous variables. Each point on the plot represents a single observation, with the x-axis representing one variable and the y-axis representing the other. Patterns in the scatter plot can indicate correlations or trends between the variables.

In conclusion, descriptive statistics and data visualization techniques are essential tools for understanding the structure and patterns within data. By effectively summarizing and visualizing data, AI practitioners can make informed decisions, identify potential issues, and build more accurate and robust models. As we delve deeper into AI, the importance of probability and statistics only grows, making these foundational concepts indispensable for success.

Inferential Statistics: Drawing Conclusions from Data

In artificial intelligence, making informed decisions based on data is crucial. This is where inferential statistics come into play. This section will delve into the fascinating world of inferential statistics, exploring how it enables us to draw conclusions from data and make predictions about future events or unknown parameters. We will also discuss the importance of hypothesis testing and confidence intervals in decision-making.

The Essence of Inferential Statistics

Inferential statistics is a branch of statistics that focuses on drawing conclusions about a population based on a sample of data. Unlike descriptive statistics, which merely summarize and visualize data, inferential statistics allow us to make predictions and generalizations about a larger group. This is particularly useful in AI, enabling machines to learn from limited data and make informed decisions.

Sampling and Sampling Distributions

The foundation of inferential statistics lies in the concept of sampling. A sample is a population subset selected to represent the entire group. On the other hand, sampling distributions describe the probability of obtaining different samples from the same population. Understanding sampling distributions is essential, as it allows us to quantify the uncertainty associated with our estimates and predictions.

Hypothesis Testing: The Art of Decision Making

One of the most critical aspects of inferential statistics is hypothesis testing. Hypothesis testing is a systematic method used to determine whether a claim about a population parameter is true or false. In AI, hypothesis testing can be employed to evaluate the performance of algorithms, compare different models, or validate assumptions.

The process of hypothesis testing involves the following steps:

- Formulate the null hypothesis (Ho) and the alternative hypothesis (H1).
- Choose a significance level (α), which represents the probability of rejecting the null hypothesis when it is true.
- Calculate the test statistic and the corresponding p-value.
- Compare the p-value with the significance level to make a decision.

Confidence Intervals: Quantifying Uncertainty

Another essential concept in inferential statistics is the confidence interval. A confidence interval is a range of values within which we expect the true population parameter to lie with a certain level of confidence. Confidence intervals measure the uncertainty associated with our estimates, allowing us to make more informed decisions in AI development.

The Power of Inferential Statistics in AI

In conclusion, inferential statistics play a vital role in developing and applying artificial intelligence. By enabling us to draw conclusions from data, make predictions, and quantify uncertainty, inferential statistics provide the foundation for informed decision-making in AI. As we continue to push the boundaries of AI technology, a solid understanding of probability and statistics will remain indispensable in creating intelligent systems that can learn from data and adapt to new situations.

Bayesian Inference: Updating Beliefs with Data

As we delve deeper into probability and statistics, it is crucial to understand the concept of Bayesian inference. This powerful tool allows us to update our beliefs based on new data. In artificial intelligence, Bayesian inference plays a significant role in decision-making, prediction, and modeling. In this section, we will explore the foundations of Bayesian inference, its applications in AI, and how it helps us make sense of uncertainty.

First, let us revisit the concept of conditional probability, which forms the basis of Bayesian inference. Conditional probability is the probability of an event occurring, given that another event has already occurred. In mathematical terms, the conditional probability of event A happening, given that event B has occurred, is denoted as $P(A|B)$. The vertical bar represents the phrase "given that."

Bayesian inference is built upon Bayes' theorem, a fundamental principle in probability theory that relates the conditional probabilities of two events. Mathematically, Bayes' theorem is expressed as:

$$P(A|B) = (P(B|A) * P(A)) / P(B)$$

In the context of AI, we can interpret A as a hypothesis or model and B as the observed data. The theorem allows us to update our belief in the hypothesis ($P(A|B)$) based on the likelihood of observing the data given the hypothesis ($P(B|A)$), the prior probability of the hypothesis ($P(A)$), and the probability of observing the data ($P(B)$).

Now, let's explore how Bayesian inference is applied in AI. One common application is in natural language processing (NLP), where Bayesian models are used to predict the next word in a sentence or classify a document's topic. For instance, a spam filter may use Bayesian inference to determine the probability that an email is spam, given the words it contains. By continuously updating the model with new data, the filter becomes more accurate in identifying spam emails.

Another application of Bayesian inference in AI is robotics, where robots use sensor data to update their beliefs about their environment. For example, a self-driving car may use Bayesian inference to estimate its position on the road, given the data from its sensors. As the car gathers more data, its position estimate becomes more accurate, allowing it to navigate safely and efficiently.

In conclusion, Bayesian inference is a powerful technique that enables AI systems to update their beliefs based on new data. By incorporating uncertainty and continuously refining their models, AI systems can make more informed decisions, predictions, and inferences. As we continue to develop and refine AI technologies, the role of probability and statistics, particularly Bayesian inference, will remain a critical component in our quest to create intelligent machines.

The Role of Probability and Statistics in AI Development

As we conclude this enlightening journey through probability and statistics, it is crucial to reflect on the significance of these mathematical concepts in the development of artificial intelligence. The intricate relationship between AI and the mathematical principles discussed in this chapter is undeniable, and understanding this connection is vital for anyone seeking to delve into the world of AI.

This chapter has explored the fundamentals of probability theory, descriptive and inferential statistics, and Bayesian inference. Each of these concepts plays a critical role in designing, implementing, and improving AI systems. By providing a solid foundation in these areas, we empower ourselves with the necessary tools to create intelligent systems that can learn from data, adapt to new information, and make informed decisions.

Probability theory is the backbone of AI, as it allows machines to reason under uncertainty. By quantifying the likelihood of various outcomes, AI systems can make informed decisions even when faced with incomplete or ambiguous information. This ability to reason probabilistically is essential for tasks such as natural language processing, computer vision, and robotics, where uncertainty is an inherent part of the problem.

Descriptive statistics, on the other hand, enable AI systems to summarize and visualize data effectively. By understanding the central tendency, dispersion, and distribution of data, AI developers can gain valuable insights into the underlying patterns and relationships within the data. This knowledge is crucial for designing algorithms that efficiently process and analyze large datasets, a common requirement in AI applications.

Inferential statistics play a pivotal role in AI by allowing developers to draw conclusions from data. Through hypothesis testing and confidence intervals, AI systems can make generalizations about populations based on samples, enabling them to learn from limited data and make predictions about future events. This ability to infer patterns and relationships from data is at the heart of machine learning, a subfield of AI that focuses on creating algorithms to learn from and make predictions based on data.

Lastly, Bayesian inference provides a powerful framework for updating beliefs with data. By combining prior knowledge with new information, AI systems can continuously refine their understanding of the world and make better decisions as they encounter new data. This dynamic learning process is particularly valuable in AI applications where the environment is constantly changing, such as autonomous vehicles or financial markets.

In conclusion, probability and statistics are indispensable tools in developing AI systems. By mastering these mathematical concepts, AI developers can create intelligent systems that can reason under uncertainty, learn from data, and adapt to new information. As AI advances and permeates various aspects of our lives, a strong foundation in probability and statistics will remain essential for those seeking to contribute to this exciting and rapidly evolving field.

Chapter Summary

- Probability and statistics are interconnected branches of mathematics that play a pivotal role in AI, providing a powerful toolkit for understanding and managing uncertainty.
- Probability theory focuses on the likelihood of events occurring and is essential for AI systems to make informed decisions based on data, particularly in natural language processing, computer vision, and robotics.
- Descriptive statistics help summarize and visualize data, enabling AI developers to gain valuable insights into the underlying patterns and relationships within the data, which is crucial for designing efficient algorithms.
- Inferential statistics allow AI systems to draw conclusions from data, predict future events, and generalize about populations based on samples, which is at the heart of machine learning.
- Bayesian inference is a powerful technique that enables AI systems to update their beliefs based on new data, allowing them to make more informed decisions, predictions, and inferences.
- Hypothesis testing and confidence intervals are essential components of inferential statistics, providing a systematic method for determining the validity of claims about population parameters and quantifying the uncertainty associated with estimates.

- AI applications such as natural language processing, robotics, and machine learning rely heavily on probability and statistics for decision-making, prediction, and modeling.
- A strong foundation in probability and statistics is essential for AI developers to create intelligent systems that can reason under uncertainty, learn from data, and adapt to new information.

3

CALCULUS: OPTIMIZING AI MODELS

W
hen building artificial intelligence (AI), the ability to create efficient and accurate models is of utmost importance. The need for optimization becomes increasingly apparent as AI continues to permeate various industries and applications. One of the most powerful mathematical tools at our disposal for optimizing AI models is calculus. This branch of mathematics, which deals with the study of change and

motion, has proven to be an invaluable asset in developing and fine-tuning AI systems.

At its core, calculus is the study of continuous change, and this concept makes it so well-suited for AI model optimization. AI models often involve complex mathematical functions that must be adjusted and fine-tuned to achieve the desired level of accuracy and efficiency. By applying the principles of calculus, we can gain a deeper understanding of these functions and how they can be manipulated to optimize the performance of our AI models.

A key concept in calculus that plays a crucial role in AI model optimization is the derivative. Derivatives allow us to analyze the rate of change of a function, which in turn helps us understand how minor adjustments to the input variables can impact the output of the model. This understanding is essential for gradient descent algorithms, widely used in AI to minimize model prediction errors.

As we delve deeper into calculus and AI model optimization, we will also explore the integration of calculus concepts in neural networks. Neural networks are a fundamental component of many AI systems, and understanding how calculus can be applied to these networks is essential for optimizing their performance.

Furthermore, we will examine the role of partial derivatives and multivariable optimization in AI models. As AI systems become more complex and involve a greater number of variables, the ability to optimize these models using multivariable calculus becomes increasingly important.

Throughout this chapter, we will also discuss real-world applications of calculus in AI models, showcasing the power and versatility of this mathematical tool in the context of AI optimization. From natural language processing to computer vision, calculus ensures that AI models are as efficient and accurate as possible.

In conclusion, the power of calculus in AI model optimization cannot be overstated. By understanding and applying the principles of calculus, we can unlock the full potential of AI systems and ensure that they continue to revolutionize the world around us. As we explore the various facets of calculus in AI model optimization, we will gain a deeper appreciation for the beauty and utility of this mathematical discipline in artificial intelligence.

The Role of Derivatives in Gradient Descent Algorithms

In artificial intelligence (AI), calculus is pivotal in optimizing AI models. One of the most significant applications of calculus in AI is using derivatives in gradient descent algorithms. In this section, we will delve into the importance of derivatives in these algorithms and explore how they contribute to optimizing AI models.

To begin with, let us first understand what gradient descent algorithms are. In simple terms, gradient descent is an optimization technique to minimize a function iteratively. It is widely employed in machine learning and deep learning for training AI models, particularly in scenarios that aim to minimize the error or loss function. The ultimate goal of gradient descent is to find the optimal set of parameters that minimize the loss function, thereby improving the model's performance.

Let us focus on derivatives and their role in gradient descent algorithms. In the context of calculus, a derivative represents the rate of change of a function concerning its input variable. In other words, it measures how sensitive the output of a function is to small changes in its input. In AI model optimization, derivatives are crucial in determining the direction and magnitude of the adjustments needed to minimize the loss function.

Gradient descent algorithms leverage the power of derivatives to update the model's parameters iteratively. The algorithm starts with an initial set of parameters and computes the gradient (i.e., the first-order derivative) of the loss function concerning each parameter. The gradient points in the direction of the steepest increase in the function's value. However, since our goal is to minimize the loss function, we move in the opposite direction of the gradient, taking steps proportional to the negative of the gradient.

A hyperparameter called the learning rate determines the size of the steps taken in the gradient descent algorithm. A smaller learning rate results in smaller steps, leading to a more gradual convergence to the optimal solution. Conversely, a larger learning rate may cause the algorithm to overshoot the optimal solution, potentially resulting in divergence. Striking the right balance in the learning rate is crucial for the success of the gradient descent algorithm.

In summary, derivatives play a vital role in gradient descent algorithms, widely used for optimizing AI models. By computing the gradient of the loss function, we can determine the direction and magnitude of the adjustments needed to minimize the loss function and improve the model's performance. The power of calculus, specifically the concept of derivatives, is indispensable in AI model optimization.

Integrating Calculus Concepts in Neural Networks

As we delve into the fascinating world of artificial intelligence, it becomes increasingly evident that calculus plays a pivotal role in optimizing AI models. One of the most prominent applications of calculus in AI is the integration of its concepts in neural networks. This section will explore how calculus concepts, particularly derivatives, and integrals, are employed in designing and optimizing neural networks.

Understanding Neural Networks

Before we discuss the role of calculus in neural networks, it is essential to understand what neural networks are and how they function. Neural networks are a series of interconnected nodes or neurons inspired by the human brain's structure. These networks are designed to recognize patterns, make decisions, and learn from experience. They consist of multiple layers, including an input layer, one or more hidden layers, and an output layer. Each neuron in a layer is connected to every neuron in the subsequent layer, with each connection having an associated weight.

The Role of Calculus in Neural Networks

In neural networks, the activation function is a crucial component that determines the output of a neuron based on its input. Common activation functions include the sigmoid, hyperbolic tangent (tanh), and rectified linear unit (ReLU) functions. The choice of activation function can significantly impact the network's performance and learning ability.

Calculus comes into play when we consider the derivatives of these activation functions. During the training process, neural networks use backpropagation to adjust the weights of the connections between neurons. This process involves computing the gradient of the error function with respect to each weight by using the chain rule, a fundamental concept in calculus. The chain rule requires the derivatives of the activation functions, making calculus an indispensable tool in optimizing neural networks.

Another essential aspect of neural networks is the loss function, which quantifies the difference between the network's predicted output and the actual target output. The goal of training a neural network is to minimize this loss function, and calculus plays a vital role in achieving this objective.

Gradient descent, a first-order optimization algorithm, is commonly used to minimize the loss function. It involves iteratively updating the weights of the connections in the neural network by moving in the direction of the steepest decrease of the loss function. This direction is determined by the gradient of the loss function, a vector of its partial derivatives with respect to each weight. Once again, calculus proves to be an essential tool in the optimization process.

In summary, calculus concepts are deeply ingrained in the design and optimization of neural networks. The use of derivatives in activation functions and the calculation of gradients in loss functions are just a few examples of how calculus plays a critical role in developing efficient and effective AI models. By understanding and applying these calculus concepts, AI practitioners can harness the power of neural networks to create innovative solutions to complex problems and drive advancements in artificial intelligence.

Partial Derivatives and Multivariable Optimization

In the realm of artificial intelligence, optimization is a crucial aspect of model development. As we delve deeper into calculus, we encounter partial derivatives and multivariable optimization, which significantly refine AI models. In this section, we will explore the concept of partial derivatives, their application in multivariable optimization, and how they contribute to the overall performance of AI models.

Understanding Partial Derivatives

To comprehend partial derivatives, we must first revisit the concept of a derivative. In single-variable calculus, a derivative represents the rate of change of a function concerning a single variable. However, in multivariable calculus, we deal with functions that have multiple input variables. This is where partial derivatives come into play.

Partial derivatives measure the rate of change of a multivariable function with respect to one variable while keeping the other variables constant. In other words, they allow us to examine how a function changes when we alter just one of its input variables. This is particularly useful in AI models, as they often involve multiple variables that interact with one another.

Multivariable Optimization Techniques

Multivariable optimization is finding the optimal values of multiple variables in a function to achieve a specific goal, such as minimizing error or maximizing efficiency. In AI models, this often involves adjusting the weights and biases of a neural network to improve its performance.

One popular technique for multivariable optimization is gradient descent, which we briefly touched upon in Section II. Gradient descent is an iterative algorithm that adjusts the variables of a function to minimize its output, such as the error in a neural network. It does this by computing the gradient, a vector of partial derivatives, and updating the variables accordingly.

Another technique is the Newton-Raphson method, which is an iterative method that uses second-order partial derivatives (also known as the Hessian matrix) to find the optimal values of a function. This method can be more efficient than gradient descent in certain situations, as it considers the curvature of the function, allowing for faster convergence to the optimal solution.

The Impact of Partial Derivatives and Multivariable Optimization on AI Models

Incorporating partial derivatives and multivariable optimization techniques into AI models can significantly improve their performance. By fine-tuning the variables within a model, we can minimize error and maximize efficiency, leading to more accurate predictions and better decision-making capabilities.

For instance, adjusting the weights and biases using gradient descent in a neural network can lead to a more accurate model that can better generalize to new data. Similarly, optimizing the parameters of an agent's policy in reinforcement learning can result in more effective decision-making and improved overall performance.

In conclusion, partial derivatives and multivariable optimization are essential tools in developing and refining AI models. By understanding and applying these concepts, we can create more efficient, accurate, and powerful artificial intelligence systems that profoundly impact various aspects of our lives.

Real-World Applications of Calculus in AI Models

In today's rapidly evolving technological landscape, artificial intelligence (AI) has become integral to various industries, from healthcare and finance to entertainment and transportation. The optimization of AI models is crucial for their performance, and calculus plays a pivotal role in achieving this. In this section, we will delve into some real-world applications of calculus in AI models, showcasing its significance in enhancing the efficiency and effectiveness of these systems.

Autonomous Vehicles

One of the most exciting applications of AI is in developing autonomous vehicles. These self-driving cars rely on many sensors and algorithms to navigate complex environments. Calculus comes into play in optimizing control algorithms, determining the vehicle's acceleration, braking, and steering. Engineers can fine-tune these algorithms using derivatives and integrals to ensure smooth and safe navigation, minimizing the risk of accidents and enhancing the overall driving experience.

Image Recognition and Computer Vision

AI-powered image recognition and computer vision systems have become increasingly prevalent in various applications, such as facial recognition, medical imaging, and surveillance. These systems rely on neural networks trained to identify patterns and features within images. Calculus is essential in optimizing these networks, as it helps adjust the weights and biases of the neurons during the training process. By employing gradient descent algorithms based on the concept of derivatives, these systems can learn to recognize and classify images with remarkable accuracy.

Natural Language Processing

Natural language processing (NLP) is another domain where AI has made significant strides, enabling machines to understand and generate human language. Applications like chatbots, voice assistants, and sentiment analysis rely on NLP algorithms to function effectively. Calculus is crucial in optimizing these algorithms, particularly in training recurrent neural networks (RNNs) and transformers, which are widely used in NLP tasks. By leveraging the power of partial derivatives and multivariable optimization, developers can fine-tune these models to comprehend better and respond to complex language patterns.

Financial Forecasting and Risk Management

AI has also found its way into finance, which is used to forecast market trends, manage investment portfolios, and assess risks. Calculus is instrumental in optimizing these AI models, as it enables the development of more accurate and reliable prediction algorithms. By using concepts such as derivatives and integrals, financial analysts can create models that can adapt to changing market conditions and make more informed decisions, ultimately leading to increased profitability and reduced risk.

In conclusion, the real-world applications of calculus in AI models are vast and varied, spanning numerous industries and domains. By harnessing the power of calculus, developers and engineers can optimize AI systems to perform at their peak, resulting in more accurate, efficient, and practical solutions to complex problems. As AI continues to advance and permeate our daily lives, the importance of calculus in optimizing these models will only grow, further solidifying its status as an essential mathematical tool in artificial intelligence.

The Power of Calculus in AI Model Optimization

As we reach the end of our exploration into the fascinating world of calculus and its applications in artificial intelligence, it is essential to take a moment to appreciate the power and significance of this mathematical discipline in optimizing AI models. Throughout this chapter, we have delved into the intricacies of calculus, from the role of derivatives in gradient descent algorithms to the integration of calculus concepts in neural networks. We have also examined the importance of partial derivatives and multivariable optimization, and real-world applications of calculus in AI models.

The power of calculus in AI model optimization cannot be overstated. It is the backbone of many optimization techniques that enable AI models to learn and adapt to new data, ultimately improving their performance and accuracy. By understanding the underlying mathematical principles, we can better comprehend the inner workings of these models and develop more efficient and effective algorithms.

One of the most significant contributions of calculus to AI is its ability to help us understand and navigate the complex, multidimensional landscapes that AI models often inhabit. We can determine the direction and magnitude of change in these landscapes using derivatives and partial derivatives, allowing us to make informed decisions about adjusting our models to achieve optimal performance.

Furthermore, the integration of calculus concepts in neural networks has led to the development of powerful learning algorithms, such as backpropagation, which have revolutionized the field of AI and enabled the creation of sophisticated models capable of tackling a wide range of tasks. These models have found applications in various industries, from healthcare and finance to entertainment and transportation, transforming how we live, work, and interact with the world around us.

In conclusion, the power of calculus in AI model optimization is undeniable. It is a critical tool that allows us to harness the full potential of artificial intelligence, pushing the boundaries of what is possible and paving the way for a future where AI models continue to improve and evolve, ultimately leading to a more intelligent, efficient, and connected world. As we explore and develop new AI technologies, the importance of calculus and its applications in AI model optimization will continue to grow, solidifying its status as an indispensable component of the AI toolkit.

Chapter Summary

- Calculus is a powerful mathematical tool for optimizing AI models, as it deals with the study of continuous change, making it well-suited for understanding complex functions in AI systems.
- Derivatives play a crucial role in gradient descent algorithms, widely used in AI to minimize model prediction errors. They help determine the direction and magnitude of adjustments needed to optimize the model's performance.
- Calculus concepts, particularly derivatives and integrals, are integrated into neural networks, a fundamental component of many AI systems. Understanding how calculus can be applied to these networks is essential for optimizing their performance.
- Partial derivatives and multivariable optimization are important in AI models, as they allow for examining how a function changes when altering just one of its input variables. This is particularly useful in complex AI systems with multiple interacting variables.
- Gradient descent and the Newton-Raphson method are popular techniques for multivariable optimization, which rely on calculus concepts to find the optimal values of a function.
- Real-world applications of calculus in AI models span various industries, including autonomous vehicles, image recognition and computer vision, natural language processing, financial forecasting, and risk management.

- By harnessing the power of calculus, developers and engineers can optimize AI systems to perform at their peak, resulting in more accurate, efficient, and practical solutions to complex problems.
- As AI continues to advance and permeate our daily lives, the importance of calculus in optimizing AI models will only grow, further solidifying its status as an essential mathematical tool in artificial intelligence.

4

GRAPH THEORY: MODELING COMPLEX RELATIONSHIPS

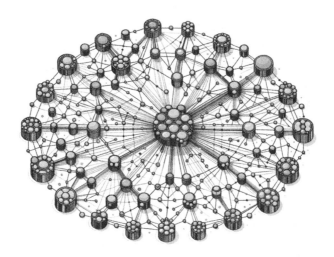

I n the ever-evolving landscape of artificial intelligence (AI), the ability to model and analyze complex relationships is crucial for developing intelligent systems that can effectively solve real-world problems. One of the most powerful mathematical tools for achieving this is graph theory, a branch of discrete mathematics that studies graphs. This chapter will delve into the fascinating world of graph theory and explore its significance in AI.

At its core, graph theory is the study of structures called graphs, which consist of vertices (also known as nodes) and edges (also known as links or connections) that connect these vertices. These graphs can represent various systems and relationships, from social networks and transportation systems to molecular structures and neural networks. By analyzing the properties and patterns within these graphs, we can gain valuable insights into the underlying systems they represent and develop more effective algorithms and AI models.

The importance of graph theory in AI cannot be overstated. As AI systems grow in complexity and sophistication, the need for efficient and accurate methods to model and analyze complex relationships becomes increasingly vital. Graph theory provides a versatile and robust framework for representing and processing information that closely mirrors the interconnected nature of the real world. This enables AI researchers and practitioners to tackle various problems, from natural language processing and computer vision to recommendation systems and robotics.

In this chapter, we will first introduce graph theory's key concepts and terminology, providing a solid foundation for understanding the subject. Next, we will discuss some of the essential graph algorithms and their applications in AI, showcasing the versatility and utility of graph theory in solving complex problems. We will then present real-world examples of graph theory in action, demonstrating its impact on the development and performance of AI systems. Finally, we will address the challenges and future directions in graph theory for AI, highlighting the potential for further advancements and breakthroughs in this exciting field.

As we embark on this journey through graph theory, we hope you will gain a deeper appreciation for its power and potential in advancing AI. By understanding and harnessing the capabilities of graph theory, we can unlock new possibilities for AI systems, paving the way for a future where intelligent machines can better understand and navigate the intricate web of relationships that define our world.

Key Concepts and Terminology in Graph Theory

As we delve into the fascinating world of graph theory, we must familiarize ourselves with the key concepts and terminology that form the foundation of this mathematical discipline. In this section, we will explore the essential terms and ideas that will enable us better to understand graph theory's applications in artificial intelligence.

A graph is a mathematical representation of a set of objects, called vertices (or nodes), and the relationships between them, called edges (or links). In AI, vertices can represent entities such as people, places, or things, while edges represent the relationships or connections between these entities.

Graphs can be classified into two main types based on the nature of their edges. In an undirected graph, edges have no specific direction, implying that the relationship between vertices is bidirectional. Conversely, a directed graph (or digraph) has edges with a specific direction, indicating that the relationship between vertices is unidirectional.

Another classification of graphs is based on the presence or absence of weights assigned to their edges. In a weighted graph, each edge is assigned a numerical value, representing the strength or cost of the connection between the vertices. An unweighted graph, on the other hand, does not have any values assigned to its edges.

The degree of a vertex is the number of edges connected to it. In a directed graph, we distinguish between the in-degree (number of incoming edges) and the out-degree (number of outgoing edges) of a vertex.

A path in a graph is a sequence of vertices connected by edges. The length of a path is the number of edges in the sequence. In a weighted graph, the weight of a path is the sum of the weights of its edges.

A cycle is a path that starts and ends at the same vertex, with no other vertices repeated in the sequence. A graph is called acyclic if it contains no cycles.

A graph is connected if there is a path between every pair of vertices. In a directed graph, we distinguish between strongly connected (a path exists in both directions between every pair of vertices) and weakly connected (the graph is connected if we ignore the direction of the edges) graphs.

A subgraph is a graph formed by a subset of the vertices and edges of a larger graph. A subgraph is induced if it contains all the edges of the larger graph that connect the selected vertices.

A tree is a connected, acyclic graph. A forest is a collection of trees, i.e., a graph that is acyclic but not necessarily connected.

Two graphs are isomorphic if a one-to-one correspondence exists between their vertices and edges, such that the connectivity between vertices is preserved.

With these fundamental concepts and terminology in mind, we are better equipped to explore the various graph algorithms and their applications in artificial intelligence. As we progress through this chapter, we will see how graph theory plays a pivotal role in modeling complex relationships and solving intricate problems in AI.

Graph Algorithms and Their Applications in AI

In artificial intelligence (AI), graph theory plays a pivotal role in modeling complex relationships and solving intricate problems. Graph algorithms, the mathematical procedures designed to analyze and manipulate graph structures, are indispensable tools for AI researchers and practitioners. In this section, we will delve into the world of graph algorithms, exploring their applications in AI and how they contribute to the development of intelligent systems.

Graph algorithms allow us to traverse, search, and analyze graphs systematically and efficiently. These algorithms can be broadly classified into two categories: traversal algorithms and optimization algorithms. Traversal algorithms, such as depth-first search (DFS) and breadth-first search (BFS), are used to explore the vertices and edges of a graph, while optimization algorithms, like Dijkstra's and Bellman-Ford, are employed to find the shortest path between two nodes or solve other optimization problems.

Applications of Graph Algorithms in AI

Natural Language Processing (NLP): Graph algorithms are widely used in NLP to model and analyze the relationships between words, phrases, and sentences. For instance, the PageRank algorithm, initially developed by Google to rank web pages, can be applied to text corpora to identify the most important words or phrases in a document. This technique is beneficial in keyword extraction, summarization, and sentiment analysis tasks.

Computer Vision: In computer vision, graph algorithms are employed to model the relationships between pixels, regions, and objects in an image. For example, the minimum spanning tree (MST) algorithm can segment an image into distinct regions based on color or texture similarity. Additionally, graph-based techniques like spectral clustering can be applied to group similar images together, aiding in object recognition and scene understanding tasks.

Social Network Analysis: AI systems that analyze social networks rely heavily on graph algorithms to uncover patterns and trends in individual relationships. Algorithms like community detection and betweenness centrality can help identify influential users, detect tightly-knit groups, and predict the spread of information or influence through a network.

Recommender Systems: Graph algorithms play a crucial role in developing recommender systems, which provide personalized suggestions to users based on their preferences and behavior. Collaborative filtering, a popular technique in recommender systems, utilizes graph algorithms to identify users with similar tastes and recommend items based on their collective preferences.

The Impact of Graph Algorithms on AI: The applications of graph algorithms in AI are vast and varied, enabling researchers and practitioners to model complex relationships and solve intricate problems easily. By leveraging the power of graph algorithms, AI systems can better understand and interpret the world around them, leading to more accurate predictions, improved decision-making, and enhanced user experiences.

In conclusion, graph algorithms are indispensable tools in the AI toolbox, providing valuable insights and solutions to various challenges. As AI advances and evolves, the importance of graph theory and its associated algorithms will only grow, paving the way for more sophisticated and intelligent systems.

Challenges and Future Directions in Graph Theory for AI

As we delve deeper into the world of artificial intelligence, the significance of graph theory in modeling complex relationships becomes increasingly apparent. However, despite its numerous applications and potential, challenges still need to be addressed, and future directions need to be explored to fully harness the power of graph theory in advancing AI.

One of the primary challenges in applying graph theory to AI is the sheer size and complexity of real-world graphs. As the number of nodes and edges in a graph increases, so does the computational complexity of graph algorithms. This can lead to scalability issues, mainly when dealing with massive datasets common in AI applications. Researchers continuously develop more efficient algorithms and parallel processing techniques to overcome these scalability challenges.

Another challenge lies in the dynamic nature of many real-world graphs. In many AI applications, the relationships between entities are not static but change over time. This requires the development of dynamic graph algorithms that can adapt to these changes and still provide accurate and timely insights. Additionally, incorporating uncertainty and probabilistic reasoning into graph models is an area that needs further exploration, as real-world relationships often involve a degree of uncertainty.

In terms of future directions, one promising area of research is integrating graph theory with other AI techniques, such as machine learning and natural language processing. By combining the strengths of these different approaches, we can develop more powerful and versatile AI systems that tackle a wider range of problems. For example, graph-based machine learning algorithms can be used to analyze and learn from the structure of large-scale networks, while natural language processing can help extract meaningful relationships from unstructured text data.

Another exciting direction is the development of new graph-based AI models that can better capture the complexity of real-world relationships. For instance, hypergraphs, which allow edges to connect more than two nodes, can be used to model higher-order relationships and interactions between entities. Similarly, multilayer graphs can be employed to represent multiple types of relationships or different aspects of a single relationship, providing a richer and more nuanced understanding of complex systems.

In conclusion, graph theory holds immense potential in advancing the field of artificial intelligence. By addressing the challenges of scalability, dynamic relationships, and uncertainty and exploring new directions, such as integrating graph theory with other AI techniques and developing more sophisticated graph models, we can unlock the full power of graph theory in AI.

The Power of Graph Theory in Advancing AI

As we have explored throughout this chapter, graph theory plays a pivotal role in developing and advancing artificial intelligence. By providing a robust mathematical framework for modeling complex relationships, graph theory enables AI systems to understand better, analyze, and navigate the intricate web of connections within various domains. In this conclusion, we will briefly recap the key points discussed in this chapter and highlight the immense potential of graph theory in propelling AI to new heights.

We began our journey into graph theory by introducing its fundamental concepts and terminology, such as vertices, edges, and adjacency matrices. These building blocks serve as the foundation for more advanced topics and applications in AI. We then delved into graph algorithms, essential tools for AI systems to process and analyze graph data efficiently. These algorithms, such as Dijkstra's shortest path and the PageRank algorithm, have been instrumental in solving complex problems in AI, from natural language processing to social network analysis.

Throughout the chapter, we showcased real-world examples of graph theory in action within AI systems. These examples illustrated the versatility and power of graph theory in addressing diverse challenges, such as detecting fraud in financial transactions, predicting protein interactions in bioinformatics, and optimizing transportation networks. These applications underscore the immense value of graph theory in enhancing the capabilities of AI systems across various industries and disciplines.

However, we also acknowledged the challenges and future directions in graph theory for AI. As AI systems evolve and tackle increasingly complex problems, researchers must develop novel graph algorithms and techniques to keep pace with these advancements. Moreover, the ethical implications of AI systems that rely on graph theory, such as privacy concerns and potential biases in graph data, must be carefully addressed.

In conclusion, the power of graph theory in advancing AI cannot be overstated. Graph theory has become an indispensable tool in the AI toolkit by enabling AI systems to model and navigate complex relationships. As we continue to push the boundaries of what AI can achieve, graph theory will undoubtedly remain a critical component in the ongoing quest to develop intelligent systems that can solve the most pressing challenges of our time.

Chapter Summary

- Graph theory is a branch of discrete mathematics that deals with the study of graphs, which consist of vertices (nodes) and edges (connections). It is crucial for modeling and analyzing complex relationships in artificial intelligence (AI).
- Key concepts and terminology in graph theory include graphs, directed and undirected graphs, weighted and unweighted graphs, degree, path, cycle, connectivity, subgraph, trees, forests, and graph isomorphism.
- Graph algorithms are essential tools for AI systems to process and analyze graph data efficiently. They can be broadly classified into traversal algorithms (e.g., depth-first search and breadth-first search) and optimization algorithms (e.g., Dijkstra's and Bellman-Ford).
- Graph theory has numerous applications in AI, including natural language processing (NLP), computer vision, social network analysis, recommender systems, and autonomous vehicles and robotics.
- Real-world examples of graph theory in AI systems include social network analysis, recommendation systems, natural language processing, computer vision, autonomous vehicles, and robotics.
- Challenges in applying graph theory to AI include the size and complexity of real-world graphs, the dynamic nature of many real-world graphs, and incorporating uncertainty and probabilistic reasoning into graph models.
- Future directions in graph theory for AI include the integration of graph theory with other AI techniques (e.g., machine learning and NLP), the development of new graph-based AI models (e.g., hypergraphs and

multilayer graphs), and addressing ethical implications of AI systems that rely on graph theory.

- Graph theory holds immense potential in advancing the field of AI by providing a robust mathematical framework for modeling complex relationships, enabling AI systems to understand better, analyze, and navigate the intricate web of connections within various domains.

5

DISCRETE MATHEMATICS: EXPLORING COMBINATORIAL PROBLEMS

I n the world of artificial intelligence (AI), the need for a solid mathematical foundation cannot be overstated. Discrete mathematics is one of the most crucial branches of mathematics that plays a pivotal role in AI development. This chapter aims to provide an insightful overview of discrete mathematics, its core concepts, and its significance in AI.

Discrete mathematics, as the name suggests, deals with discrete or distinct objects, as opposed to continuous mathematics, which focuses on continuous objects. In simpler terms, discrete mathematics is the study of countable, separate values, while continuous mathematics deals with values that can vary continuously. The former is particularly relevant to AI, as it helps understand and solve problems involving finite or countable structures, such as networks, algorithms, and data manipulation.

The importance of discrete mathematics in AI stems from its ability to model and analyze complex relationships, optimize problem-solving, and make informed decisions. As AI systems are designed to process and interpret vast amounts of data, discrete mathematics provides the necessary tools to handle these tasks efficiently and accurately. Moreover, discrete mathematics is the backbone of many AI algorithms, as it enables the development of efficient and reliable solutions to a wide range of problems.

One of the critical aspects of discrete mathematics that makes it indispensable for AI is its focus on combinatorial problems. Combinatorial problems involve finding, counting, or optimizing arrangements of objects under specific constraints. These problems are ubiquitous in AI, arising in various applications, such as natural language processing, computer vision, and machine learning.

This chapter will delve into the fascinating world of discrete mathematics and explore its various concepts, such as permutations, combinations, and partitions. We will also discuss graph theory, which is instrumental in modeling and analyzing complex relationships in AI systems. Furthermore, we will examine probability theory, which plays a crucial role in making informed decisions in AI, and algorithmic efficiency, which is vital for optimizing combinatorial problem-solving.

By the end of this chapter, you will have a comprehensive understanding of the power of discrete mathematics in AI development and its potential to revolutionize how we approach and solve complex problems. So, let us embark on this exciting journey and unravel the mysteries of discrete mathematics and its applications in AI.

Combinatorial Concepts: Permutations, Combinations, and Partitions

In artificial intelligence, discrete mathematics is pivotal in solving complex problems and making informed decisions. One of the most fascinating aspects of discrete mathematics is combinatorial concepts, which involve the study of finite or countable discrete structures. This section will delve into the world of permutations, combinations, and partitions, exploring their significance in AI development.

Permutations: Ordering Matters

Permutations are a fundamental concept in combinatorial mathematics, which deals with the arrangement of objects in a specific order. In AI, permutations are often used to analyze and solve problems that involve sequencing, such as determining the optimal route for a delivery truck or finding the best sequence of moves in a game.

A permutation is an arrangement of objects in a specific order without repetition. The number of permutations of a set of n objects is given by the factorial function, denoted as n! (n factorial). For example, the number of permutations of a set of 3 objects (A, B, C) is 3! = 3 × 2 × 1 = 6. These permutations are ABC, ACB, BAC, BCA, CAB, and CBA.

Combinations: Order Doesn't Matter

While permutations focus on the arrangement of objects in a specific order, combinations are concerned with the selection of objects without regard to their arrangement. Combinations are used in AI to solve problems that involve selecting a subset of items from a larger set, such as choosing the best features for a machine learning model or selecting a group of sensors for optimal data collection.

The number of combinations of a set of n objects taken r at a time, denoted as C(n, r) or "n choose r," is calculated using the formula:

$$C(n, r) = n! \, / \, (r! \, (n\text{-}r)!)$$

For example, the number of combinations of a set of 3 objects (A, B, C) taken 2 at a time is C(3, 2) = 3! / (2! (3-2)!) = 3. These combinations are AB, AC, and BC.

Partitions: Dividing into Distinct Groups

Partitions, another essential combinatorial concept, involve dividing a set of objects into distinct, non-overlapping groups. Partitions are used in AI to solve problems that require dividing data into clusters or groups, such as image segmentation or customer segmentation in marketing.

The number of partitions of a set of n objects into k non-empty groups is denoted as P(n, k) and can be calculated using the Stirling numbers of the second kind or recursive formulas. For example, the number of partitions of a set of 4 objects (A, B, C, D) into 2 non-empty groups is P(4, 2) = 7. These partitions are (AB, CD), (AC, BD), (AD, BC), (ABC, D), (ABD, C), (ACD, B), and (BCD, A).

In conclusion, combinatorial concepts such as permutations, combinations, and partitions are indispensable tools in developing AI systems. By understanding and applying these concepts, AI developers can efficiently solve complex problems, optimize decision-making processes, and ultimately create more intelligent and effective AI solutions.

Graph Theory: Modeling and Analyzing Complex Relationships

In artificial intelligence, the ability to model and analyze complex relationships is crucial for developing intelligent systems that can navigate and make sense of the intricate web of connections in the real world. Graph theory, a branch of discrete mathematics, provides a robust framework for representing and understanding these relationships. In this section, we will delve into the fundamentals of graph theory, explore its applications in AI, and discuss how it can be used to solve combinatorial problems.

At its core, graph theory studies mathematical structures called graphs, consisting of vertices (nodes) and edges (links) connecting these vertices. Graphs can be used to represent a wide variety of relationships, such as social networks, transportation systems, and even the structure of the Internet. There are two main types of graphs: directed and undirected. In directed graphs, the edges have a specific direction, indicating a one-way relationship between vertices. In contrast, undirected graphs have edges without direction, signifying a mutual relationship between vertices.

To work with graphs, it is essential to understand their representation and the terminology associated with them. Graphs can be represented using adjacency matrices, adjacency lists, or edge lists. An adjacency matrix is a square matrix where the entry at position (i, j) indicates the presence of an edge between vertices i and j. Adjacency lists store the neighbors of each vertex in a list, while edge lists store all the edges in a graph as pairs of vertices.

Some common terms in graph theory include:

- **Degree:** The number of edges connected to a vertex.
- **Path:** A sequence of vertices connected by edges.
- **Cycle:** A path that starts and ends at the same vertex without repeating other vertices.
- **Connected graph:** A graph with a path between every pair of vertices.
- **Subgraph:** A graph formed by a subset of vertices and edges from a larger graph.
- **Tree:** A connected graph without cycles.

Graph theory has numerous applications in AI, ranging from

natural language processing to computer vision. Some examples include:

- **Social network analysis:** Graphs can be used to model relationships between individuals in a social network, enabling AI systems to identify influential users, detect communities, and predict the spread of information.
- **Recommendation systems:** By representing users and items as vertices and their interactions as edges, AI algorithms can analyze the graph's structure to make personalized recommendations.
- **Image segmentation:** In computer vision, graphs can model the relationships between pixels in an image, allowing AI systems to identify and separate distinct objects.
- **Pathfinding:** Graphs can represent the layout of physical spaces, such as road networks or game maps, enabling AI agents to find the shortest or most efficient path between two points.

Graph theory provides a rich toolbox for tackling combinatorial problems in AI. For example, the traveling salesperson problem, which involves finding the shortest route that visits a set of cities and returns to the starting city, can be modeled as a graph with cities as vertices and distances as edge weights. Similarly, the maximum flow problem, which seeks to maximize the flow of resources through a network, can be represented as a directed graph with capacities assigned to each edge.

By leveraging graph algorithms and optimization techniques, AI developers can efficiently solve these and other combinatorial problems, unlocking the full potential of discrete mathematics in AI development.

In conclusion, graph theory plays a vital role in modeling and analyzing complex relationships in artificial intelligence. By understanding the fundamentals of graph theory and its applications in

AI, developers can harness its power to create intelligent systems capable of navigating and making sense of the intricate connections that define our world.

Probability Theory: Making Informed Decisions in AI Systems

As we delve deeper into discrete mathematics, we encounter probability theory, a branch that plays a crucial role in developing and functioning artificial intelligence (AI) systems. Probability theory allows us to make informed decisions by quantifying the likelihood of various outcomes. This section will explore the fundamentals of probability theory and its applications in AI systems.

Probability theory is a mathematical framework that deals with the analysis of random phenomena. It provides us with the tools to model and predict the behavior of complex systems under uncertainty. In AI, probability theory represents and manipulates uncertain information, enabling machines to reason and make decisions in the face of incomplete or ambiguous data.

One of the key concepts in probability theory is the notion of a random variable. A random variable is a function that assigns a numerical value to each outcome of a random experiment. For example, in a coin toss experiment, we can define a random variable X that takes the value 1 if the coin lands heads and 0 if it lands tails. The probability distribution of a random variable describes the likelihood of each possible outcome. In our coin toss example, if the coin is fair, the probability distribution of X would assign a probability of 0.5 to both 1 (heads) and 0 (tails).

In AI systems, we often deal with multiple random variables related to each other. For instance, consider a robot navigating through an environment with obstacles. The robot's position, the positions of the obstacles, and the robot's sensor readings can all be modeled as random variables. We use joint probability distributions to reason about the relationships between these variables, which describe the likelihood of different combinations of variable values.

Conditional probability is another essential concept in probability theory. It allows us to update our beliefs about a random variable based on new information. In the context of AI, this is particularly useful for incorporating sensor readings or user input into the system's decision-making process. Bayes' theorem, a fundamental result in probability theory, provides a way to compute conditional probabilities by relating them to the joint probabilities of the variables involved.

AI systems often need to make decisions based on uncertain information. To do this, they employ decision theory, combining probability and utility theories to determine the best course of action. In decision theory, an AI system evaluates the expected utility of each possible action, considering both the likelihood of different outcomes and the desirability of those outcomes. The system then selects the action with the highest expected utility.

In conclusion, probability theory is a powerful tool for modeling and reasoning about uncertainty in AI systems. By representing and manipulating uncertain information, AI systems can make informed decisions even in the face of incomplete or ambiguous data. As we continue developing increasingly sophisticated AI technologies, our understanding and application of probability theory will remain vital to their success.

Algorithmic Efficiency: Optimizing Combinatorial Problem Solving

In the realm of artificial intelligence, the ability to solve complex combinatorial problems efficiently is of paramount importance. Optimizing algorithms becomes even more critical as AI systems evolve and tackle increasingly intricate tasks. In this section, we will delve into the concept of algorithmic efficiency, explore its significance in combinatorial problem-solving, and discuss various techniques to enhance the performance of AI systems.

Understanding Algorithmic Efficiency

Algorithmic efficiency refers to the effectiveness of an algorithm in terms of the resources it consumes, such as time and memory, to solve a given problem. In the context of combinatorial problems, efficient algorithms can quickly find optimal solutions while minimizing the computational resources required. The efficiency of an algorithm is often measured using its time complexity, which is a function of the input size that describes the number of basic operations the algorithm performs.

The Importance of Algorithmic Efficiency in AI

As AI systems tackle more complex problems, efficient algorithms become increasingly crucial. Inefficient algorithms can lead to slow processing times, excessive memory usage, and the inability to find optimal solutions within a reasonable timeframe. This can be particularly detrimental in real-world applications, where timely decision-making is often essential. By optimizing algorithmic efficiency, AI developers can create systems that are more responsive, accurate, and capable of handling large-scale combinatorial problems.

Techniques for Optimizing Combinatorial Problem Solving

There are several techniques that can be employed to optimize the efficiency of combinatorial problem-solving algorithms. Some of these include:

- **Divide and Conquer:** This approach involves breaking a problem down into smaller subproblems, solving each subproblem independently, and then combining the solutions to form the overall solution. By tackling smaller, more manageable tasks, the algorithm can arrive at a solution more quickly.
- **Dynamic Programming:** This technique involves solving a problem by breaking it down into overlapping

subproblems and storing the results of these subproblems to avoid redundant computations. By reusing previously computed results, dynamic programming can significantly reduce the time complexity of an algorithm.

- **Greedy Algorithms:** Greedy algorithms make locally optimal choices at each step to find a globally optimal solution. While they may not always yield the best possible solution, they can often provide a good approximation relatively quickly.
- **Heuristics:** Heuristic methods involve using problem-specific knowledge or intuition to guide the search for a solution. By incorporating domain-specific insights, heuristics can focus the search on more promising areas of the solution space, thereby reducing the time required to find an optimal solution.

The Power of Discrete Mathematics in AI Development

In conclusion, algorithmic efficiency is vital in developing AI systems capable of solving complex combinatorial problems. By employing techniques such as divide and conquer, dynamic programming, greedy algorithms, and heuristics, AI developers can create systems that are more responsive, accurate, and capable of handling large-scale problems. As the field of AI continues to advance, the importance of discrete mathematics, particularly the optimization of combinatorial problem-solving algorithms, will only continue to grow.

In this final section, we shall reflect on the significance of discrete mathematics in artificial intelligence (AI) and how it empowers developers to create innovative and efficient solutions. Throughout this chapter, we have delved into the various aspects of discrete mathematics, including combinatorial concepts, graph theory, probability theory, and algorithmic efficiency. Each of these components plays a crucial role in developing and optimizing AI systems, enabling them to tackle complex problems and make informed decisions.

Discrete mathematics is the foundation for understanding and analyzing AI systems' intricate structures and relationships. By employing combinatorial concepts such as permutations, combinations, and partitions, developers can explore the vast possibilities and configurations that arise in AI problems. This, in turn, allows them to design algorithms that can efficiently navigate through these possibilities and arrive at optimal solutions.

Graph theory, another essential aspect of discrete mathematics, enables developers to model and analyze complex relationships within AI systems. By representing these relationships as graphs, developers can gain valuable insights into the structure and behavior of their AI systems. This understanding is vital for designing algorithms that can effectively traverse and manipulate these relationships, leading to more robust and adaptable AI solutions.

Probability theory plays a significant role in AI development by providing a framework for making informed decisions in uncertain environments. AI systems often need to make choices based on incomplete or noisy data, and probability theory equips them with the tools to do so in a principled manner. By incorporating probabilistic reasoning into their algorithms, developers can create AI systems capable of making intelligent decisions even when uncertain.

Algorithmic efficiency is a critical consideration in AI development, as it directly impacts the performance and scalability of AI systems. Discrete mathematics offers a wealth of techniques for optimizing combinatorial problem-solving, allowing developers to create algorithms that can efficiently tackle complex problems. By harnessing the power of discrete mathematics, developers can ensure that their AI systems are effective and computationally efficient.

In conclusion, discrete mathematics is an indispensable tool in developing AI systems. Its various components, including combinatorial concepts, graph theory, probability theory, and algorithmic efficiency, provide developers with the necessary knowledge and techniques to create innovative and powerful AI solutions. As AI continues to advance and permeate various aspects of our lives, the importance of discrete mathematics in AI development will only grow, making it an essential area of study for aspiring AI developers and researchers.

Chapter Summary

- Discrete mathematics is a crucial branch of mathematics in AI development, as it helps understand and solve problems involving finite or countable structures, such as networks, algorithms, and data manipulation.
- Combinatorial concepts, including permutations, combinations, and partitions, are essential tools in AI development, enabling efficient problem-solving, optimization, and decision-making processes.
- Graph theory plays a vital role in modeling and analyzing complex relationships in AI systems, allowing developers to create intelligent systems capable of navigating and making sense of intricate connections.
- Probability theory is a powerful tool for modeling and reasoning about uncertainty in AI systems, enabling machines to make informed decisions even in the face of incomplete or ambiguous data.
- Algorithmic efficiency is paramount in AI development, as it directly impacts the performance and scalability of AI systems. Optimizing algorithms ensures that AI systems are effective and computationally efficient.
- Techniques for optimizing combinatorial problem-solving include divide and conquer, dynamic programming, greedy algorithms, and heuristics. These

methods can help AI developers create more responsive, accurate, and capable systems.

- Decision theory, which combines probability theory with utility theory, is used in AI systems to evaluate the expected utility of each possible action and select the action with the highest expected utility.
- As AI continues to advance and permeate various aspects of our lives, the importance of discrete mathematics in AI development will only grow, making it an essential area of study for aspiring AI developers and researchers.

6

NUMERICAL METHODS: SOLVING EQUATIONS AND APPROXIMATING FUNCTIONS

In the constantly-changing world of artificial intelligence (AI), the ability to solve complex problems and make accurate predictions is paramount. As AI systems advance, they increasingly rely on mathematical models and algorithms to process vast amounts of data and make informed decisions. One of the key components in developing these AI systems is using numerical methods, which are techniques for solving mathematical problems using numerical approximations.

Numerical methods play a crucial role in AI, as they provide the foundation for many algorithms and models used in machine learning, data analysis, and optimization. These methods enable AI systems to tackle problems that are too complex or time-consuming to solve analytically, allowing for more efficient and accurate solutions.

This chapter will delve into the fascinating world of numerical methods and their applications in AI. We will explore various techniques for solving equations, approximating functions and optimizing solutions, all essential tools in the AI developer's toolkit.

First, we will examine root-finding techniques used to solve equations and find the points where a given function equals zero. These methods are fundamental in AI, as they can be applied to a wide range of problems, from optimizing neural networks to solving systems of linear equations.

Next, we will discuss interpolation and curve fitting, which are techniques for approximating functions based on a set of data points. These methods are instrumental in AI for tasks such as data analysis, pattern recognition, and function approximation, as they allow for creating smooth and continuous functions that can be easily analyzed and manipulated.

Following this, we will explore numerical integration and differentiation, which are essential tools for analyzing and understanding the behavior of functions. These techniques are invaluable in AI, as they enable the calculation of areas, volumes, and rates of change, all of which are critical for understanding the dynamics of complex systems.

Finally, we will delve into optimization techniques used to find the best possible solution to a given problem. In AI, optimization is a critical component of many algorithms, as it allows for fine-tuning models and discovering optimal solutions to complex problems.

In conclusion, numerical methods are an indispensable part of AI development, providing the mathematical foundation for many algorithms and models that drive modern AI systems. By understanding and mastering these techniques, AI developers can unlock the full potential of their creations and push the boundaries of what is possible in the realm of artificial intelligence.

Root Finding Techniques for Solving Equations

In the fascinating artificial intelligence (AI) world, numerical methods play a crucial role in solving complex mathematical problems that arise in various applications. One such essential aspect is finding the roots of equations, the foundation for many AI algorithms. In this section, we will delve into the realm of root-finding techniques, exploring their significance and how they contribute to the development of AI systems.

Understanding Roots of Equations

Before diving into the techniques, let's first understand the roots of equations. In mathematics, a root of an equation is a value that makes it true when substituted into the equation. In other words, it is the point where the function intersects the x-axis. Finding the roots of an equation is a fundamental problem in mathematics and has numerous applications in AI, such as optimization, computer graphics, and machine learning.

Bracketing Methods

Bracketing methods are a class of root-finding techniques that involve isolating the root within an interval and successively narrowing it down. These methods guarantee convergence, provided the function is continuous, and the initial interval contains a root. Two popular bracketing methods are:

- **Bisection Method:** This technique involves dividing the interval into two equal parts and determining which half contains the root. The process is repeated until the desired level of accuracy is achieved. The bisection method is simple, reliable, and easy to implement, but it can be relatively slow compared to other methods.
- **Regula Falsi (False Position) Method:** This method is an improvement over the bisection method. Instead of dividing the interval into two equal parts, it uses a linear interpolation between the function values at the interval endpoints to estimate the root. This approach generally converges faster than the bisection method but may sometimes be slower due to specific function properties.

Iterative Methods

Iterative methods are another class of root-finding techniques that involve refining an initial guess of the root through a series of iterations. These methods can be faster than bracketing methods but may only sometimes guarantee convergence. Some widely used iterative methods are:

- **Newton-Raphson Method:** This technique uses the function's derivative to approximate the root. It involves linearizing the function at the initial guess and finding the intersection point with the x-axis. The process is repeated until convergence is achieved. The Newton-Raphson method is known for its fast convergence rate but may fail if the initial guess is not close enough to the root or if the function's derivative is zero.
- **Secant Method:** The secant method is a modification of the Newton-Raphson method that does not require the derivative of the function. Instead, it uses two initial guesses and approximates the derivative using the finite

difference between the function values. The secant method converges faster than the bisection method but may be slower than the Newton-Raphson method.

In conclusion, root-finding techniques are indispensable tools in the AI developer's arsenal, enabling them to solve complex equations that arise in various applications. By understanding and implementing these methods, AI systems can be developed more efficiently and accurately, paving the way for groundbreaking innovations.

Interpolation and Curve Fitting for Function Approximation

In artificial intelligence (AI), the ability to approximate functions is a crucial skill that enables machines to learn from data and make predictions. Interpolation and curve fitting are two powerful techniques that allow us to create mathematical models that closely mimic real-world phenomena' behavior. This section will delve into the fascinating world of function approximation, exploring the concepts of interpolation and curve fitting and discussing their significance in AI development.

Understanding Interpolation

Interpolation is a mathematical technique used to estimate the value of a function at a specific point, given a set of known data points. The primary goal of interpolation is to construct a smooth curve that passes through all the given data points, thereby providing a means to predict the function's behavior in between these points. This is particularly useful in AI when we have limited data and need to make inferences about the underlying function.

There are several interpolation methods, each with its strengths and weaknesses. Some of the most common techniques include:

- **Linear Interpolation:** This method connects adjacent data points with straight lines, creating a piecewise linear function. It is simple to implement and computationally efficient but may only accurately capture the true behavior of the function if it is linear between the given points.
- **Polynomial Interpolation:** This technique involves fitting a polynomial function to the data points. The degree of the polynomial is typically chosen to be one less than the number of data points, ensuring the curve passes through all of them. While this method can provide a smooth and continuous curve, it may suffer from oscillations and overfitting, especially when dealing with a large number of data points.
- **Spline Interpolation:** This method divides the data into intervals and fits a separate polynomial function to each interval. The polynomials are chosen to be smooth and continuous at the interval boundaries. Spline interpolation balances simplicity and accuracy, making it a popular choice for many applications.

Curve Fitting: A Generalization of Interpolation

While interpolation focuses on constructing a curve that passes through all the given data points, curve fitting takes a more generalized approach. Curve fitting aims to find a function that best approximates the underlying relationship between the variables, even if it does not pass through every data point. This is particularly useful in AI when dealing with noisy or imperfect data, as it allows us to capture the overall trend without being overly influenced by individual outliers.

Curve fitting typically involves selecting a suitable function (e.g., linear, polynomial, exponential) and adjusting its parameters to minimize the discrepancy between the predicted and actual values. This process is often achieved using optimization techniques, such as least squares or gradient descent.

The Role of Interpolation and Curve Fitting in AI

Interpolation and curve fitting play a vital role in developing AI systems. They enable machines to learn from data, generalize patterns, and predict unseen instances. Some of the key applications of these techniques in AI include:

- **Regression Analysis:** In supervised learning, interpolation and curve fitting can be used to create regression models that predict the output of a continuous variable based on one or more input features.
- **Image Processing:** These techniques can be employed to enhance image resolution, fill in missing pixels, or correct distortions by estimating the values of neighboring pixels.
- **Time Series Forecasting:** Interpolation and curve fitting can be used to analyze and predict trends in time series data, such as stock prices, weather patterns, or sales figures.

In conclusion, interpolation and curve fitting are indispensable tools in the AI toolbox, allowing us to approximate functions and extract meaningful insights from data. By mastering these techniques, we can empower machines to learn from the world around them and make increasingly accurate predictions, ultimately driving the advancement of AI technology.

Numerical Integration and Differentiation

This section will delve into the fascinating world of numerical integration and differentiation, two essential mathematical techniques that play a crucial role in developing artificial intelligence (AI) systems. As we explore these methods, we will gain a deeper understanding of their underlying principles and appreciate their significance in the context of AI.

Numerical integration, also known as quadrature, is a method used to approximate the definite integral of a function. In AI, this technique is often employed to solve problems that involve continuous variables, such as calculating the area under a curve or determining the probability distribution of a random variable. Numerical integration is beneficial when dealing with difficult or impossible functions to integrate analytically.

There are several numerical integration techniques, each with its own set of advantages and limitations. Some of the most popular methods include the trapezoidal rule, Simpson's rule, and Gaussian quadrature. These techniques involve dividing the area under the curve into smaller sections, approximating the function within each section, and then summing the results to obtain the overall integral. The choice of method depends on factors such as the desired accuracy, computational efficiency, and the nature of the function being integrated.

On the other hand, numerical differentiation is the process of approximating the derivative of a function using discrete data points. In AI, this technique is often used to estimate the rate of change of a variable, which can be crucial for tasks such as optimization, control systems, and sensitivity analysis. Numerical differentiation is particularly valuable when dealing with difficult or impossible functions to differentiate analytically.

There are several numerical differentiation techniques, including finite difference methods, such as forward, backward, and central differences, as well as more advanced methods like Richardson extrapolation and automatic differentiation. These techniques involve estimating the slope of the function at a given point by considering the values of the function at nearby points. The choice of method depends on factors such as the desired accuracy, computational efficiency, and the nature of the function being differentiated.

In AI, numerical integration and differentiation are indispensable tools that enable us to tackle complex problems involving continuous variables. By approximating the integral and derivative of functions, we can gain valuable insights into the behavior of AI systems, optimize their performance, and, ultimately, create more intelligent and efficient solutions.

In conclusion, numerical integration and differentiation are vital mathematical techniques that significantly contribute to the development and success of AI systems. As we continue to push the boundaries of AI, it is essential for researchers and practitioners to have a solid grasp of these methods and their applications. By mastering these techniques, we can unlock AI's full potential and revolutionize how we live, work, and interact with the world around us.

Optimization Techniques in AI

In artificial intelligence (AI), optimization techniques play a crucial role in developing and improving algorithms and models. These methods are employed to find the best possible solution to a given problem, often by minimizing or maximizing a specific objective function. In this section, we will delve into the importance of optimization in AI, explore various optimization techniques, and discuss their applications in the field.

The Importance of Optimization in AI

Optimization is at the heart of many AI tasks, such as machine learning, neural networks, and natural language processing. Optimization techniques enable AI systems to learn from data, adapt to new inputs, and make accurate predictions by fine-tuning the parameters of a model. Furthermore, optimization methods can help reduce computational complexity and improve the efficiency of AI algorithms, making them more practical for real-world applications.

Gradient Descent and Its Variants

Gradient descent is a widely used optimization technique in AI, particularly in training neural networks. It is an iterative method that seeks to minimize a given objective function by updating the model's parameters in the direction of the negative gradient of the function. The learning rate, a hyperparameter that controls the step size of each update, plays a crucial role in the convergence of the algorithm.

Several variants of gradient descent, such as stochastic gradient descent (SGD) and mini-batch gradient descent, introduce randomness and batch processing, respectively, to improve the algorithm's efficiency and convergence properties. Additionally, adaptive gradient methods, such as AdaGrad, RMSProp, and Adam, have been developed to adjust the learning rate dynamically based on the history of gradients, further enhancing the optimization process.

Evolutionary Algorithms

Inspired by natural selection and evolution principles, evolutionary algorithms (EAs) are a family of optimization techniques that operate on a population of candidate solutions. EAs typically involve selection, crossover (recombination), and mutation to generate new solutions and evolve the population toward an optimal solution. Genetic algorithms, genetic programming, and differential evolution are popular examples of EAs used in AI applications.

Swarm Intelligence

Swarm intelligence is another class of optimization techniques that draws inspiration from the collective behavior of social organisms, such as ants, bees, and birds. These methods rely on the interaction of simple agents to explore the search space and converge toward an optimal solution. Particle swarm optimization (PSO) and ant colony optimization (ACO) are two well-known swarm intelligence techniques that have been successfully applied to various AI problems, including neural network training, clustering, and combinatorial optimization.

Other Optimization Techniques

Numerous other optimization techniques have been employed in AI, such as simulated annealing, tabu search, and hill climbing. These methods offer different trade-offs between exploration and exploitation, convergence speed, and computational complexity, making them suitable for different types of problems and constraints.

In conclusion, optimization techniques are indispensable tools in the development of AI systems, as they enable the fine-tuning of algorithms and models to achieve better performance and efficiency. By understanding and selecting the appropriate optimization method for a given problem, AI practitioners can harness the full potential of these techniques to advance the state of the art in artificial intelligence.

The Importance of Numerical Methods in AI Development

As we reach the end of this enlightening journey through the world of numerical methods, it is crucial to reflect on the significance of these mathematical techniques in artificial intelligence. The development of AI systems has been a groundbreaking endeavor, and the role of numerical methods in this process cannot be overstated. In this conclusion, we shall recapitulate the key points discussed in this chapter and emphasize the indispensable nature of numerical methods in AI development.

This chapter has explored various numerical techniques instrumental in solving equations and approximating functions. These methods, ranging from root-finding techniques to optimization algorithms, have proven invaluable tools for AI researchers and developers. By providing efficient and accurate solutions to complex mathematical problems, numerical methods have facilitated the creation of sophisticated AI models that can learn, adapt, and make decisions in myriad situations.

One of the most significant contributions of numerical methods to AI development is their ability to handle large-scale data and high-dimensional problems. As AI systems continue to evolve, they are required to process and analyze vast amounts of information. Numerical methods, such as interpolation and curve fitting, enable AI models to approximate functions and make predictions based on this data, enhancing their learning capabilities and overall performance.

Moreover, numerical integration and differentiation techniques have been crucial in developing AI algorithms that adapt and respond to dynamic environments. These methods allow AI systems to compute gradients and estimate the impact of various factors on their decision-making processes. Consequently, AI models can optimize their actions and make more informed choices, leading to improved outcomes and increased efficiency.

Optimization techniques, such as gradient descent and genetic algorithms, have also played a pivotal role in AI development. These methods enable AI systems to fine-tune their parameters and minimize errors, resulting in more accurate and reliable models. Furthermore, optimization techniques have facilitated the creation of AI models that tackle complex, real-world problems, such as natural language processing, image recognition, and autonomous navigation.

In conclusion, the importance of numerical methods in AI development is undeniable. These mathematical techniques have provided the foundation for AI algorithms and enabled the creation of advanced AI systems that can learn, adapt, and make decisions in an ever-changing world. As AI continues to progress and permeate various aspects of our lives, the role of numerical methods in shaping the future of this technology will remain paramount. By understanding and harnessing the power of these methods, we can unlock AI's full potential and revolutionize how we live, work, and interact with the world around us.

Chapter Summary

- Numerical methods are essential in AI development, providing the foundation for algorithms and models used in machine learning, data analysis, and optimization.
- Root-finding techniques, such as the bisection method and Newton-Raphson method, are crucial for solving equations and optimizing AI systems.
- Interpolation and curve fitting techniques, including linear interpolation and spline interpolation, enable AI models to approximate functions and make predictions based on limited data.
- Numerical integration and differentiation techniques, such as the trapezoidal rule and finite difference methods, are vital for analyzing and understanding the behavior of functions in AI systems.
- Optimization techniques, including gradient descent and evolutionary algorithms, are indispensable for fine-tuning AI models and improving their performance and efficiency.
- Numerical methods allow AI systems to handle large-scale data and high-dimensional problems, enhancing their learning capabilities and overall performance.
- AI models can optimize their actions and make more informed choices using numerical integration and

differentiation techniques, leading to improved outcomes and increased efficiency.

- As AI continues to progress, the role of numerical methods in shaping the future of this technology will remain paramount, enabling the creation of advanced AI systems that can revolutionize how we live, work, and interact with the world around us.

7

OPTIMIZATION TECHNIQUES: ENHANCING AI PERFORMANCE

rtificial Intelligence (AI) has become integral to our daily lives, revolutionizing various industries and transforming how we interact with technology. From self-driving cars to personalized recommendations on streaming platforms, AI systems have proven their ability to learn and adapt to complex situations. However, the efficiency and effectiveness of these systems are heavily reliant on the optimization techniques employed during their development. This chapter will delve into the fascinating world of optimization techniques, exploring their significance in enhancing AI performance and their diverse applications.

Optimization techniques play a crucial role in developing AI systems, enabling fine-tuning algorithms and models to achieve the best possible performance. These techniques involve the process of adjusting the parameters and configurations of an AI system to minimize or maximize a specific objective function. The objective function, also known as the cost or loss function, is a mathematical representation of the system's performance, quantifying the difference between the predicted and actual output. By minimizing the value of the objective function, we can ensure that the AI system is making accurate predictions and decisions, thereby improving its overall performance.

Various optimization techniques are available, each with its unique approach to problem-solving and suitability for different types of AI systems. Some of the most widely used techniques include gradient descent and its variants, evolutionary algorithms, swarm intelligence, and reinforcement learning. These techniques have been instrumental in the success of AI systems across diverse domains, such as computer vision, natural language processing, robotics, and game playing.

The following sections will explore these optimization techniques in detail, discussing their underlying principles, advantages, and limitations. We will begin with gradient descent, the backbone of AI optimization, and its variants, which have been extensively used in training deep learning models. Next, we will delve into the world of evolutionary algorithms inspired by the process of natural selection and their applications in AI. Following that, we will examine swarm intelligence, a fascinating approach to collaborative problem-solving in AI inspired by the behavior of social insects. Finally, we will discuss reinforcement learning, a technique that teaches AI systems through trial and error, enabling them to learn from their interactions with the environment.

As we embark on this journey through optimization techniques, we hope to provide you with a comprehensive understanding of their significance in AI and inspire you to appreciate the intricate balance between mathematical rigor and creative problem-solving at the heart of AI performance optimization. With the rapid advancements in AI research and development, the future of AI performance optimization promises to be even more exciting and transformative, paving the way for more innovative, efficient, and human-like AI systems.

Gradient Descent and Its Variants: The Backbone of AI Optimization

In artificial intelligence (AI), optimization techniques play a crucial role in enhancing the performance of machine learning models. One of the most widely used and fundamental optimization algorithms is Gradient Descent. This powerful technique has been the backbone of AI optimization, enabling machines to learn and adapt to complex tasks efficiently. In this section, we will delve into the concept of Gradient Descent, its variants, and their significance in the world of AI.

Understanding Gradient Descent

Gradient Descent is an iterative optimization algorithm that aims to find the minimum value of a function, typically a cost or loss function, which measures the discrepancy between the predicted and actual outcomes. In simpler terms, Gradient Descent helps AI models minimize the error in their predictions by adjusting the model's parameters, such as weights and biases, in the direction of the steepest decrease in the cost function.

The core idea behind Gradient Descent is to compute the gradient (the vector of partial derivatives) of the cost function with respect to each parameter. The gradient represents the direction of the steepest increase in the function. By moving in the opposite direction of the gradient, we can iteratively update the parameters to minimize the cost function, ultimately reaching the optimal solution.

Variants of Gradient Descent

While the basic concept of Gradient Descent is straightforward, several variants of the algorithm cater to different scenarios and computational constraints. These variants primarily differ in how they update the model's parameters and how much data they use to compute the gradient. Let's explore the three main types of Gradient Descent:

- **Batch Gradient Descent:** This is the most basic form of Gradient Descent, where the gradient is calculated using the entire dataset. While this approach guarantees convergence to the global minimum for convex functions, it can be computationally expensive and slow for large datasets.
- **Stochastic Gradient Descent (SGD):** Unlike Batch Gradient Descent, SGD computes the gradient using only a single data point at each iteration. This makes the algorithm much faster and more suitable for large datasets. However, the trade-off is that the path to the optimal solution can be noisy and less direct due to the randomness introduced using a single data point.
- **Mini-batch Gradient Descent:** This variant balances Batch Gradient Descent and SGD by computing the gradient using a small subset of the dataset, called a mini-batch. Mini-batch Gradient Descent offers a compromise between computational efficiency and convergence stability, making it a popular choice in practice.

The Significance of Gradient Descent in AI

Gradient Descent and its variants have been instrumental in AI's success, particularly in deep learning. The algorithm's ability to efficiently navigate high-dimensional parameter spaces and find optimal solutions has made it the go-to optimization technique for training neural networks. Moreover, the flexibility offered by its variants allows practitioners to tailor the algorithm to their specific needs and computational resources.

In conclusion, Gradient Descent has undoubtedly earned its place as the backbone of AI optimization. Its simplicity, adaptability, and effectiveness have made it an indispensable tool in developing intelligent machines capable of tackling complex tasks. As AI continues to evolve, Gradient Descent and its variants will undoubtedly remain at the forefront of optimization techniques, driving the performance of AI models to new heights.

Evolutionary Algorithms: Harnessing the Power of Natural Selection

In artificial intelligence, optimization techniques play a crucial role in enhancing the performance of AI systems. One such technique that has gained significant attention in recent years is evolutionary algorithms. Drawing inspiration from the process of natural selection, these algorithms have proven to be highly effective in solving complex optimization problems. This section will delve into the fascinating world of evolutionary algorithms, exploring their underlying principles, various types, and applications in AI.

The Principles of Evolutionary Algorithms

Evolutionary algorithms are a family of optimization techniques that mimic the process of natural selection, the driving force behind the evolution of species. These algorithms operate on a population of potential solutions to a given problem, iteratively applying a set of biologically-inspired operators such as selection, crossover (recombination), and mutation. The population evolves over time through these operations, gradually converging towards an optimal or near-optimal solution.

The fundamental steps of an evolutionary algorithm can be summarized as follows:

1. **Initialization:** Generate an initial population of candidate solutions, typically at random.
2. **Evaluation:** Assess each individual's fitness in the population, i.e., how well it solves the problem at hand.
3. **Selection:** Choose a subset of individuals from the current population based on their fitness, favoring those with higher fitness values.
4. **Variation:** Apply crossover and mutation operators to the selected individuals, creating a new generation of offspring.
5. **Replacement:** Replace the current population with the newly generated offspring.
6. **Termination:** Repeat steps 2-5 until a stopping criterion is met, such as reaching a maximum number of generations or achieving a desired fitness level.

Types of Evolutionary Algorithms

There are several types of evolutionary algorithms, each with its unique characteristics and strengths. Some of the most widely used variants include:

- **Genetic Algorithms (GAs):** Perhaps the most well-known type of evolutionary algorithm, GAs employ binary strings to represent candidate solutions and use genetic operators such as selection, crossover, and mutation to evolve the population.
- **Genetic Programming (GP):** An extension of genetic algorithms, GP focuses on evolving computer programs or symbolic expressions to solve a given problem.

- **Evolutionary Strategies (ES):** Originating from the engineering optimization field, ES emphasizes using real-valued representations and self-adaptive mutation rates.
- **Differential Evolution (DE):** A population-based optimization technique that employs a unique mutation strategy, combining elements from multiple individuals to generate new offspring.

Applications of Evolutionary Algorithms in AI

The versatility and adaptability of evolutionary algorithms have made them a popular choice for tackling a wide range of optimization problems in AI. Some notable applications include:

- **Neural Network Training:** Evolutionary algorithms can optimize the weights and architecture of artificial neural networks, enhancing their performance in tasks such as pattern recognition, classification, and regression.
- **Feature Selection:** In machine learning, evolutionary algorithms can help identify the most relevant features for a given problem, reducing the dimensionality of the data and improving the efficiency of learning algorithms.
- **Game Playing:** Evolutionary algorithms have evolved strategies and heuristics for playing various games, from classic board games like chess and Go to modern video games.
- **Robotics:** In robotics, evolutionary algorithms have been used to optimize the design and control of robotic systems, enabling them to adapt to different environments and tasks.

In conclusion, evolutionary algorithms represent a powerful and versatile optimization technique that has found numerous applications in artificial intelligence. By harnessing the power of natural selection, these algorithms offer a unique approach to problem-solving, allowing AI systems to evolve and adapt in the face of complex and dynamic challenges. As AI advances, evolutionary algorithms will likely play an increasingly important role in shaping the future of AI performance optimization.

Swarm Intelligence: Collaborative Problem Solving in AI

In the vast and ever-evolving world of artificial intelligence, one of the most fascinating and effective optimization techniques is inspired by the natural world: swarm intelligence. This powerful approach to problem-solving is derived from the collective behavior of decentralized, self-organized systems, such as those observed in ant colonies, bird flocks, and fish schools. This section will delve into the captivating realm of swarm intelligence, exploring its origins, fundamental principles, and applications in AI.

The Inspiration: Nature's Collective Wisdom

The concept of swarm intelligence is rooted in observing nature's remarkable ability to solve complex problems through the collaborative efforts of simple agents. For instance, ants are individually limited in their cognitive abilities, yet as a colony, they can efficiently locate and transport food, build intricate nests, and defend against predators. Similarly, birds in a flock can navigate vast distances and avoid obstacles with remarkable precision, all without a central leader or explicit communication. These examples demonstrate the power of collective intelligence, where the whole is greater than the sum of its parts.

Principles of Swarm Intelligence

Swarm intelligence in AI is based on several key principles that mirror the behavior of natural swarms. These principles include:

- **Decentralization**: Swarm intelligence systems are composed of multiple agents that operate independently, without a central authority. This allows for greater flexibility, adaptability, and robustness in changing environments and problem parameters.
- **Local Interactions**: Agents in a swarm intelligence system rely on local information and interactions with their neighbors rather than global knowledge of the entire system. This enables the swarm to respond quickly to changes and efficiently distribute tasks among its members.
- **Emergence**: The collective behavior of a swarm intelligence system emerges from the simple, local interactions of its agents. This emergent behavior is often more sophisticated and effective than the behavior of any single agent, allowing the swarm to solve complex problems that would be difficult or impossible for an individual agent to tackle alone.

Applications of Swarm Intelligence in AI

Swarm intelligence has been successfully applied to various AI problems, including optimization, robotics, and data analysis. Some notable examples include:

- **Particle Swarm Optimization (PSO)** is a popular optimization algorithm inspired by the social behavior of bird flocks. In PSO, a swarm of particles moves through a search space, adjusting their positions based on their own experiences and those of their neighbors. This collaborative search process allows the swarm to

    locate optimal solutions to complex problems
    efficiently.

- **Ant Colony Optimization (ACO)** is another powerful
  optimization technique inspired by the foraging
  behavior of ants. In ACO, artificial ants traverse a graph
  representing a problem space, depositing pheromone
  trails that guide other ants toward promising solutions.
  Over time, the collective pheromone trails converge on
  the optimal solution, allowing the swarm to solve
  complex combinatorial problems, such as the traveling
  salesperson problem.
- **Swarm intelligence** principles have been applied to
  robotics, enabling the development of multi-robot
  systems that can collaboratively perform tasks such as
  exploration, mapping, and search and rescue. These
  swarm robotic systems are highly robust and adaptable,
  as they can continue to function even if individual
  robots fail or are removed from the swarm.

In conclusion, swarm intelligence offers a captivating and powerful approach to problem-solving in AI, drawing inspiration from the collective wisdom of nature's swarms. By harnessing the principles of decentralization, local interactions, and emergence, swarm intelligence techniques have demonstrated remarkable success in a wide range of AI applications, from optimization to robotics. As we continue to explore and develop new swarm intelligence algorithms, we expect to see even greater advancements in AI performance optimization, further unlocking the potential of artificial intelligence to tackle the most complex and challenging problems of our time.

Reinforcement Learning: Teaching AI through Trial and Error

In the ever-evolving landscape of artificial intelligence, one of the most promising and exciting areas of research is reinforcement learning (RL). This powerful optimization technique, inspired by how humans and animals learn from their experiences, can potentially revolutionize AI performance. In this section, we will delve into the fascinating world of reinforcement learning, exploring its core concepts, applications, and the challenges it presents.

At its core, reinforcement learning is a trial-and-error approach to problem-solving. An AI agent, or learner, interacts with its environment, taking action and receiving feedback through rewards or penalties. The agent aims to learn an optimal policy, a set of rules that dictate the best action to take in each situation to maximize its cumulative reward over time. This process of exploration and exploitation allows the AI to adapt and improve its performance, even in complex and uncertain environments.

One of the critical components of reinforcement learning is the concept of the Markov Decision Process (MDP). MDPs provide a mathematical framework for modeling decision-making when the outcome is uncertain and depends on the current state and the chosen action. The AI agent can determine the optimal policy and improve its decision-making capabilities by solving the MDP.

Several algorithms and approaches are used in reinforcement learning, including value iteration, policy iteration, Q-learning, and deep Q-networks (DQNs). Each of these methods has its strengths and weaknesses, and the choice of algorithm depends on the specific problem and the desired level of performance.

Reinforcement learning has found numerous applications in various fields, such as robotics, finance, healthcare, and gaming. For instance, Google's DeepMind developed AlphaGo. This AI program defeated the world champion in the ancient board game of Go, using a combination of deep neural networks and reinforcement learning. Similarly, RL has been used to optimize trading strategies in financial markets, develop adaptive treatment plans for patients with chronic conditions, and even teach drones to navigate complex environments autonomously.

Despite its immense potential, reinforcement learning also presents several challenges. One of the primary issues is the trade-off between exploration and exploitation. The AI agent must balance the need to explore new actions and states to learn more about the environment with the need to exploit its current knowledge to maximize rewards. This balance is crucial for achieving optimal performance, but finding the right balance can be a complex and computationally expensive task.

Another challenge is the so-called "curse of dimensionality," which arises when the AI agent must deal with a large number of states and actions. As the size of the state-action space increases, the computational complexity of reinforcement learning algorithms grows exponentially, making it difficult to find optimal solutions in a reasonable amount of time.

In conclusion, reinforcement learning is a powerful optimization technique with great promise for enhancing AI performance across various applications. By harnessing the power of trial and error, AI agents can learn to navigate complex and uncertain environments, adapting their behavior to achieve optimal results. As research in this field advances, we can expect to see even more impressive achievements and breakthroughs in artificial intelligence.

The Future of AI Performance Optimization

As we have explored throughout this chapter, optimization techniques play a crucial role in enhancing artificial intelligence systems' performance. From the fundamental gradient descent algorithm to the more advanced evolutionary algorithms, swarm intelligence, and reinforcement learning, these methods have significantly contributed to the development and success of AI applications across various domains.

Looking ahead, AI performance optimization's future is promising and challenging. With the rapid advancements in technology and the ever-growing demand for more efficient and intelligent systems, researchers and practitioners are continuously seeking innovative ways to improve the performance of AI algorithms. In this pursuit, we expect to witness the emergence of new optimization techniques and the refinement of existing ones.

One potential area of growth lies in the integration of different optimization methods. By combining the strengths of various techniques, such as the adaptability of evolutionary algorithms and the collaborative problem-solving capabilities of swarm intelligence, we can develop hybrid optimization approaches to tackle complex problems more effectively.

Moreover, as AI systems become increasingly sophisticated, the need for optimization techniques to handle large-scale, high-dimensional problems will become more pressing. This may lead to developing novel algorithms that can efficiently explore vast search spaces and promptly identify optimal solutions.

Another exciting prospect for the future of AI performance optimization is incorporating human intuition and expertise into the optimization process. By leveraging the unique problem-solving abilities of humans, AI systems can overcome some of the limitations of traditional optimization techniques and achieve even greater performance levels.

Furthermore, as AI continues to permeate various aspects of our lives, ethical considerations surrounding optimizing AI systems will become increasingly important. Ensuring that AI algorithms are optimized fairly, transparently, and respect society's values will be a critical challenge for researchers and practitioners alike.

In conclusion, the future of AI performance optimization is filled with opportunities and challenges. As we continue to push the boundaries of what AI systems can achieve, developing and refining optimization techniques will remain an essential component of this journey. By embracing the spirit of innovation and collaboration, we can look forward to a future where AI systems are more efficient, effective, and aligned with the values and needs of our diverse world.

Chapter Summary

- Optimization techniques are crucial for enhancing AI performance, as they enable fine-tuning algorithms and models to achieve the best possible results.
- Gradient descent and its variants, such as batch, stochastic, and mini-batch gradient descent, are widely used optimization techniques in AI, particularly deep learning.
- Evolutionary algorithms, inspired by the process of natural selection, offer a unique approach to problem-solving and have been applied to various AI domains, including neural network training and feature selection.
- Swarm intelligence, derived from the collective behavior of decentralized, self-organized systems in nature, has been successfully applied to AI problems such as particle swarm optimization and ant colony optimization.
- Reinforcement learning, a trial-and-error approach to problem-solving, has shown great potential in various fields, including robotics, finance, healthcare, and gaming.
- The future of AI performance optimization may involve integrating different optimization methods, developing novel algorithms for large-scale problems, and incorporating human intuition and expertise.
- Ethical considerations surrounding the optimization of AI systems, such as fairness and transparency, will become increasingly important as AI continues to permeate various aspects of our lives.
- By embracing innovation and collaboration, we can look forward to a future where AI systems are more efficient, effective, and aligned with the values and needs of our diverse world.

8

GAME THEORY: ANALYZING STRATEGIC DECISION-MAKING

Game theory, a branch of mathematics and economics, has emerged as a powerful tool for understanding and predicting the behavior of intelligent agents in various situations. It is a study of strategic decision-making, where multiple players interact and make decisions based on their objectives and the actions of others. In artificial intelligence (AI), game theory is crucial in designing algorithms and systems that can adapt and respond to the complex and dynamic environments they encounter.

The importance of game theory in AI stems from its ability to model and analyze the interactions between multiple agents, whether human or artificial. As AI systems become more advanced and integrated into our daily lives, they must be able to navigate and make decisions in environments that involve other intelligent agents. Game theory provides a framework for understanding these interactions and designing AI systems that can make optimal decisions in the face of uncertainty and competition.

This chapter will explore the fundamentals of game theory and its applications in AI. We will begin by introducing key concepts and terminology used in game theory, such as players, strategies, payoffs, and equilibria. Next, we will delve into the different types of games and their relevance to AI, including zero-sum games, cooperative games, and non-cooperative games. We will then discuss various techniques and algorithms for solving game theory problems, focusing on their implementation in AI systems.

To illustrate the practical applications of game theory in AI and machine learning, we will present real-world examples that showcase how game theory has improved decision-making in areas such as robotics, natural language processing, and autonomous vehicles. Finally, we will conclude by discussing the future of game theory in AI and its potential impact on strategic decision-making in the rapidly evolving world of artificial intelligence.

By the end of this chapter, readers will have a solid understanding of game theory and its significance in developing AI systems. They will also gain insights into the various techniques and algorithms used to solve game theory problems and how they can be applied to create intelligent agents capable of making strategic decisions in complex environments.

Key Concepts and Terminology in Game Theory

In this section, we will delve into the essential concepts and terminology that form the foundation of game theory. Understanding these fundamental ideas, you will be better equipped to analyze strategic decision-making in artificial intelligence (AI) and other fields.

Players and Strategies

At the core of any game are the players, who are the decision-makers in the game. Players can be algorithms, agents, or even human beings in AI. Each player has a set of possible actions or decisions, known as strategies, that they can choose from to achieve their objectives. Strategies can be simple, like choosing a number in a lottery, or complex, like deciding the next move in a chess game.

Payoffs and Utility

The outcome of a game depends on the strategies chosen by the players. Each player prefers the possible outcomes represented by a payoff or utility function. The utility function assigns a numerical value to each outcome, reflecting the player's satisfaction or benefit from that outcome. In AI, the utility function can represent an algorithm's performance or an agent's success in achieving its goal.

Nash Equilibrium

A central concept in game theory is the Nash equilibrium, named after the mathematician John Nash. A Nash equilibrium is a stable state in which no player can improve their payoff by unilaterally changing their strategy, given the other players' strategies. In other words, it is a situation where each player's strategy is the best response to the other players' strategies. The existence of a Nash equilibrium in a game is a powerful tool for predicting the outcome of strategic interactions.

Zero-Sum and Non-Zero-Sum Games

Games can be classified as zero-sum or non-zero-sum based on the relationship between the players' payoffs. In a zero-sum game, the total payoff for all players is constant, meaning that one player's gain is another player's loss. Classic examples of zero-sum games include poker and chess. In contrast, non-zero-sum games allow for the possibility of mutual gain or loss, such as in cooperative games or negotiation scenarios.

Perfect and Imperfect Information

Another important distinction in game theory is between games of perfect and imperfect information. In a game of perfect information, all players have complete knowledge of the game's structure, including the strategies and payoffs of the other players. Chess is an example of a game with perfect information. In games of imperfect information, players have incomplete knowledge about the game, such as the strategies or payoffs of other players. Poker is an example of a game with imperfect information, as players do not know the cards held by their opponents.

By understanding these key concepts and terminology in game theory, you will be better prepared to analyze strategic decision-making in AI and other fields. In the next section, we will explore the different types of games and their applications in AI, further expanding your knowledge of this fascinating subject.

Solving Game Theory Problems: Techniques and Algorithms

This section will delve into the various techniques and algorithms used to solve game theory problems. These methods are crucial for understanding strategic decision-making in AI and machine learning applications. By mastering these techniques, AI systems can make more informed decisions and better predict the actions of other agents in a given environment.

Dominant Strategy Equilibrium

A dominant strategy equilibrium occurs when a player has a strategy that yields the best outcome, regardless of the strategies chosen by other players. In such cases, the player will always choose this dominant strategy. To identify a dominant strategy equilibrium, one must analyze each player's payoff and determine if a particular strategy consistently yields the highest payoff.

Nash Equilibrium

Named after the mathematician John Nash, a Nash equilibrium is a set of strategies where no player can improve their payoff by unilaterally changing their strategy. In other words, each player's strategy is the best response to the strategies of all other players. To find a Nash equilibrium, one can use various algorithms, such as the best-response algorithm or the Lemke-Howson algorithm.

Minimax Algorithm

The minimax algorithm is a decision-making technique used in two-player, zero-sum games. It involves each player minimizing the maximum possible loss they could incur. The algorithm works by recursively evaluating the game tree, assigning a value to each node based on the best possible outcome for the player. The minimax algorithm is handy in AI applications, such as board games like chess or tic-tac-toe, where the AI must make decisions based on the possible moves of its opponent.

Alpha-Beta Pruning

Alpha-beta pruning is an optimization technique used in conjunction with the minimax algorithm. It reduces the number of nodes that need to be evaluated in the game tree by eliminating branches that do not contribute to the final decision. This allows the AI to search deeper into the game tree and make more informed decisions while reducing computational time.

Reinforcement Learning

Reinforcement learning is a type of machine learning where an AI agent learns to make decisions by interacting with its environment and receiving feedback in the form of rewards or penalties. In game theory, reinforcement learning can be used to train AI agents to find optimal strategies in various games. Techniques like Q-learning and deep reinforcement learning have been successfully applied to complex games like Go and poker, allowing AI systems to outperform human players.

In conclusion, solving game theory problems is essential for AI systems to make strategic decisions and predict the actions of other agents. By mastering techniques such as dominant strategy equilibrium, Nash equilibrium, minimax algorithm, alpha-beta pruning, and reinforcement learning, AI systems can become more effective in a wide range of applications, from board games to complex real-world scenarios. As AI advances, we can expect to see even more sophisticated game theory techniques and algorithms being developed and applied to strategic decision-making.

Real-World Examples of Game Theory in AI and Machine Learning

In this section, we will delve into the fascinating world of real-world applications of game theory in artificial intelligence (AI) and machine learning. By examining these examples, we can better understand how game theory principles are employed to solve complex problems and make strategic decisions in various domains.

Autonomous Vehicles and Traffic Management

One of the most promising applications of game theory in AI is in the realm of autonomous vehicles. As self-driving cars become more prevalent, traffic management systems must adapt to accommodate these vehicles' unique characteristics. Game theory can be used to model the interactions between autonomous vehicles and human-driven cars, allowing for the development of optimal traffic management strategies that minimize congestion and maximize safety.

For instance, researchers have used game theory to design algorithms that enable autonomous vehicles to negotiate intersections without traffic signals. By treating each vehicle as a player in a game, the vehicles can make strategic decisions about when to enter the intersection, taking into account the actions of other vehicles and minimizing the risk of collisions.

Multi-Agent Systems and Robotics

Game theory is also a valuable tool in the design and analysis of multi-agent systems, where multiple AI agents interact with each other to achieve a common goal. In robotics, for example, game theory can be used to model the interactions between multiple robots working together to complete a task, such as assembling a structure or exploring an unknown environment.

By applying game theory principles, researchers can develop algorithms enabling robots to cooperate effectively, allocate resources efficiently, and avoid conflicts. This can lead to more robust and resilient multi-agent systems adapting to changing conditions and achieving their objectives more efficiently.

Auctions and Market Design

AI and machine learning have been increasingly employed in designing and analyzing auctions and markets. Game theory plays a crucial role in understanding the strategic behavior of participants in these settings, allowing for the development of more efficient and fair mechanisms.

For example, AI-powered algorithms have been used to design auctions for allocating radio spectrum licenses, ensuring that the licenses are allocated to the parties that value them the most while generating revenue for the government. Similarly, game theory has been applied to the design of online advertising markets, where advertisers bid for the opportunity to display their ads to users.

Cybersecurity and Network Defense

In cybersecurity, game theory has emerged as a powerful tool for modeling the interactions between attackers and defenders. By treating cybersecurity as a game, researchers can develop strategies for defending networks and systems against various types of attacks, taking into account the actions and motivations of the attackers.

For instance, machine learning algorithms can predict attackers' behavior based on historical data, allowing defenders to allocate resources more effectively and prioritize their efforts. Game theory can also be used to design incentives for users to adopt secure practices, such as using strong passwords and keeping their software up-to-date.

Social Network Analysis and Influence Maximization

Finally, game theory has found applications in analyzing social networks and designing strategies for maximizing influence in these networks. By modeling the interactions between individuals in a social network as a game, researchers can develop algorithms that identify the most influential nodes and devise strategies for spreading information or promoting products and services.

Machine learning techniques can be employed to analyze large-scale social network data, allowing for identifying patterns and trends that can inform the design of influence maximization strategies. This has applications in areas such as viral marketing, political campaigns, and public health interventions.

In conclusion, the real-world examples of game theory in AI and machine learning demonstrate the versatility and power of this mathematical framework in addressing complex problems and enabling strategic decision-making. As AI continues to advance and permeate various domains, we can expect game theory to play an increasingly important role in shaping the future of AI-driven systems and applications.

The Future of Game Theory in AI and Strategic Decision-Making

As we have explored throughout this chapter, game theory plays a crucial role in developing and advancing artificial intelligence. By providing a mathematical framework for analyzing strategic decision-making, game theory enables AI systems to make more informed choices and adapt to complex, dynamic environments. In this concluding section, we will discuss the future of game theory in AI and its potential impact on strategic decision-making.

Multi-agent systems are one of the most promising areas for applying game theory in AI. These systems consist of multiple autonomous agents that interact with each other to achieve specific goals. By incorporating game theory into the design of multi-agent systems, researchers can develop AI agents capable of cooperating, competing, and negotiating with one another in a wide range of scenarios. This could lead to more efficient and robust AI systems that tackle complex problems in transportation, logistics, and resource allocation.

Another exciting avenue for the future of game theory in AI is the development of new algorithms and techniques for solving game-theoretic problems. As AI systems become more sophisticated, they will need to be able to handle larger and more complex games. This will require the development of new algorithms that can efficiently compute optimal strategies and equilibria in these games. Researchers are already making progress in this area, with recent advances in techniques such as deep reinforcement learning and neural network-based approaches showing great promise for solving game-theoretic problems.

In addition to these technical advancements, the future of game theory in AI will also be shaped by its integration with other disciplines and methodologies. For example, researchers are increasingly exploring the connections between game theory and fields such as economics, psychology, and sociology. By combining insights from these disciplines with game-theoretic models, AI systems can be designed to understand better and predict human behavior, leading to more effective and ethical decision-making.

Finally, as AI continues to permeate various aspects of our lives, understanding and addressing the ethical implications of AI systems that utilize game theory cannot be overstated. As AI systems become more capable of making strategic decisions, ensuring that these decisions align with our values and ethical principles is essential. This will require ongoing collaboration between AI researchers, ethicists, policymakers, and other stakeholders to develop guidelines and best practices for the responsible use of game theory in AI.

In conclusion, the future of game theory in AI and strategic decision-making is bright, with numerous opportunities for innovation and growth. By continuing to explore the applications of game theory in AI, developing new algorithms and techniques, and addressing the ethical implications of AI systems that utilize game theory, we can unlock the full potential of this powerful mathematical framework and pave the way for a new era of intelligent, strategic decision-making.

Chapter Summary

- Game theory is a powerful tool for understanding and predicting the behavior of intelligent agents in various situations, making it crucial for designing AI algorithms and systems that can adapt to complex environments.
- Key concepts in game theory include players, strategies, payoffs, Nash equilibrium, zero-sum and non-zero-sum games, and perfect and imperfect information.
- Different types of games, such as zero-sum, non-zero-sum, cooperative and non-cooperative, and stochastic and deterministic games, have various applications in AI and can help develop intelligent agents capable of strategic decision-making.
- Techniques and algorithms for solving game theory problems include dominant strategy equilibrium, Nash equilibrium, minimax algorithm, alpha-beta pruning, and reinforcement learning.
- Game theory has real-world applications in AI and machine learning, such as autonomous vehicles and traffic management, multi-agent systems and robotics, auctions, and market design, cybersecurity and network defense, and social network analysis and influence maximization.
- The future of game theory in AI lies in developing multi-agent systems, new algorithms and techniques for solving game-theoretic problems, and integration with other disciplines such as economics, psychology, and sociology.
- Addressing the ethical implications of AI systems that utilize game theory is essential to ensure that strategic decisions align with our values and ethical principles, requiring collaboration between AI researchers, ethicists, policymakers, and other stakeholders.

- By exploring the applications of game theory in AI, developing new algorithms and techniques, and addressing ethical implications, we can unlock the full potential of game theory and pave the way for a new era of intelligent, strategic decision-making.

9

INFORMATION THEORY: QUANTIFYING AND ENCODING DATA

I n the world of artificial intelligence (AI), the ability to process, analyze, and understand vast amounts of data is crucial. As AI systems become more sophisticated, they require efficient methods to manage and utilize this data effectively. This is where Information Theory comes into play. In this chapter, we will delve into the fascinating realm of Information Theory and explore its significance in the development and advancement of AI.

Information Theory, a branch of mathematics and computer science, was introduced by Claude Shannon in his groundbreaking 1948 paper, "A Mathematical Theory of Communication." At its core, Information Theory is concerned with quantifying, encoding, and transmitting data in the most efficient and reliable manner possible. It provides a mathematical framework for understanding the fundamental limits of communication systems and offers valuable insights into the design and optimization of these systems.

In the context of AI, Information Theory plays a pivotal role in various aspects of data processing and analysis. From data compression techniques that enable efficient storage and transmission of information to error detection and correction mechanisms that ensure data integrity, Information Theory serves as a foundation for many AI applications.

One of the key concepts in Information Theory is entropy, which measures the uncertainty or randomness of data. In AI, understanding entropy is essential for tasks such as feature selection, model complexity, and decision-making processes. AI systems can make more informed decisions and improve their overall performance by quantifying data uncertainty.

Moreover, Information Theory is instrumental in developing machine learning algorithms, particularly in unsupervised learning and reinforcement learning. These algorithms rely on the principles of Information Theory to discover patterns, extract meaningful features, and optimize their learning processes.

As AI advances, the importance of Information Theory cannot be overstated. By providing a solid foundation for understanding the intricacies of data and communication systems, Information Theory enables AI researchers and practitioners to push the boundaries of what is possible in the field. In the following sections, we will delve deeper into the key concepts of Information Theory, such as entropy, data compression, error detection and correction, and channel capacity, and explore their applications in AI.

Entropy: Measuring the Uncertainty of Data

In the realm of artificial intelligence, the ability to quantify and manage the uncertainty of data is of paramount importance. This is where the concept of entropy comes into play. Entropy, a term borrowed from thermodynamics, is a measure of the uncertainty or randomness of a set of data. This section will delve into the significance of entropy, its mathematical representation, and its applications in AI.

To begin with, let us understand why entropy is crucial in the context of AI. Artificial intelligence systems often deal with vast amounts of data, which may contain varying degrees of uncertainty. By quantifying this uncertainty, AI algorithms can make better-informed decisions, optimize their performance, and reduce the risk of errors. In essence, entropy serves as a guiding force for AI systems to navigate through the complex landscape of data.

Now, let us explore the mathematical representation of entropy. Entropy is denoted by the letter 'H' and is calculated using the following formula:

$$H(X) = - \sum P(x) * log2(P(x))$$

Here, 'X' represents a discrete random variable with possible outcomes x_1, x_2, ..., x_n, and P(x) denotes the probability of each outcome. The logarithm is base 2, meaning entropy is measured in bits. In simpler terms, entropy quantifies the average amount of information required to describe the outcome of a random variable.

To illustrate this concept, let us consider a simple example. Suppose we have a fair coin with equal probabilities of landing heads (H) or tails (T). The entropy of this coin can be calculated as follows:

$$H(Coin) = - [P(H) * log2(P(H)) + P(T) * log2(P(T))]$$

$$= - [(0.5 * log2(0.5)) + (0.5 * log2(0.5))]$$
$$= 1 \ bit$$

This result indicates that, on average, we need 1 bit of information to describe the outcome of a fair coin toss. In contrast, if we had a biased coin with a 90% chance of landing heads, the entropy would be lower, reflecting the reduced uncertainty in the outcome.

In AI, entropy is vital in various applications, such as decision trees, data compression, and natural language processing. For instance, in decision tree algorithms, entropy determines the best attribute for splitting the data at each node, optimizing the classification process. Similarly, in data compression techniques, entropy helps identify the most efficient encoding schemes to minimize storage and transmission costs.

In conclusion, entropy is a powerful tool for measuring data uncertainty in artificial intelligence systems. By quantifying this uncertainty, AI algorithms can optimize their performance, make better-informed decisions, and ultimately contribute to advancing the field. As we continue to explore the fascinating world of information theory, we will uncover more ways in which entropy and other related concepts can help shape the future of AI.

Data Compression Techniques: Efficient Storage and Transmission

In the realm of artificial intelligence, the ability to store and transmit data efficiently is of paramount importance. As AI systems grow in complexity and the volume of data they process increases, the need for effective data compression techniques becomes increasingly crucial. This section will explore various data compression methods that enable AI systems to store and transmit data more efficiently, enhancing their overall performance.

Data compression refers to the process of reducing the size of a data file without compromising its original content. This is achieved by identifying and eliminating redundancies within the data, allowing it to be represented in a more compact form. There are two primary types of data compression: lossless and lossy.

Lossless Compression

Lossless compression techniques ensure that the original data can be perfectly reconstructed from the compressed data. This is particularly important in AI applications where data integrity is critical, such as in medical imaging or financial analysis. Some common lossless compression algorithms include:

- **Huffman Coding:** This technique assigns shorter binary codes to more frequently occurring data elements, resulting in a reduced overall file size. Huffman coding is widely used in text compression and forms the basis of several popular file formats, such as ZIP and GZIP.
- **Run-Length Encoding (RLE):** RLE is a simple compression method that replaces consecutive occurrences of the same data element with a single instance of the element, followed by the number of repetitions. This technique is particularly effective for compressing data with large areas of uniformity, such as images with solid color backgrounds.
- **Lempel-Ziv-Welch (LZW) Algorithm:** LZW is a dictionary-based compression algorithm that replaces repeated occurrences of data with references to a dictionary entry. This method is employed in various file formats, including GIF and TIFF images.

Lossy Compression

On the other hand, Lossy compression techniques sacrifice some degree of data fidelity in exchange for greater compression efficiency. These methods are typically employed in situations where a small loss of data quality is acceptable, such as in audio or video compression. Some widely used lossy compression algorithms include:

- **JPEG (Joint Photographic Experts Group):** JPEG is a popular image compression standard that utilizes discrete cosine transform (DCT) and quantization to reduce the size of image files. By adjusting the level of compression, users can balance the trade-off between file size and image quality.
- **MP3 (MPEG-1 Audio Layer III):** MP3 is a widely used audio compression format that employs perceptual coding techniques to remove audio data that is less perceptible to the human ear. This allows for significant reductions in file size while maintaining an acceptable level of audio quality.
- **H.264/AVC (Advanced Video Coding):** H.264 is a video compression standard that utilizes motion compensation, spatial prediction, and other advanced techniques to achieve high compression efficiency while maintaining good video quality. It is widely used in video streaming and broadcasting applications.

In conclusion, data compression techniques play a vital role in efficiently storing and transmitting data in AI systems. By employing a combination of lossless and lossy compression methods, AI developers can optimize their systems to handle vast amounts of data without sacrificing performance or integrity. As AI advances, developing new and improved data compression techniques will remain an essential area of research and innovation.

Error Detection and Correction: Ensuring Data Integrity

In the realm of artificial intelligence, the accuracy and reliability of data are of paramount importance. As AI systems process vast amounts of information, even the smallest errors can have significant consequences. This is where error detection and correction techniques come into play, ensuring the integrity of data as it is transmitted and stored. In this section, we will delve into the fundamental concepts of error detection and correction and explore how these methods contribute to AI systems' overall efficiency and effectiveness.

The Need for Error Detection and Correction

As data travels through various channels, it is susceptible to noise, interference, and other factors that can introduce errors. These errors manifest as flipped bits, missing data, or corrupted information. To maintain the integrity of the data, it is crucial to identify and correct these errors as they occur. Error detection and correction techniques are designed to address this need, providing a means to identify and rectify inaccuracies in the data.

Error Detection Techniques

Error detection techniques are the first line of defense in ensuring data integrity. These methods involve adding redundant information to the original data, which can be used to detect errors upon receipt. Some common error detection techniques include:

- **Parity Bits:** A parity bit is a binary digit added to a group of bits, ensuring that the total number of 1s in the group is either even (even parity) or odd (odd parity). This simple technique can detect single-bit errors but is not effective for multiple-bit errors.

- **Checksums:** A checksum is a value calculated from the original data transmitted alongside the data. Upon receipt, the receiver calculates the checksum from the received data and compares it to the transmitted checksum. If the values match, the data is assumed to be error-free.
- **Cyclic Redundancy Check (CRC):** CRC is a more advanced error detection technique that involves generating a polynomial code from the original data. This code is then transmitted alongside the data, and the receiver uses it to verify the integrity of the received information.

Error Correction Techniques

While error detection techniques can identify errors, they do not provide a means to correct them. On the other hand, error correction techniques detect errors and enable the receiver to reconstruct the original data. Some common error correction techniques include:

The **Hamming code** is a linear block code that adds redundant bits to the original data, allowing the receiver to detect and correct single-bit errors. This technique is widely used in computer memory systems and other applications where single-bit errors are common.

The **Reed-Solomon code** is a more advanced error correction technique that can correct multiple errors in a data block. This method is particularly useful in communication systems, where noise and interference can cause multiple errors in a single transmission.

Turbo Codes and LDPC Codes are modern error correction techniques that employ iterative decoding algorithms to achieve near-optimal error correction performance. They are widely used in applications such as deep-space communication and wireless communication systems.

In conclusion, error detection and correction techniques are vital in ensuring data integrity in AI systems. By identifying and rectifying errors, these methods contribute to AI algorithms' overall efficiency and effectiveness, enabling them to make accurate predictions and decisions based on reliable information. As AI advances, the importance of robust error detection and correction mechanisms will only grow, paving the way for even more sophisticated and reliable AI systems.

Channel Capacity and the Noisy Channel Coding Theorem

Artificial intelligence's ability to transmit and process information accurately and efficiently is of utmost importance. As we delve into the fascinating world of information theory, we must explore the concept of channel capacity and the noisy channel coding theorem, which plays a crucial role in understanding the limits and potential of communication systems.

Channel capacity refers to the maximum rate at which information can be transmitted over a communication channel without losing accuracy due to noise or interference. It is measured in bits per second (bps) and serves as a benchmark for the performance of communication systems. In AI, channel capacity is vital as it determines the speed and reliability of data transmission between various components of a system.

The noisy channel coding theorem, a cornerstone of information theory, was introduced by Claude Shannon in 1948. This theorem addresses the fundamental question of how to transmit information reliably over a noisy channel, which is a communication channel that introduces errors or distortions in the transmitted data. The theorem states that, given a noisy channel with a certain capacity, it is possible to transmit information at a rate close to this capacity with an arbitrarily low probability of error, provided that an appropriate coding scheme is used.

Let's consider a simple example to understand better the noisy channel coding theorem. Imagine you are trying to send a message to a friend using a walkie-talkie. However, the signal is weak, and there is a lot of static noise. You may repeat the message several times to ensure that your friend receives the message accurately. This repetition is a form of error-correcting code, which increases the reliability of the transmission at the cost of a reduced effective data rate.

In the context of AI, the noisy channel coding theorem has significant implications. It highlights the importance of developing efficient coding schemes that maximize the information transmission rate while minimizing the probability of errors. This is particularly relevant in applications such as speech recognition, natural language processing, and computer vision, where the input data is often noisy or incomplete.

Moreover, the noisy channel coding theorem also provides a theoretical foundation for understanding the limits of communication systems. By quantifying the trade-off between data rate and error probability, it offers valuable insights into designing robust and efficient AI systems that can operate in real-world conditions with varying noise and interference levels.

In conclusion, channel capacity and the noisy channel coding theorem are essential concepts in information theory that profoundly impact the field of artificial intelligence. By understanding the limits and potential of communication systems, researchers and engineers can develop innovative AI solutions that can effectively process and transmit information in a noisy and uncertain world.

The Role of Information Theory in Advancing AI

As we reach the end of our journey through the fascinating world of Information Theory, it is essential to reflect on its significant role in advancing Artificial Intelligence. Throughout this chapter, we have explored various concepts and techniques that form the foundation of Information Theory and contribute to the development and optimization of AI systems.

The importance of Information Theory in AI cannot be overstated. It provides a robust framework for quantifying and encoding data, which is the lifeblood of any AI system. By understanding data uncertainty through entropy, we can develop more efficient algorithms to process and analyze vast amounts of information. This, in turn, allows AI systems to make better predictions and decisions, ultimately enhancing their performance.

Data compression techniques, as discussed in this chapter, are crucial for efficiently storing and transmitting information. As AI systems grow in complexity and the amount of data they process increases exponentially, the need for effective data compression becomes even more critical. By employing these techniques, we can reduce AI systems' storage and bandwidth requirements, making them more accessible and cost-effective.

Error detection and correction methods are vital in ensuring data integrity, which is paramount for the reliability and accuracy of AI systems. By identifying and rectifying errors in data transmission, we can maintain the quality of information being fed into AI algorithms. This improves the overall performance of AI systems and helps build trust in their outputs.

The concept of channel capacity and the Noisy Channel Coding Theorem provides valuable insights into data transmission limits and the trade-offs between speed, reliability, and efficiency. By understanding these limits, AI researchers and engineers can design better communication protocols and optimize the performance of AI systems in real-world scenarios.

In conclusion, Information Theory is an indispensable tool in the ever-evolving field of Artificial Intelligence. Its principles and techniques profoundly impact how we design, develop, and optimize AI systems. As we continue to push the boundaries of AI, Information Theory will undoubtedly remain a cornerstone in our quest to create intelligent machines that can learn, adapt, and thrive in an increasingly complex and data-driven world.

Chapter Summary

- Information Theory, introduced by Claude Shannon, is a branch of mathematics and computer science that focuses on quantifying, encoding, and transmitting data efficiently and reliably, making it crucial for AI systems.
- Entropy is a key concept in Information Theory, measuring the uncertainty or randomness of data. Understanding entropy is essential for AI tasks such as feature selection, model complexity, and decision-making processes.
- Data compression techniques, including lossless and lossy compression, are vital for efficiently storing and transmitting information in AI systems, enabling them to handle vast amounts of data without sacrificing performance or data integrity.
- Error detection and correction techniques are crucial in ensuring data integrity in AI systems and identifying and rectifying errors to maintain the quality of information fed into AI algorithms.
- Channel capacity refers to the maximum rate at which information can be transmitted over a communication channel without losing accuracy due to noise or interference, determining the speed and reliability of data transmission in AI systems.
- The Noisy Channel Coding Theorem, introduced by Shannon, states that transmitting information at a rate close to the channel capacity with an arbitrarily low probability of error is possible, provided that an appropriate coding scheme is used.
- Information Theory provides a theoretical foundation for understanding the limits of communication systems, offering valuable insights into designing robust and

efficient AI systems that can operate in real-world conditions with varying levels of noise and interference.

- As AI continues to advance, Information Theory will remain an indispensable tool in developing and optimizing AI systems, enabling researchers and engineers to create intelligent machines that can learn, adapt, and thrive in an increasingly complex and data-driven world.

10

TOPOLOGY AND GEOMETRY: UNCOVERING HIDDEN STRUCTURES

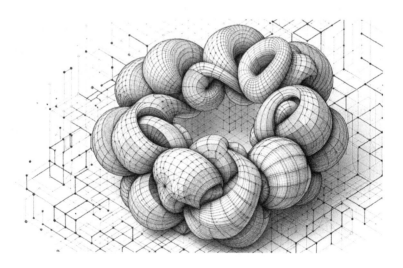

I n artificial intelligence (AI), the quest for understanding and replicating human intelligence has led researchers to explore various mathematical concepts and techniques. Topology and geometry have emerged as essential tools in developing advanced AI algorithms and applications. This chapter aims to provide an insightful overview of the significance of topology and geometry in AI, delving into their foundational concepts, applications, and future prospects.

Topology, a branch of mathematics concerned with the study of spatial properties that are preserved under continuous transformations, has proven invaluable in analyzing complex data structures. Topology allows AI researchers to uncover hidden structures and patterns that may not be apparent through traditional analytical methods by focusing on the intrinsic relationships between data points. This ability to discern the underlying data structure is crucial in various AI applications, such as computer vision, natural language processing, and network analysis.

Geometry, however, studies shapes, sizes, and relative positions of objects in space. In the context of AI, geometry plays a vital role in understanding and representing the physical world. Geometric transformations, such as rotations, translations, and scaling, enable AI algorithms to manipulate and analyze data more intuitively and efficiently. This is particularly important in fields like robotics, where the accurate representation and manipulation of spatial information are critical for tasks such as navigation, object recognition, and manipulation.

Topology and geometry provide a powerful framework for AI researchers to model, analyze, and interpret complex data. By leveraging these mathematical concepts, AI algorithms can better understand the world around them, leading to more accurate and robust solutions to various problems. In the following sections, we will explore the foundational concepts of topological spaces and geometric transformations, delve into the fascinating world of manifold learning, and examine the various applications of topology and geometry in AI. Finally, we will discuss the prospects of these mathematical tools in the ongoing quest to develop more advanced and human-like artificial intelligence.

Exploring Topological Spaces: The Foundation of Geometric Analysis

In artificial intelligence, the study of topology and geometry plays a crucial role in understanding and interpreting complex data structures. To appreciate the significance of these mathematical disciplines, we must first delve into the concept of topological spaces, which serve as the foundation for geometric analysis.

Topology, often referred to as "rubber sheet geometry," is a branch of mathematics that deals with the properties of space that are preserved under continuous transformations. Topology is more concerned with the qualitative aspects of shapes and spaces than quantitative aspects, such as distance and angle measurements. This unique perspective allows us to analyze and classify data flexibly and intuitively.

A topological space is a set of points and a collection of open subsets that satisfy certain axioms. These axioms are designed to capture the essence of continuity and closeness, which are fundamental concepts in the study of geometry. By defining a topological space, we can explore various properties of the space, such as connectedness, compactness, and convergence, which are essential in understanding the underlying structure of the data.

One of the most important aspects of topological spaces is the concept of a continuous function. A function between two topological spaces is continuous if the preimage of every open set in the target space is an open set in the domain space. This notion of continuity is crucial in AI, as it allows us to study the behavior of algorithms and models under small perturbations of the input data.

As we venture further into topology, we encounter the fascinating subject of geometric transformations. These transformations, which include translations, rotations, and scaling, are the key to unraveling complex patterns and structures hidden within the data. By understanding how these transformations affect the topological properties of a space, we can develop powerful tools and techniques for AI applications, such as pattern recognition, image processing, and data visualization.

In summary, exploring topological spaces lays the groundwork for studying geometry in artificial intelligence. By understanding the fundamental concepts of continuity, connectedness, and convergence, we can develop a deeper appreciation for the hidden structures that govern the behavior of complex data sets. This knowledge, in turn, enables us to create more robust and efficient AI algorithms, pushing the boundaries of what is possible in the ever-evolving field of artificial intelligence.

Delving into Geometric Transformations: The Key to Unraveling Complex Patterns

As we venture deeper into topology and geometry, it becomes increasingly evident that geometric transformations are pivotal in uncovering the hidden structures within complex patterns. In this section, we will delve into the intricacies of geometric transformations, elucidating their significance in the context of artificial intelligence.

Geometric transformations can be defined as operations that alter an object's position, orientation, or size while preserving its essential properties. These transformations are instrumental in data analysis and manipulation, particularly in AI, where the ability to recognize and adapt to patterns is of paramount importance. There are four primary types of geometric transformations: translation, rotation, scaling, and reflection.

Translation refers to moving an object from one location to another without altering its orientation or size. In AI, this transformation is crucial for tasks such as object recognition and tracking, where the position of an object in an image or a sequence of images must be determined.

Rotation, on the other hand, involves pivoting an object around a fixed point or axis. This transformation is particularly relevant in computer vision, where the orientation of an object must be discerned to facilitate tasks such as image registration and 3D reconstruction.

Scaling entails resizing an object while maintaining its proportions. This transformation is vital in AI applications that require comparing objects with varying sizes, such as facial recognition and object detection. By scaling images or features to a standard size, AI algorithms can analyze and compare them more effectively.

Lastly, reflection involves flipping an object across a line or plane, creating a mirror image. This transformation is useful in AI applications that necessitate identifying symmetrical patterns or generating novel perspectives on existing data.

The power of geometric transformations lies in their ability to reveal hidden structures within complex patterns. By applying these transformations to high-dimensional data, AI algorithms can uncover relationships and patterns that may not be readily apparent. For instance, manifold learning techniques, such as t-distributed stochastic neighbor embedding (t-SNE) and Isomap, leverage geometric transformations to reduce the dimensionality of data, thereby facilitating the visualization and analysis of intricate structures.

In conclusion, geometric transformations are vital in the AI toolbox, enabling the discovery and manipulation of hidden structures within complex patterns. As we continue to push the boundaries of AI research and development, the significance of topology and geometry, mainly geometric transformations, will only grow. By harnessing the power of these transformations, we can unlock new insights and capabilities, propelling AI to new heights.

Manifold Learning: Unveiling the Hidden Structures in High-Dimensional Data

Manifold learning emerges as a powerful technique in artificial intelligence that allows us to uncover hidden structures within high-dimensional data. As we delve into this fascinating topic, we will explore the concept of manifolds, the significance of manifold learning, and the various algorithms employed to achieve this feat.

The Concept of Manifolds: A Gateway to Simplification

A manifold is a mathematical construct representing a continuous, smooth surface embedded within a higher-dimensional space. It is a lower-dimensional representation of complex data that retains the essential structure and relationships between data points. The concept of manifolds is crucial in manifold learning, as it enables us to simplify high-dimensional data while preserving its inherent properties.

The Significance of Manifold Learning in AI

High-dimensional data is common in AI, with applications ranging from image recognition to natural language processing. However, analyzing and interpreting such data can be daunting due to the "curse of dimensionality," which refers to the exponential increase in complexity as the number of dimensions grows.

Manifold learning comes to the rescue by reducing the dimensionality of the data, making it more manageable and easier to analyze. Manifold learning allows AI algorithms to identify patterns, make predictions, and ultimately improve their performance by unveiling the hidden structures within the data.

Algorithms for Manifold Learning: A Comparative Overview

Several manifold learning algorithms have been developed to tackle the challenges posed by high-dimensional data. Some of the most popular ones include:

- **Principal Component Analysis (PCA):** PCA is a linear technique that projects high-dimensional data onto a lower-dimensional subspace, maximizing the variance of the projected data. While PCA effectively reduces dimensionality, it may not capture the underlying non-linear structures in the data.

- **Isomap:** Isomap is a non-linear technique that seeks to preserve the geodesic distances between data points while reducing dimensionality. By constructing a neighborhood graph and computing shortest paths, Isomap can uncover the intrinsic geometry of the data.

- **Locally Linear Embedding (LLE):** LLE is another non-linear technique that aims to preserve local relationships between data points. LLE can effectively map high-dimensional data onto a lower-dimensional manifold by reconstructing each **data point as a linear combination of its neighbors.**

- **t-Distributed Stochastic Neighbor Embedding (t-SNE):** t-SNE is a probabilistic technique that minimizes the divergence between probability distributions in high-dimensional and low-dimensional spaces. This approach is particularly effective in visualizing high-dimensional data, as it preserves local and global structures.

Manifold Learning in Action: Real-World Applications

Manifold learning has found numerous applications in AI, some of which include:

- **Computer Vision:** By reducing the dimensionality of image data, manifold learning can improve the performance of image recognition and classification algorithms.

- **Natural Language Processing:** Manifold learning can analyze high-dimensional text data, enabling AI algorithms to understand better and process human language.

- **Robotics:** In robotics, manifold learning can simplify sensor data, allowing robots to navigate and interact with their environment more effectively.

In conclusion, manifold learning is a powerful tool in the AI toolbox, enabling us to unveil the hidden structures within high-dimensional data and, ultimately, enhance the performance of AI algorithms. As we continue to push the boundaries of AI research and development, the importance of topology and geometry and manifold learning, in particular, will only grow.

Applications of Topology and Geometry in AI: From Computer Vision to Robotics

The fascinating world of topology and geometry has far-reaching implications in artificial intelligence (AI). These mathematical disciplines have become indispensable tools for researchers and developers by uncovering hidden structures and patterns in complex data. In this section, we will delve into the myriad applications of topology and geometry in AI, focusing on two key areas: computer vision and robotics.

Computer Vision: Seeing the World Through Geometric Lenses

Computer vision, a subfield of AI, aims to teach machines how to interpret and understand the visual world. Topology and geometry are crucial in this endeavor, as they provide the mathematical framework to analyze and process images and videos.

One of the most prominent applications of geometry in computer vision is feature extraction. By identifying and describing distinctive geometric structures in images, such as corners, edges, and contours, algorithms can efficiently recognize and classify objects. For instance, the Scale-Invariant Feature Transform (SIFT) and Oriented FAST and Rotated BRIEF (ORB) algorithms rely on geometric transformations to detect and describe local features invariant to scale, rotation, and illumination changes.

Topology also contributes significantly to computer vision, particularly in image segmentation. Topological data analysis (TDA) techniques, such as persistent homology, enable the identification of meaningful structures and patterns in images. By capturing the underlying topology of an image, TDA can distinguish between different objects and regions, even in the presence of noise and occlusions.

Robotics: Navigating the World with Geometric Precision

Robotics, another subfield of AI, deals with the design, construction, and operation of robots. Topology and geometry are integral to developing advanced robotic systems, as they provide the mathematical tools to model and navigate complex environments.

In robotic path planning, for instance, geometric algorithms are employed to find the shortest and safest routes for robots to traverse. By representing the environment as a geometric space, researchers can devise efficient algorithms to avoid obstacles and reach target destinations. Topological methods, such as homotopy classes, can also classify different paths based on their qualitative properties, enabling robots to choose the most suitable route according to specific criteria.

Moreover, topology and geometry are essential in developing robotic manipulation and grasping techniques. By modeling the shape and structure of objects, robots can determine the most effective way to grasp and manipulate them. Geometric reasoning can also be applied to analyze the kinematics and dynamics of robotic systems, allowing for precise control and coordination of their movements.

In conclusion, the applications of topology and geometry in AI are vast and varied, spanning from computer vision to robotics. By leveraging these mathematical disciplines, researchers and developers can uncover hidden structures and patterns in complex data, paving the way for more advanced and intelligent systems. As AI continues to evolve, the significance of topology and geometry will only grow, shaping the future of AI research and development.

The Future of Topology and Geometry in AI Research and Development

As we have journeyed through the fascinating world of topology and geometry, it is evident that these mathematical concepts play a crucial role in developing and advancing artificial intelligence. From the foundations of topological spaces to the intricacies of manifold learning, applying these ideas has enabled AI researchers to uncover hidden structures and patterns in complex, high-dimensional data. In this concluding section, we will explore the potential future directions of topology and geometry in AI research and development and the challenges and opportunities that lie ahead.

One promising avenue for the future of topology and geometry in AI is the integration of these concepts with deep learning techniques. Deep learning, a subset of machine learning, has recently gained significant attention due to its ability to learn and extract features from raw data automatically. By incorporating topological and geometric principles into deep learning algorithms, researchers can develop more robust and efficient models to understand better and interpret complex data structures.

Another exciting direction for topology and geometry in AI is the development of new algorithms and techniques that can efficiently handle large-scale, high-dimensional data. As the amount of data generated by various sources continues to grow exponentially, it becomes increasingly important for AI systems to process and analyze this information effectively. By leveraging the power of topology and geometry, researchers can create novel methods for dimensionality reduction, data compression, and pattern recognition that can scale to meet the demands of the ever-growing data landscape.

Moreover, applying topology and geometry in AI is not limited to computer vision and robotics. These mathematical concepts can also be applied to other domains, such as natural language processing, bioinformatics, and social network analysis, to name a few. By extending the reach of topology and geometry to these areas, researchers can uncover new insights and develop innovative solutions to a wide range of problems.

Despite the immense potential of topology and geometry in AI, some challenges must be addressed. One such challenge is the need for more efficient computational methods and tools to handle the complex calculations involved in topological and geometric analysis. Additionally, there is a need for more interdisciplinary collaboration between mathematicians, computer scientists, and AI researchers to further advance the understanding and application of these concepts in AI.

In conclusion, the future of topology and geometry in AI research and development is undoubtedly bright and full of possibilities. By continuing to explore and harness the power of these mathematical concepts, AI researchers can unlock new levels of understanding and innovation, ultimately pushing the boundaries of what artificial intelligence can achieve. As we move forward into this exciting future, researchers, practitioners, and enthusiasts must remain curious, open-minded, and collaborative in their pursuit of knowledge and discovery.

Chapter Summary

- Topology and geometry are essential tools in AI research, as they help uncover hidden structures and patterns in complex data, leading to more accurate and robust solutions in various applications such as computer vision, natural language processing, and network analysis.

- Topological spaces, which focus on the intrinsic relationships between data points, serve as the foundation for geometric analysis and are crucial for understanding the underlying structure of data.
- Geometric transformations, including translations, rotations, and scaling, enable AI algorithms to manipulate and analyze data more intuitively and efficiently, particularly in robotics.
- Manifold learning is a powerful technique that uncovers hidden structures within high-dimensional data, simplifying the data while preserving its inherent properties and enhancing the performance of AI algorithms.
- Popular manifold learning algorithms include Principal Component Analysis (PCA), Isomap, Locally Linear Embedding (LLE), and t-Distributed Stochastic Neighbor Embedding (t-SNE).
- Topology and geometry have numerous applications in AI, such as feature extraction, image segmentation in computer vision, path planning, and robotic manipulation in robotics.
- Future directions for topology and geometry in AI include integrating these concepts with deep learning techniques, developing new algorithms for handling large-scale data, and extending their applications to other domains like natural language processing and bioinformatics.
- Challenges in the field include more efficient computational methods, topological and geometric analysis tools, and increased interdisciplinary collaboration between mathematicians, computer scientists, and AI researchers.

THE FUTURE OF MATHEMATICS
IN AI

As we stand on the precipice of a new era in artificial intelligence, it is crucial to recognize mathematics's indispensable role in shaping this rapidly evolving landscape. The purpose of this concluding chapter is to provide a comprehensive overview of the essential mathematical concepts and techniques discussed throughout this book and to explore their implications for the future of AI. By synthesizing the significant themes and findings, we aim to highlight the significance of these mathematical foundations in driving advancements in AI while also acknowledging the limitations and critiques accompanying such a complex and interdisciplinary field.

In this epilogue, we will delve into the broader implications of our findings, examining how the mathematical principles we have explored can be applied to real-world AI applications and challenges. Furthermore, we will address our approach's potential shortcomings and critiques, fostering a balanced and nuanced understanding of the subject matter. Finally, we will offer recommendations for future research and development in AI, charting a path forward that is both innovative and grounded in the rich mathematical heritage that has brought us to this point.

By providing a straightforward and engaging narrative, we aim to inspire readers to appreciate the beauty and power of mathematics in AI and recognize its potential to shape the future of technology and society.

A Comprehensive Recap

As we reach the culmination of our exploration into the world of essential mathematics for artificial intelligence, it is crucial to take a moment to reflect on the major themes and findings that have emerged throughout this journey. By revisiting these key concepts, we can better understand the significance of mathematics in the development and advancement of AI and its potential to shape the future of this rapidly evolving field.

First and foremost, we have delved into the foundational mathematical concepts that underpin AI, including linear algebra, probability and statistics, calculus, and optimization. These core principles are the building blocks for AI algorithms and models, enabling them to learn, adapt, and make data-based decisions. By mastering these essential mathematical tools, AI practitioners can harness the power of AI to solve complex problems and drive innovation across various domains.

Another central theme throughout this book is the importance of interdisciplinary collaboration. As AI continues to permeate diverse fields such as healthcare, finance, and transportation, it becomes increasingly vital for AI practitioners to work closely with domain experts to ensure that mathematical models are grounded in real-world contexts and address relevant challenges. This collaborative approach enhances the efficacy of AI solutions and fosters a deeper understanding of the underlying mathematical principles.

We have also explored the role of ethics and responsibility in AI development, emphasizing the need for transparency, fairness, and accountability in mathematical models. As AI systems become more prevalent and influential in our daily lives, we must consider the potential consequences of their actions and strive to mitigate any negative impacts. By incorporating ethical considerations into the mathematical foundations of AI, we can work towards creating a more just and equitable future for all.

Throughout this book, we have examined various case studies and real-world applications of AI, showcasing the versatility and potential of mathematics in addressing diverse challenges. From natural language processing to autonomous vehicles, these examples have demonstrated the power of mathematical models in driving AI innovation and transforming industries.

Finally, we have discussed the importance of continuous learning and adaptation in AI. As new mathematical techniques and algorithms emerge, AI practitioners must remain agile and open to change, embracing the evolving landscape of AI and its potential to revolutionize how we live, work, and interact with the world around us.

In conclusion, this comprehensive recap serves as a testament to mathematics's critical role in the development and advancement of AI. By understanding and mastering these essential mathematical concepts, we can unlock the full potential of AI and shape a future that is both innovative and responsible.

Shaping the AI Landscape

As we delve into the implications and significance of essential mathematics in artificial intelligence, it is crucial to recognize the profound impact these mathematical concepts have on the development and advancement of AI technologies. The symbiotic relationship between mathematics and AI has not only shaped the AI landscape but has also paved the way for groundbreaking innovations that continue to revolutionize various industries and aspects of human life.

One of the most significant implications of essential mathematics in AI is its role in developing machine learning algorithms. These algorithms, the backbone of AI systems, rely heavily on mathematical concepts such as linear algebra, probability, and calculus to analyze and process vast amounts of data. By understanding and applying these mathematical principles, AI researchers and engineers can create more efficient and accurate algorithms to learn from data, adapt to new information, and ultimately make intelligent decisions.

Moreover, the significance of essential mathematics in AI extends beyond machine learning. It also plays a vital role in optimizing AI systems, ensuring they operate at peak performance. For instance, mathematical concepts such as graph theory and combinatorics are instrumental in solving complex optimization problems in AI applications, such as routing and scheduling in logistics or resource allocation in cloud computing.

Furthermore, essential mathematics is a foundation for developing new AI techniques and methodologies. As AI evolves, researchers constantly explore novel mathematical concepts and theories that can unlock new capabilities and applications for AI systems. For example, the emerging field of topological data analysis, which leverages the principles of algebraic topology, has shown promise in enhancing the robustness and interpretability of machine learning models.

In addition to its direct impact on AI technologies, essential mathematics fosters interdisciplinary collaboration and innovation. By bridging the gap between mathematics and AI, researchers from diverse fields such as computer science, engineering, and even social sciences can come together to tackle complex problems and develop innovative solutions that have far-reaching implications for society.

However, the significance of essential mathematics in AI has its challenges. As AI systems become increasingly sophisticated and complex, the demand for individuals with a strong foundation in mathematics and AI-related disciplines continues to grow. To ensure that the AI landscape continues to thrive and evolve, it is imperative to invest in education and training programs that equip the next generation of AI researchers and engineers with the necessary mathematical skills and knowledge.

In conclusion, the implications and significance of essential mathematics in AI are vast and far-reaching. By understanding and harnessing the power of these mathematical concepts, we can continue to shape the AI landscape, drive innovation, and unlock the full potential of artificial intelligence in transforming our world for the better.

Addressing the Inevitable Shortcomings

As we delve into the limitations and critiques of essential mathematics in AI, it is crucial to acknowledge that no field is without its shortcomings. This section will address some of the most pressing concerns and challenges when applying mathematical concepts to artificial intelligence. By doing so, we aim to provide a balanced perspective and encourage further research and development in this fascinating domain.

The Complexity Conundrum

One of the most significant limitations of using mathematics in AI is the inherent complexity of both fields. As AI systems become more advanced, the mathematical models and algorithms required to support them grow increasingly intricate. This complexity can make it difficult for researchers and practitioners to fully comprehend and optimize the AI systems they are working with. Moreover, the steep learning curve associated with mastering advanced mathematical concepts may deter some individuals from pursuing careers in AI, potentially limiting the field's growth and innovation.

The Black Box Dilemma

Another critique of using mathematics in AI is the so-called "black box" problem. This issue arises when AI systems become so complex that their inner workings are difficult, if possible, to understand. As a result, explaining how these systems arrive at their conclusions can take time and effort, leading to concerns about transparency, accountability, and trustworthiness. While mathematical models can provide a solid foundation for AI systems, they may only sometimes offer clear insights into the decision-making processes of these systems.

The Bias Pitfall

The application of mathematics in AI is not immune to the issue of bias. AI systems are often trained on large datasets, which may contain inherent biases that can be inadvertently perpetuated by the algorithms. Furthermore, the mathematical models may be designed with certain assumptions that introduce bias into the AI system. Addressing these biases is essential to ensure that AI systems are fair, ethical, and effective.

The Adaptability Challenge

Lastly, one of the limitations of using mathematics in AI is the difficulty in adapting mathematical models to the ever-evolving landscape of AI. As new technologies and techniques emerge, keeping mathematical models up-to-date and relevant can be challenging. This adaptability challenge underscores the importance of interdisciplinary collaboration between mathematicians, computer scientists, and other experts in the field of AI.

In conclusion, while essential mathematics plays a critical role in the development and advancement of AI, it is important to recognize and address the limitations and critiques accompanying its application. By doing so, we can work towards refining our understanding of the complex relationship between mathematics and AI, ultimately contributing to the growth and success of this exciting field.

Charting the Path Forward

As we reach the end of our mathematical journey through artificial intelligence, we must reflect on the insights gained and the path ahead. Mathematics has always been the backbone of scientific progress, and its role in AI is no exception. In this final section, we will provide a synthesis of our findings and offer recommendations for future research and development in the field of AI.

Throughout this book, we have explored the essential mathematical concepts that underpin AI, delving into topics such as linear algebra, probability theory, optimization, and more. We have seen how these mathematical tools have enabled the development of sophisticated AI algorithms and models, empowering machines to learn, reason, and adapt in ways that were once the exclusive domain of human intelligence.

The implications of these advancements are profound, with AI poised to revolutionize industries, economies, and societies across the globe. From healthcare and education to finance and transportation, the potential applications of AI are vast and varied. However, as we have also discussed, some limitations and critiques must be acknowledged and addressed to ensure the responsible and ethical development of AI technologies.

In light of these considerations, we offer the following recommendations for charting the path forward in the field of AI:

- **Foster interdisciplinary collaboration:** The development of AI requires expertise from a diverse range of fields, including mathematics, computer science, engineering, and the social sciences. Encouraging collaboration between these disciplines will facilitate the exchange of ideas and promote the development of innovative solutions to complex AI challenges.
- **Prioritize ethical considerations:** As AI continues to permeate various aspects of our lives, it is essential to ensure that ethical considerations are at the forefront of AI research and development. This includes addressing issues such as algorithmic bias, data privacy, and the potential displacement of human labor.
- **Invest in education and training:** To keep pace with the rapid advancements in AI, it is crucial to invest in education and training programs that equip individuals with the necessary mathematical and computational skills. This will help address the growing demand for AI talent and empower individuals to participate in the AI-driven economy.
- **Promote open research and collaboration:** The sharing of knowledge and resources is vital to the continued progress of AI. By promoting open research and collaboration, we can accelerate the pace of innovation and ensure that the benefits of AI are accessible to all.
- **Encourage public engagement and dialogue:** As AI technologies become increasingly integrated into our daily lives, it is essential to foster public engagement and dialogue around the potential benefits, risks, and ethical implications of AI. This will help to ensure that AI

development is guided by the needs and values of the communities it serves.

In conclusion, the future of mathematics in AI is both promising and challenging. By embracing the recommendations outlined above, we can work together to harness the power of mathematics and AI for the betterment of society while also addressing the potential pitfalls that may arise along the way. The journey may be complex, but the rewards are undoubtedly worthwhile.

AI AND ML FOR CODERS

A COMPREHENSIVE GUIDE TO
ARTIFICIAL INTELLIGENCE AND
MACHINE LEARNING TECHNIQUES,
TOOLS, REAL-WORLD APPLICATIONS,
AND ETHICAL CONSIDERATIONS FOR
MODERN PROGRAMMERS

INTRODUCTION TO ARTIFICIAL INTELLIGENCE AND MACHINE LEARNING FOR CODERS

In the ever-evolving landscape of technology, artificial intelligence (AI) and machine learning (ML) have emerged as two of the most transformative forces shaping our world today. As we stand at the cusp of a new era, coders, developers, and enthusiasts must understand and harness the power of these groundbreaking technologies. This book, "AI and ML for Coders," aims to serve as a comprehensive guide, providing readers with the knowledge and tools necessary to navigate the fascinating world of AI and ML.

AI and ML are vast and diverse, encompassing various techniques, algorithms, and applications. From natural language processing and computer vision to predictive analytics and autonomous systems, the potential of AI and ML to revolutionize industries and improve our daily lives is immense. As a coder, you are uniquely positioned to contribute to this revolution, leveraging your skills and creativity to develop innovative solutions that can change the world.

In this introductory chapter, we will embark on a journey through the history and evolution of AI and ML, tracing their roots and exploring the milestones that have shaped their development. We will also discuss the purpose and scope of this book, highlighting the unique blend of theory, practice, and real-world applications that sets it apart from other resources in the field. Furthermore, we will delve into the author's perspective, offering insights into the experiences and expertise that have informed the creation of this comprehensive guide.

As we progress through the chapters, we will delve deeper into the intricacies of AI and ML, equipping you with the knowledge and skills necessary to implement these technologies in your projects. Whether you are a seasoned developer looking to expand your repertoire or a curious enthusiast eager to learn more about AI and ML, this book caters to your needs and interests.

So, let us embark on this transformative journey together as we unveil the world of AI and ML for coders and unlock the potential of these powerful technologies to shape the future of our world.

Tracing the Evolution of Artificial Intelligence and Machine Learning

The fascinating world of Artificial Intelligence (AI) and Machine Learning (ML) has come a long way since its inception. To truly appreciate the power and potential of these technologies, it is essential to understand their historical roots and the milestones that have shaped their development. In this section, we will embark on a captivating journey through time, tracing the evolution of AI and ML and highlighting the key moments that have defined their growth.

The concept of AI dates back to ancient times, with myths and legends featuring intelligent machines and automatons. However, the modern era of AI began in the mid-20th century, when British mathematician and computer scientist Alan Turing proposed the Turing Test in 1950. This test assessed a machine's ability to exhibit intelligent behavior indistinguishable from a human's. Turing's work laid the foundation for the field of AI, sparking the imagination of researchers and visionaries alike.

In 1956, the Dartmouth Conference marked the birth of AI as a formal academic discipline. This gathering of scientists and mathematicians aimed to explore the possibilities of creating machines capable of simulating human intelligence. Early AI research focused on symbolic reasoning and problem-solving, giving rise to the development of programming languages like LISP and Prolog.

The 1960s and 1970s saw the emergence of various AI techniques, including knowledge representation, natural language processing, and expert systems. These approaches aimed to replicate human expertise in specific domains, such as medical diagnosis or financial planning. However, the limitations of these early AI systems soon became apparent as they needed help to cope with the complexity and ambiguity of real-world problems.

The 1980s marked a turning point in the evolution of AI and ML with the advent of connectionism and neural networks. Inspired by the structure and function of the human brain, these models sought to emulate how neurons process and transmit information. The development of the backpropagation algorithm enabled the efficient training of neural networks, paving the way for the emergence of deep learning in the subsequent decades.

The 1990s and 2000s witnessed significant advancements in ML, fueled by the increasing availability of data and computational power. The introduction of support vector machines, decision trees, and ensemble methods expanded the ML toolkit, enabling the development of more sophisticated and accurate models. During this period, AI and ML began to permeate various industries, from finance and healthcare to entertainment and e-commerce.

The 2010s saw the rise of deep learning, a subset of ML that leverages neural networks with multiple layers to learn complex patterns and representations. Breakthroughs in image recognition, natural language processing, and reinforcement learning have propelled AI and ML to the forefront of technological innovation. Today, AI and ML are transforming how we live, work, and interact with applications ranging from self-driving cars and virtual assistants to medical diagnostics and personalized recommendations.

In conclusion, the evolution of AI and ML has been remarkable, marked by groundbreaking discoveries, innovative techniques, and visionary thinkers. As we delve deeper into the world of AI and ML for coders, it is crucial to appreciate the rich history that has shaped these technologies and their immense potential for the future.

Empowering Coders to Harness the Power of AI and ML

The dawn of the digital age has brought many technological advancements. Among these innovations, Artificial Intelligence (AI) and Machine Learning (ML) have emerged as game-changers in computing. As we delve deeper into the 21st century, the significance of AI and ML in shaping our lives and industries is becoming increasingly apparent. Consequently, the demand for skilled coders who can harness the power of these technologies is on the rise.

The primary purpose of this book is to empower coders like you to tap into the immense potential of AI and ML. By providing a comprehensive understanding of these technologies' fundamental concepts, techniques, and applications, this book aims to equip you with the knowledge and skills required to excel in the rapidly evolving landscape of AI and ML.

This book is designed to serve as a valuable resource for coders, developers, and enthusiasts who wish to explore the fascinating world of AI and ML. It offers a unique blend of theory, practice, and real-world applications, ensuring that you not only grasp the underlying principles of these technologies but also learn how to apply them effectively in various contexts.

As you progress through the chapters, you will be introduced to various AI and ML techniques, ranging from basic algorithms to advanced neural networks. Each topic is presented clearly and concisely, emphasizing practical examples and hands-on exercises that will enable you to implement your newfound knowledge.

Moreover, this book adopts an engaging and persuasive writing style, encouraging you to embrace the transformative power of AI and ML and inspiring you to become an active participant in the ongoing technological revolution. By the time you reach the final pages, you will have gained a solid foundation in AI and ML and the confidence to apply these technologies in your projects and contribute to the broader coding community.

In summary, this book aims to empower you, the coder, to harness the power of AI and ML and embark on a transformative journey into these cutting-edge technologies. By providing a comprehensive, practical, and engaging learning experience, this book aims to equip you with the tools and knowledge necessary to thrive in the exciting world of AI and ML. So, let us begin this adventure together and unlock the limitless possibilities that await us in the fascinating world of Artificial Intelligence and Machine Learning.

Exploring the Breadth and Depth of AI and ML Techniques

In this groundbreaking book, we will embark on an enlightening journey that delves into the vast and intricate world of Artificial Intelligence (AI) and Machine Learning (ML) for coders. Our expedition will traverse the expansive landscape of these revolutionary technologies, providing readers with a comprehensive understanding of their underlying principles, techniques, and applications.

To begin, we will explore the foundational concepts and theories that form the bedrock of AI and ML. This will include examining the various types of AI, such as narrow, general, and superintelligence, and the fundamental principles of ML, including supervised, unsupervised, and reinforcement learning. By establishing a solid theoretical base, coders will be well-equipped to appreciate the practical aspects of these technologies.

Next, we will delve into the heart of AI and ML techniques, dissecting the inner workings of popular algorithms and models. This will encompass various topics, from neural networks and deep learning to natural language processing and computer vision. By examining these techniques in detail, readers will gain a thorough understanding of the mechanics behind these powerful tools, enabling them to harness their full potential in coding projects.

As we venture further into AI and ML, we will also discuss these technologies' ethical considerations and potential pitfalls. This will include an analysis of the implications of AI and ML on privacy, security, and employment, as well as a discussion of the measures that can be taken to mitigate these concerns. By addressing these critical issues, we aim to foster a responsible and conscientious approach to developing and deploying AI and ML solutions.

In addition to providing a comprehensive overview of AI and ML techniques, this book will also showcase many real-world applications and case studies. These examples will span various industries and domains, such as healthcare, finance, and transportation, demonstrating the transformative impact of AI and ML on our everyday lives. By examining these practical applications, readers will gain valuable insights into how AI and ML can be harnessed to solve complex problems and drive innovation.

Finally, this book will cater to a diverse audience of coders, developers, and enthusiasts, regardless of their expertise in AI and ML. Through clear explanations, engaging examples, and practical exercises, we aim to make these cutting-edge technologies accessible and enjoyable for all readers. Whether you are a seasoned programmer seeking to expand your skillset or a curious enthusiast eager to explore the world of AI and ML, this book will serve as your indispensable guide on this transformative journey.

A Unique Blend of Theory, Practice, and Real-World Applications

I aim to provide readers with a comprehensive understanding of artificial intelligence (AI) and machine learning (ML) from a coder's perspective. This book is designed to be a unique blend of theory, practice, and real-world applications, ensuring that readers not only grasp the fundamental concepts but also learn how to apply them in their coding projects.

In the theoretical aspect of this book, I delve into the history and evolution of AI and ML, discussing the key milestones and breakthroughs that have shaped the field. This background information is crucial for coders to appreciate the significance of these technologies and their potential impact on the future of computing.

The practical component of the book focuses on the hands-on implementation of AI and ML techniques. Through step-by-step tutorials and examples, readers will learn how to build and train various models, such as neural networks, decision trees, and clustering algorithms. These practical exercises reinforce the theoretical concepts and provide coders with the necessary skills to integrate AI and ML into their projects.

Lastly, the real-world applications section showcases the versatility and potential of AI and ML across various industries, such as healthcare, finance, and transportation. By exploring case studies and success stories, readers will gain insights into how these technologies revolutionize our lives and work. This section also serves as a source of inspiration for coders, encouraging them to think creatively and develop innovative AI and ML solutions.

Throughout the book, I try to make complex concepts accessible to readers of all levels. I aim to demystify AI and ML, empowering coders to harness the power of these technologies and contribute to the ongoing advancements in the field.

In conclusion, this book offers a unique blend of theory, practice, and real-world applications, providing coders with a comprehensive understanding of AI and ML. By combining these elements, I aim to inspire and equip readers with the knowledge and skills to embark on their transformative journey into AI and ML.

Embarking on a Transformative Journey into the Realm of AI and ML

As we stand on the precipice of a new era in technology, the significance of artificial intelligence and machine learning cannot be overstated. These powerful tools have the potential to revolutionize industries, streamline processes, and, ultimately, improve the quality of life for people around the world. For coders, developers, and enthusiasts alike, the opportunity to harness AI and ML's power is exciting and transformative.

In this book, we have endeavored to provide a comprehensive and accessible introduction to the world of AI and ML for coders. By tracing the evolution of these technologies, exploring their breadth and depth, and offering a unique blend of theory, practice, and real-world applications, we aim to empower our readers to take full advantage of the opportunities that AI and ML present.

As you embark on this transformative journey, it is essential to remember that the field of AI and ML is vast and ever-evolving. As such, it is crucial to approach your studies with an open mind, a willingness to learn, and a commitment to staying current with the latest developments and advancements. By doing so, you will be well-equipped to navigate the complexities of AI and ML and ultimately make a meaningful impact in your chosen field.

In conclusion, we invite you to join us on this exciting adventure into artificial intelligence and machine learning. As you delve into this book's pages, we hope you will find inspiration, knowledge, and the tools necessary to participate actively in the AI and ML revolution. Together, let us explore the limitless possibilities these technologies offer and work towards a brighter, more efficient, and more connected future.

1

FOUNDATIONS OF AI: HISTORY, CONCEPTS, AND TERMINOLOGY

I n recent years, artificial intelligence (AI) and machine learning (ML) fields have experienced a meteoric rise in popularity and application. These cutting-edge technologies have permeated nearly every aspect of our lives, from how we communicate and consume information to how we work and make decisions. As a coder, it is essential to understand the foundations of AI and ML, as they have become integral components of modern software development and innovation.

This chapter aims to provide a comprehensive overview of the history, core concepts, techniques, and terminology associated with AI and ML. By gaining a solid understanding of these topics, coders will be better equipped to harness the power of these technologies and stay ahead in the ever-evolving programming world.

The journey begins with a brief history of artificial intelligence, tracing its roots from the early days of computer science to the present day. This section will highlight key milestones and visionaries who have shaped the field, providing context for the development of AI and ML.

Next, we delve into the core concepts of AI, exploring the building blocks that underpin this fascinating field. From algorithms and heuristics to neural networks and natural language processing, this section will provide a solid foundation for understanding the inner workings of AI systems.

The focus then shifts to machine learning, a subset of AI that has garnered significant attention in recent years. This section will explore various techniques and applications of ML, demonstrating how coders can leverage these methods to create intelligent, adaptive software solutions.

A comprehensive glossary of essential terminology will be provided to ensure that readers are well-versed in the language of AI and ML. This vocabulary will serve as a valuable reference for coders navigating the complex landscape of AI and ML technologies.

Finally, the chapter will conclude with a look toward the future, examining the potential impact of AI and ML on the coding profession and beyond. As these technologies continue to advance rapidly, coders must stay informed and adapt to the changing landscape.

In summary, this chapter thoroughly introduces the world of AI and ML, equipping coders with the knowledge and tools necessary to excel in this exciting and dynamic field. By understanding the history, concepts, techniques, and terminology associated with AI and ML, coders will be well-prepared to harness the power of these technologies and shape the future of software development.

A Brief History of Artificial Intelligence: From Turing to Today

The fascinating journey of artificial intelligence (AI) and machine learning (ML) has its roots in the early 20th century, with the groundbreaking work of British mathematician and computer scientist Alan Turing. In this section, we will explore the milestones that have shaped the development of AI and ML and how they have become indispensable tools for coders in the modern world.

The Turing Test: The Birth of AI

In 1950, Alan Turing proposed a test to determine whether a machine could exhibit intelligent behavior indistinguishable from a human's. This test, known as the Turing Test, laid the foundation for AI. Turing's work sparked a wave of interest in the possibility of creating intelligent machines, and researchers began to explore the potential of computers to mimic human thought processes.

The Dartmouth Conference: Defining AI

In 1956, a group of scientists and mathematicians gathered at Dartmouth College to discuss the future of AI. This conference marked the birth of AI as a formal academic discipline. The attendees, including John McCarthy, Marvin Minsky, and Claude Shannon, defined AI as the science of creating machines that can perform tasks requiring human intelligence. This definition set the stage for decades of research and development in the field.

Early AI Programs: Exploring the Possibilities

Throughout the 1960s and 1970s, researchers developed several early AI programs that demonstrated the potential of computers to perform tasks such as problem-solving, language understanding, and learning. Some notable examples include:

- **General Problem Solver (GPS):** Developed by Allen Newell and Herbert A. Simon, GPS was an early AI program designed to imitate human problem-solving strategies.
- **ELIZA:** Created by Joseph Weizenbaum, ELIZA was a natural language processing program that could simulate conversations with humans.
- **SHRDLU:** Developed by Terry Winograd, SHRDLU was a program that could understand and manipulate objects in a virtual world using natural language commands.

The Rise of Machine Learning

In the 1980s, researchers focused on developing algorithms that could learn from data, giving birth to machine learning. This shift was driven by the realization that teaching machines to learn from data was more efficient than programming them explicitly. Key developments during this period include:

- **Decision Trees:** Ross Quinlan's development of the ID3 algorithm for generating decision trees marked a significant milestone in ML research.
- **Neural Networks:** Inspired by the human brain, researchers developed artificial neural networks that could learn to recognize patterns in data.
- **Reinforcement Learning:** Richard Sutton and Andrew Barto pioneered the field of reinforcement learning, where algorithms learn by interacting with their environment and receiving feedback.

The AI and ML Renaissance: Deep Learning and Beyond

The 21st century has seen an explosion of interest in AI and ML, fueled by advances in computing power, large datasets' availability, and algorithm design breakthroughs. The development of deep learning, a subset of ML that involves training large neural networks, has led to significant progress in areas such as image and speech recognition, natural language processing, and game-playing. Today, AI and ML are integral components of the coding world, with applications ranging from web development and data analysis to robotics and autonomous vehicles.

In conclusion, the history of AI and ML is a testament to the ingenuity and perseverance of researchers who have sought to understand and replicate human intelligence. As we continue to push the boundaries of what machines can do, the future of AI and ML promises to be an exciting and transformative journey for coders and society.

Core Concepts in AI: Understanding the Building Blocks

As we delve into the fascinating world of artificial intelligence (AI) and machine learning (ML), coders must grasp the fundamental concepts that underpin these technologies. In this section, we will explore the core building blocks of AI, providing you with a solid foundation to better understand and utilize these powerful tools in your coding projects.

Intelligent Agents

At the heart of AI lies the concept of an intelligent agent. An intelligent agent is a system that perceives its environment, processes the gathered information, and takes appropriate actions to achieve specific goals. These agents can range from simple rule-based systems to complex neural networks capable of learning and adapting to their surroundings.

Problem Solving and Search

One of the primary tasks of AI is to solve problems. To accomplish this, AI systems employ various search algorithms to explore the solution space and identify the most suitable solution. These algorithms can be classified into two categories: uninformed search, which blindly explores the solution space, and informed search, which uses heuristics or other knowledge to guide the search process.

Knowledge Representation and Reasoning

Knowledge representation is the process of encoding information about the world in a form that an AI system can understand and manipulate. This can be achieved through various methods, such as propositional logic, first-order logic, semantic networks, and ontologies. Reasoning, on the other hand, is the process of concluding the represented knowledge. AI systems use deduction, induction, and abduction techniques to reason about the world and make decisions.

Machine Learning

Machine learning is a subset of AI that focuses on developing algorithms that enable computers to learn from and make predictions or decisions based on data. There are three main types of machine learning: supervised learning, where the algorithm is trained on a labeled dataset; unsupervised learning, where the algorithm learns patterns from an unlabeled dataset; and reinforcement learning, where the algorithm learns by interacting with its environment and receiving feedback in the form of rewards or penalties.

Neural Networks and Deep Learning

Neural networks are a machine learning model inspired by the structure and function of the human brain. These networks consist of interconnected nodes or neurons, which process and transmit information. Deep learning is a subset of neural networks that deal with large, complex models containing multiple layers of neurons. These deep neural networks have been instrumental in achieving breakthroughs in various AI applications, such as image recognition, natural language processing, and game playing.

Natural Language Processing

Natural language processing (NLP) is a branch of AI that focuses on enabling computers to understand, interpret, and generate human language. This involves speech recognition, sentiment analysis, machine translation, and text summarization. NLP techniques rely on machine learning algorithms and linguistic knowledge to process and analyze textual data.

By understanding these core concepts, you are now better equipped to appreciate the intricacies of AI and ML and their applications in the coding world. As we continue our journey, we will delve deeper into the techniques and applications of machine learning, providing you with the knowledge and tools to harness the power of AI in your coding projects.

Decoding Machine Learning: Techniques and Applications for Coders

As we delve deeper into artificial intelligence (AI), coders must understand the intricacies of machine learning (ML) – a subset of AI that focuses on developing algorithms and models that enable computers to learn and improve from experience. In this section, we will explore various ML techniques and their applications, providing you with the necessary knowledge to harness the power of AI in your coding projects.

Supervised Learning

Supervised learning is the most common ML technique, where the algorithm is trained on a labeled dataset, meaning that each data point has a corresponding output or label. Supervised learning aims to create a model that can make accurate predictions when presented with new, unseen data. This technique is widely used in applications such as image recognition, speech recognition, and natural language processing.

Some popular supervised learning algorithms include:

- **Linear Regression:** Used for predicting continuous values, such as house prices, based on various features like the number of rooms, location, and size.
- **Logistic Regression:** Used for binary classification problems, such as determining whether an email is spam.
- **Support Vector Machines (SVM):** A robust algorithm for classification and regression tasks, often used in image classification and handwriting recognition.
- **Decision Trees and Random Forests:** These algorithms are used for classification and regression tasks and are particularly useful for handling large datasets with multiple features.

Unsupervised Learning

In unsupervised learning, the algorithm is trained on an unlabeled dataset, meaning the data points do not have corresponding outputs or labels. Unsupervised learning aims to identify patterns or structures within the data, such as clustering or dimensionality reduction. This technique is often used for anomaly detection, data compression, and recommendation systems.

Some popular unsupervised learning algorithms include:

- **K-means Clustering:** A widely-used clustering algorithm that groups data points based on their similarity, often used for customer segmentation or image compression.
- **Principal Component Analysis (PCA):** A dimensionality reduction technique that transforms data into a lower-dimensional space, preserving as much information as possible. PCA is often used for data visualization and noise reduction.

Reinforcement Learning

Reinforcement learning is an ML technique where an agent learns to make decisions by interacting with its environment and receiving feedback as rewards or penalties. Reinforcement learning aims to train the agent to make the best possible decisions to maximize its cumulative reward. This technique is commonly used in robotics, game-playing, and autonomous vehicles.

Some popular reinforcement learning algorithms include:

- **Q-Learning:** A model-free algorithm that learns an action-value function, which estimates the expected reward for a specific action in a given state.
- **Deep Q-Network (DQN):** A combination of Q-learning and deep neural networks, DQN has achieved human-level performance in playing Atari games.

In conclusion, understanding the various machine learning techniques and their applications is essential for coders looking to harness the power of AI. Mastering these concepts will enable you to tackle various coding projects, from building intelligent chatbots to developing self-driving cars. As AI and ML continue to evolve, the possibilities for their integration into the coding world are virtually limitless, making it an exciting time to be a coder.

AI and ML Terminology: Essential Vocabulary for the Modern Coder

As we delve deeper into artificial intelligence (AI) and machine learning (ML), coders must familiarize themselves with the essential vocabulary that defines these fields. This section aims to provide a comprehensive overview of the key terms and concepts that every modern coder should know. By mastering this terminology, you will be better equipped to understand and navigate the ever-evolving landscape of AI and ML.

- **Artificial Intelligence (AI):** AI refers to developing computer systems that can perform tasks that typically require human intelligence. These tasks include learning, reasoning, problem-solving, perception, and natural language understanding.
- **Machine Learning (ML):** ML is a subset of AI that focuses on developing algorithms and statistical models that enable computers to learn and improve from experience without being explicitly programmed. In other words, ML allows computers to adapt and make decisions based on data input automatically.
- **Deep Learning:** Deep learning is a subfield of ML that uses artificial neural networks to model and solve complex problems. These networks are designed to mimic the structure and function of the human brain, allowing computers to process and analyze vast amounts of data with remarkable accuracy.
- **Supervised Learning:** Supervised learning is a type of ML where the algorithm is trained on a labeled dataset containing input data and the corresponding correct output. Supervised learning aims to develop a model that can accurately predict the output for new, unseen data.

- **Unsupervised Learning:** Unlike supervised learning, unsupervised learning involves training an algorithm on an unlabeled dataset, where the input data does not have a corresponding output. Unsupervised learning aims to identify patterns, relationships, or structures within the data.
- **Reinforcement Learning:** Reinforcement learning is a type of ML where an agent learns to make decisions by interacting with its environment and receiving feedback through rewards or penalties. Reinforcement learning aims to develop a policy that maximizes the cumulative reward over time.
- **Neural Network:** A neural network is a computational model inspired by the structure and function of the human brain. It consists of interconnected nodes, or neurons, that process and transmit information. Neural networks are the foundation of deep learning and are used to model complex patterns and relationships in data.
- **Algorithm:** An algorithm is a step-by-step procedure for solving or performing a problem. In AI and ML, algorithms process data, make decisions, and generate predictions or recommendations.
- **Feature:** A feature is an individual measurable property or characteristic of an observed phenomenon. In ML, features are input variables to train and test algorithms.
- **Model:** In ML, a model is a mathematical representation of a real-world process or system. Models are developed using algorithms and are trained on data to make predictions or decisions.

By understanding and incorporating these essential AI and ML terms into your coding vocabulary, you will be better prepared to tackle the challenges and opportunities that lie ahead in this rapidly evolving field. As you continue to explore the foundations of AI and ML, remember that the key to success lies in your ability to adapt, learn, and grow alongside these transformative technologies.

The Future of AI and ML in Coding and Beyond

As we have journeyed through the fascinating world of artificial intelligence (AI) and machine learning (ML), it is evident that these technologies have become an integral part of the coding landscape. From their humble beginnings with Turing's groundbreaking work to the sophisticated algorithms that power today's most advanced applications, AI and ML have come a long way. As we look towards the future, it is essential to consider the potential impact of these technologies on the coding profession and the world at large.

The rapid advancements in AI and ML have opened up many opportunities for coders. With the increasing demand for AI-powered solutions across various industries, there is a growing need for skilled professionals who can develop and implement these technologies. As a result, coders who are well-versed in AI and ML concepts and techniques are likely to be in high demand in the coming years. By staying up-to-date with the latest developments and honing their skills in these areas, coders can position themselves at the forefront of this technological revolution.

Moreover, the integration of AI and ML into coding practices has the potential to transform the way we approach problem-solving and software development. By leveraging the power of these technologies, coders can create more efficient, accurate, and intelligent applications that can adapt and learn from their environments. This can lead to the development of innovative solutions that can tackle complex challenges and improve the overall quality of life.

However, it is crucial to recognize that the widespread adoption of AI and ML also raises several ethical and societal concerns. Data privacy, algorithmic bias, and the potential displacement of human workers by automation are just a few of the challenges that need to be addressed as we continue to integrate these technologies into our daily lives. As responsible professionals, coders must be aware of these concerns and strive to develop AI and ML solutions that are transparent, fair, and beneficial to all.

In conclusion, the future of AI and ML in coding is undoubtedly promising, with immense potential for growth and innovation. As we continue to explore the capabilities of these technologies, it is up to us, the coders, to harness their power responsibly and ethically. By doing so, we can help shape a future where AI and ML not only revolutionize the coding profession but also contribute to the betterment of society.

Chapter Summary

- AI and ML have experienced a rapid rise in popularity and application, becoming integral components of modern software development and innovation.
- The history of AI and ML can be traced back to the early 20th century, with key milestones and visionaries shaping the field, such as Alan Turing and the Dartmouth Conference.
- Core concepts in AI include intelligent agents, problem-solving and search, knowledge representation and reasoning, machine learning, neural networks and deep learning, and natural language processing.
- Machine learning techniques can be classified into supervised, unsupervised, and reinforcement learning, each with its own algorithms and applications.
- Deep learning, a subset of ML, involves training large neural networks and has led to significant progress in areas such as image and speech recognition, natural language processing, and game-playing.
- Familiarity with essential AI and ML terminology, such as supervised learning, unsupervised learning,

reinforcement learning, and neural networks, is crucial for modern coders.

- The future of AI and ML in coding is promising, with immense potential for growth, innovation, and the development of intelligent, adaptive software solutions.
- Ethical and societal concerns, such as data privacy, algorithmic bias, and the potential displacement of human workers, must be addressed as AI and ML technologies continue to advance and integrate into our daily lives.

2

MACHINE LEARNING BASICS: SUPERVISED, UNSUPERVISED, AND REINFORCEMENT LEARNING

I n the 21st century, artificial intelligence (AI) and machine learning (ML) have emerged as powerful tools transforming how we approach problem-solving and decision-making. As a coder, harnessing the potential of AI and ML can significantly enhance your capabilities and open up a world of possibilities. In this chapter, we will delve into the fascinating realm of machine learning, exploring its core concepts and techniques, and providing you with a solid foundation to incorporate these cutting-edge technologies into your coding repertoire.

At its core, machine learning is a subset of artificial intelligence that focuses on the development of algorithms and models that enable computers to learn and adapt from experience without being explicitly programmed. This ability to learn from data and improve over time allows machine learning systems to make predictions, identify patterns, and optimize processes with minimal human intervention.

There are three primary types of machine learning: supervised learning, unsupervised learning, and reinforcement learning. Each approach offers unique advantages and is suited to different types of problems and datasets. In the following sections, we will examine these learning methods in detail, providing a comprehensive understanding of their underlying principles, applications, and limitations.

As we embark on this journey through machine learning, it is essential to remember that the true power of AI and ML lies in their ability to augment human intelligence and creativity. By mastering these techniques and incorporating them into your coding projects, you will be well-equipped to tackle complex challenges, drive innovation, and shape the future of technology. So, let us begin our exploration of machine learning basics and unlock the potential of AI and ML for coders.

Supervised Learning: Training with Labeled Data

In the fascinating world of artificial intelligence and machine learning, supervised learning is one of the most widely used and practical techniques. As coders, it is essential to understand the fundamentals of supervised learning to harness its full potential in your projects. In this section, we will delve into the concept of supervised learning, explore its applications, and discuss the steps involved in training a model using labeled data.

The Concept of Supervised Learning

Supervised learning is a type of machine learning where the algorithm is trained on a dataset containing input-output pairs, also known as labeled data. In other words, the algorithm learns from examples annotated with the correct output, allowing it to make predictions or decisions based on new, unseen data. The primary goal of supervised learning is to create a model that can generalize well to new instances, minimizing the error between the predicted and actual outputs.

Applications of Supervised Learning

The versatility of supervised learning has led to its widespread use across various domains. Some typical applications include:

- **Image recognition:** Identifying objects, people, or scenes in images.
- **Spam detection:** Filtering out unwanted emails based on their content.
- **Fraud detection:** Identifying suspicious activities in financial transactions.
- **Medical diagnosis:** Predicting the presence or absence of a disease based on patient data.
- **Language translation:** Converting text from one language to another.

Training a Model with Labeled Data

The process of training a supervised learning model involves several crucial steps. Let's take a closer look at each of these steps:

- **Data collection and preprocessing:** The first step is to gather a dataset containing input-output pairs. This dataset must be large and diverse enough to represent the problem space accurately. The data may need to be cleaned, normalized, or transformed to ensure the algorithm can process it efficiently.

- **Model selection:** Next, you must choose an appropriate machine learning algorithm based on the problem. Some popular supervised learning algorithms include linear regression, logistic regression, support vector machines, and neural networks.
- **Model training:** The chosen algorithm is then trained on the labeled dataset. During this phase, the algorithm adjusts its parameters to minimize errors between its predictions and outputs. This process is often iterative, with the model improving its performance over multiple passes through the data.
- **Model evaluation:** Once the model has been trained, it is essential to evaluate its performance on a separate dataset that it has not seen before. This step helps to determine the model's ability to generalize to new instances. Standard evaluation metrics include accuracy, precision, recall, and F1 score.
- **Model tuning and optimization:** If the model's performance is unsatisfactory, you may need to fine-tune its parameters or optimize the algorithm to achieve better results. This process may involve adjusting the learning rate, changing the model's complexity, or employing regularization techniques to prevent overfitting.

In conclusion, supervised learning is a powerful and versatile technique that allows coders to create intelligent applications capable of making predictions and decisions based on labeled data. By understanding the fundamentals of supervised learning and following the steps outlined in this section, you can harness the power of AI and ML to enhance your coding projects and quickly solve complex problems.

Unsupervised Learning: Discovering Hidden Patterns

As we delve deeper into artificial intelligence and machine learning, it is essential to understand the different learning methods employed to solve various problems. In this section, we will explore the fascinating realm of unsupervised learning. This technique allows machines to discover hidden patterns and structures within data without prior guidance or labeled information.

The Essence of Unsupervised Learning

Imagine a scenario where you are presented with a large dataset containing information about various fruits. In supervised learning, you would have been provided with labeled data, such as the fruit's name, color, and size. However, in unsupervised learning, you are given no such labels. Your task is identifying any underlying patterns or structures within the data, such as clustering similar fruits or finding relationships between their attributes.

Unsupervised learning is a powerful technique that can be applied to various problems, from customer segmentation in marketing to anomaly detection in cybersecurity. By allowing machines to learn from unlabeled data, unsupervised learning opens up possibilities for discovering new insights and understanding complex systems.

Key Techniques in Unsupervised Learning

Several techniques in unsupervised learning can be employed to uncover hidden patterns within data. Two of the most common methods are clustering and dimensionality reduction.

Clustering involves grouping data points based on their similarity or proximity. Clustering algorithms, such as K-means or hierarchical clustering, can identify natural groupings within the data, which can be analyzed further to reveal insights or inform decision-making processes.

High-dimensional data can be challenging to analyze and visualize. Dimensionality reduction techniques, such as Principal Component Analysis (PCA) or t-Distributed Stochastic Neighbor Embedding (t-SNE), aim to reduce the number of dimensions in the data while preserving its essential structure. This can reveal hidden patterns and simplify the analysis process.

Advantages and Limitations of Unsupervised Learning

Unsupervised learning offers several advantages over supervised learning, such as the ability to work with unlabeled data and the potential to uncover previously unknown patterns or relationships. However, it also comes with its own set of challenges and limitations.

One of the primary advantages of unsupervised learning is its ability to work with large volumes of unlabeled data. Obtaining labeled data can be time-consuming, expensive, or even impossible in many real-world scenarios. Unsupervised learning offers a solution to this problem by allowing machines to learn from the data without explicit guidance.

On the other hand, unsupervised learning can be more challenging to evaluate and interpret than supervised learning. Since there are no predefined labels or ground truth to compare the results against, it can be challenging to determine the accuracy or effectiveness of the model. Additionally, the lack of guidance can sometimes lead to unexpected or irrelevant patterns being discovered, which may not be helpful for the problem at hand.

In conclusion, unsupervised learning is a powerful and versatile technique that can be used to discover hidden patterns and structures within data. By understanding its key techniques, advantages, and limitations, coders can harness the power of AI and machine learning to tackle a wide range of problems and uncover new insights. As we continue exploring the world of AI and ML, it is essential to recognize the value of unsupervised learning and its potential to transform how we analyze and understand complex systems.

Reinforcement Learning: Learning through Interaction

As we delve deeper into the fascinating world of machine learning, we must explore the concept of reinforcement learning. This unique and powerful approach enables machines to learn through interaction. This section will discuss the fundamentals of reinforcement learning, its applications, and how it differs from supervised and unsupervised learning. By understanding the intricacies of reinforcement learning, coders can harness its potential to create intelligent systems that adapt and improve over time.

The Essence of Reinforcement Learning

Reinforcement learning is an area of machine learning that focuses on training algorithms to make decisions based on their interactions with an environment. In this learning paradigm, an agent (the learning algorithm) takes actions within a given environment to achieve a specific goal. The agent receives feedback through rewards or penalties, which it uses to adjust its behavior and improve its decision-making capabilities.

The primary objective of reinforcement learning is to enable the agent to learn an optimal policy, a set of rules that dictate the best course of action in any given situation. The agent's goal is to maximize the cumulative reward it receives over time, which requires striking a balance between exploration (trying new actions) and exploitation (choosing the best-known action).

Key Components of Reinforcement Learning

Reinforcement learning comprises several essential components, including:

- **Agent:** The learning algorithm that interacts with the environment and makes decisions.
- **Environment:** The context in which the agent operates and takes actions.
- **State:** A representation of the current situation within the environment.
- **Action:** A decision made by the agent that affects the environment.
- **Reward:** Feedback provided to the agent based on the consequences of its actions.

These components work together in a cyclical process, with the agent continually observing the environment, taking actions, receiving rewards, and updating its knowledge to improve future decision-making.

Applications of Reinforcement Learning

Reinforcement learning has applications in various fields, including robotics, finance, healthcare, and gaming. Some notable examples include:

- **Robotics:** Reinforcement learning algorithms have been used to teach robots to walk, grasp objects, and navigate complex environments.
- **Finance:** In the financial sector, reinforcement learning has been employed to optimize trading strategies and manage investment portfolios.
- **Healthcare:** Reinforcement learning has been applied to personalize treatment plans for patients with chronic conditions, such as diabetes and cancer.
- **Gaming:** Reinforcement learning has trained AI agents to defeat human players in games like Go, chess, and poker.

Reinforcement Learning vs. Supervised and Unsupervised Learning

Reinforcement learning differs from supervised and unsupervised learning in several key aspects:

- **Feedback:** While supervised learning relies on labeled data to provide explicit feedback, reinforcement learning uses rewards and penalties as indirect feedback based on the agent's actions.
- **Exploration vs. Exploitation:** Reinforcement learning requires the agent to balance exploration and exploitation, a challenge not present in supervised or unsupervised learning.
- **Decision-making:** Reinforcement learning focuses on training agents to make decisions, whereas supervised and unsupervised learning primarily involves pattern recognition and data analysis.

In conclusion, reinforcement learning offers a dynamic and interactive approach to machine learning that empowers coders to create intelligent systems capable of learning from their experiences. By understanding the principles of reinforcement learning and its differences from supervised and unsupervised learning, coders can choose the most suitable learning method for their projects and harness the full potential of AI and ML in their work.

Comparing and Choosing the Right Learning Method

As we delve deeper into the world of artificial intelligence and machine learning, it becomes increasingly important to understand the distinctions between the various learning methods and how to choose the right one for your coding project. In this section, we will compare supervised, unsupervised, and reinforcement learning, highlight their strengths and weaknesses, and guide you in selecting the most suitable approach for your needs.

Supervised Learning: Training with Labeled Data

Strengths: Supervised learning is the most common and widely used method in machine learning. It excels in situations with a clear relationship between input and output data, and labeled data is readily available. This method is particularly effective for classification, regression, and prediction tasks.

Weaknesses: The primary drawback of supervised learning is its reliance on labeled data. Obtaining and maintaining a large dataset with accurate labels can be time-consuming and expensive. Additionally, supervised learning models may struggle with generalizing to new, unseen data if the training data needs to be more diverse.

When to choose: Opt for supervised learning when you have a well-defined problem with a clear input-output relationship and access to a substantial amount of labeled data.

Unsupervised Learning: Discovering Hidden Patterns

Strengths: Unsupervised learning shines when labeled data is scarce or nonexistent. It is adept at uncovering hidden patterns, structures, and relationships within the data, making it ideal for clustering, dimensionality reduction, and anomaly detection tasks.

Weaknesses: The primary limitation of unsupervised learning is its need for more precise, interpretable results. Since it does not rely on labeled data, the output may be challenging to understand and validate. Additionally, unsupervised learning models may require more computational resources and time to process large datasets.

When to choose: Choose unsupervised learning when you have a large amount of unlabeled data and are interested in discovering underlying patterns or structures within the data.

Reinforcement Learning: Learning through Interaction

Strengths: Reinforcement learning is particularly well-suited for problems involving decision-making and interacting with an environment. Through trial and error, it can learn optimal strategies and actions, making it ideal for game playing, robotics, and autonomous systems.

Weaknesses: Reinforcement learning can be computationally expensive and may require significant time to converge on an optimal solution. Additionally, it can be challenging to design an appropriate reward function that effectively guides the learning process.

When to choose: Opt for reinforcement learning when working on a problem involving sequential decision-making and interaction with an environment, and you are willing to invest time and resources in fine-tuning the learning process.

In conclusion, the choice of learning method depends on the nature of your problem, the availability of labeled data, and the desired outcome. By understanding the strengths and weaknesses of supervised, unsupervised, and reinforcement learning, you can make an informed decision and harness the power of AI and ML to elevate your coding projects to new heights.

Embracing the Power of AI and ML in Coding

As we reach the end of our journey through the fascinating world of artificial intelligence and machine learning, it is essential to take a moment to reflect on the immense potential these technologies hold for coders. By understanding the basics of machine learning, including supervised, unsupervised, and reinforcement learning, we have unlocked the door to a new realm of possibilities in the coding field.

The power of AI and ML lies in their ability to transform how we approach problem-solving and decision-making. By harnessing these technologies, coders can create more efficient, intelligent, and adaptable software solutions that can learn and grow over time. This enhances the user experience and allows developers to tackle increasingly complex challenges with greater ease and precision.

In today's rapidly evolving digital landscape, coders must stay ahead of the curve and embrace the latest advancements in AI and ML. By doing so, they can unlock new opportunities for innovation and growth, personally and professionally. As we have seen throughout this chapter, the key to success in this endeavor lies in understanding the fundamental principles of machine learning and selecting the most appropriate method for each unique situation.

As you continue to explore the world of AI and ML, remember that the journey does not end here. Machine learning constantly evolves, with new techniques and algorithms being developed daily. As a coder, it is up to you to stay informed and adapt to these changes, ensuring that your skills remain relevant and valuable in the ever-changing world of technology.

In conclusion, the power of AI and ML in coding cannot be overstated. By embracing and incorporating these technologies into your work, you can unlock a world of possibilities and take your coding skills to new heights. So, go forth and harness the power of machine learning, and let it guide you on your path to becoming a more skilled, innovative, and successful coder.

Chapter Summary

- Machine learning, a subset of artificial intelligence, focuses on developing algorithms and models that enable computers to learn and adapt from experience without explicit programming.
- There are three primary types of machine learning: supervised learning (training with labeled data), unsupervised learning (discovering hidden patterns),

and reinforcement learning (learning through interaction).

- Supervised learning is the most common method and is effective for classification, regression, and prediction tasks. It requires a large amount of labeled data and a clear input-output relationship.
- Unsupervised learning is ideal for uncovering hidden patterns and structures within data, especially when labeled data is scarce. It is suitable for clustering, dimensionality reduction, and anomaly detection tasks.
- Reinforcement learning is well-suited for problems involving decision-making and interaction with an environment. It is ideal for game-playing, robotics, and autonomous systems.
- Choosing the right learning method depends on the nature of the problem, the availability of labeled data, and the desired outcome. Understanding the strengths and weaknesses of each method is crucial for making an informed decision.
- The power of AI and ML lies in their ability to transform problem-solving and decision-making, allowing coders to create more efficient, intelligent, and adaptable software solutions.
- Staying informed and adapting to the constantly evolving field of machine learning is essential for coders to remain relevant and valuable in the ever-changing world of technology.

3

ESSENTIAL TOOLS AND LIBRARIES
FOR AI AND ML DEVELOPMENT

I n the always-adapting world of artificial intelligence (AI) and
machine learning (ML), developers constantly seek ways to
create more efficient, accurate, and intelligent systems. To
achieve this, they rely on a wide array of tools and libraries that
simplify the development process and enhance the capabilities of
their AI and ML projects. This chapter aims to provide an overview

of the essential tools and libraries that every AI and ML developer should be familiar with, regardless of their level of expertise.

As we delve into AI and ML development, we must understand that these technologies are not limited to a single programming language or platform. Instead, they encompass various languages, libraries, and tools that cater to different needs and preferences. By exploring these options, developers can decide which tools best suit their projects and goals.

In the following sections, we will discuss popular programming languages for AI and ML and the most widely used machine learning libraries and frameworks. We will also explore deep learning libraries and tools, which have gained significant traction in recent years due to their ability to process vast amounts of data and generate highly accurate models. Finally, we will examine data visualization and analysis tools, which are essential for understanding and interpreting the results of AI and ML algorithms.

By the end of this chapter, you will have a solid understanding of the various tools and libraries available for AI and ML development, enabling you to choose the right ones for your projects and ultimately create more effective and intelligent systems. So, let's embark on this exciting journey and discover the essential tools and libraries that will empower you to harness the full potential of AI and ML technologies.

Popular Programming Languages for AI and ML

As we delve into the fascinating world of artificial intelligence (AI) and machine learning (ML), it is crucial to understand the role of programming languages in shaping this domain. The choice of a programming language can significantly impact the ease of development, performance, and scalability of AI and ML projects. This section will explore some of the most popular programming languages for AI and ML, highlighting their strengths and weaknesses to help you make an informed decision.

Python

Python has emerged as the undisputed leader in the AI and ML landscape thanks to its simplicity, readability, and extensive library support. Its syntax is clear and concise, allowing developers to focus on the logic and algorithms rather than getting bogged down by complex code structures. Python's vast ecosystem of libraries, such as TensorFlow, PyTorch, and scikit-learn, makes it an ideal choice for implementing various AI and ML techniques, including deep learning, natural language processing, and computer vision.

R

R is a powerful statistical programming language that has gained immense popularity among data scientists and statisticians. Its comprehensive statistical and graphical tools suite makes it an excellent choice for data analysis, visualization, and modeling. R's rich library support, including packages like caret, randomForest, and xgboost, enables developers to implement a wide range of ML algorithms easily. However, R's steep learning curve and less intuitive syntax may challenge beginners.

Java

Java, a versatile and widely used programming language, has also found its place in the AI and ML domain. Its platform independence, robustness, and strong object-oriented programming (OOP) capabilities make it suitable for large-scale, complex AI and ML projects. Java's extensive library support, such as Deeplearning4j, Weka, and Java-ML, facilitates the implementation of various ML algorithms and techniques. However, Java's verbosity and slower execution speed compared to Python may be a drawback for some developers.

C++

C++ is a high-performance programming language that offers fine-grained control over system resources, making it an attractive choice for computationally intensive AI and ML tasks. Its powerful OOP features and support for parallelism enable developers to build efficient and scalable AI and ML applications. Libraries like Shark, mlpack, and Dlib provide a solid foundation for implementing ML algorithms in C++. However, C++ has a steeper learning curve and lacks the extensive library support available in Python and R.

Julia

Julia is a relatively new programming language gaining traction in the AI and ML community. It combines the ease of use and readability of Python with the performance of C++, making it an appealing choice for developers. Julia's growing ecosystem of libraries, such as Flux, MLJ, and Knet, supports various AI and ML techniques. While Julia shows great promise, its relatively smaller community and limited library support compared to more established languages may concern some developers.

In conclusion, choosing a programming language for AI and ML projects largely depends on your specific requirements, existing skillset, and personal preferences. Python and R are excellent for their extensive library support and ease of use, while Java and C++ offer robustness and scalability for large-scale projects. With its blend of simplicity and performance, Julia is an exciting newcomer to the field. Ultimately, the key is to choose a language that enables you to effectively and efficiently bring your AI and ML ideas to life.

Machine Learning Libraries and Frameworks

In artificial intelligence (AI) and machine learning (ML), the right tools can make all the difference in the success of your projects. Machine learning libraries and frameworks are essential components that provide developers with pre-built algorithms, functions, and methods to simplify the process of creating and implementing ML models. This section will explore some of the most popular machine learning libraries and frameworks, discussing their features, advantages, and use cases.

Scikit-learn

Scikit-learn is an open-source Python library offering various machine learning algorithms for various tasks, including classification, regression, clustering, and dimensionality reduction. It is built on top of NumPy, SciPy, and Matplotlib, essential libraries for scientific computing in Python. Scikit-learn is known for its user-friendly interface, comprehensive documentation, and active community support. It is an excellent choice for beginners and experienced developers looking to implement traditional machine-learning techniques in their projects.

TensorFlow

Developed by Google, TensorFlow is an open-source machine learning framework that has gained immense popularity for its flexibility, scalability, and ability to work with deep learning models. TensorFlow supports multiple programming languages, including Python, C++, and Java, and can be used for various tasks such as image and speech recognition, natural language processing, and reinforcement learning. Its extensive ecosystem, including tools like TensorBoard for visualization and TensorFlow Extended (TFX) for production pipelines, makes it a powerful choice for research and production environments.

Keras

Keras is a high-level neural networks API written in Python and capable of running on top of TensorFlow, Microsoft Cognitive Toolkit, or Theano. It was designed to enable fast experimentation with deep neural networks and focuses on being user-friendly, modular, and extensible. Keras provides a simple interface for building and training complex neural network models, making it an excellent choice for developers new to deep learning or those who prefer a more intuitive approach to model creation.

PyTorch

Created by Facebook's AI Research lab, PyTorch is an open-source machine learning framework that has gained popularity for its dynamic computation graph, ease of debugging, and strong support for GPU acceleration. PyTorch is particularly well-suited for deep learning applications, offering a wide range of pre-built models and tools for computer vision, natural language processing, and reinforcement learning. Its "eager execution" mode allows developers to see the results of their code as they write it, making it easier to identify and fix errors in the development process.

XGBoost

XGBoost, short for eXtreme Gradient Boosting, is an open-source library that provides an efficient and scalable implementation of gradient-boosted decision trees. It is designed for speed and performance, with features like parallelization, regularization, and early stopping to prevent overfitting. XGBoost has been widely adopted in machine learning competitions and real-world applications due to its ability to handle large datasets and deliver accurate results. It supports multiple programming languages, including Python, R, Java, and Scala.

In conclusion, the choice of machine learning libraries and frameworks depends on your specific project requirements, programming language preferences, and level of expertise. By familiarizing yourself with these popular tools, you can make informed decisions and select the best options for your AI and ML projects. As you continue to explore the world of AI and ML development, remember that the right tools can significantly enhance your productivity and the quality of your work.

Data Visualization and Analysis Tools

In artificial intelligence (AI) and machine learning (ML), data visualization and analysis tools play a crucial role in understanding and interpreting the vast amounts of data generated by these technologies. These tools enable developers and data scientists to gain insights, identify patterns, and make informed decisions based on the data. This section will explore some of the most popular and widely used data visualization and analysis tools that can significantly enhance your AI and ML projects.

Matplotlib

Matplotlib is a versatile and powerful Python library for creating static, animated, and interactive visualizations. It offers many plotting options, including line plots, scatter plots, bar plots, and more. With its extensive customization options, Matplotlib allows users to create visually appealing and informative graphics that can effectively communicate the results of their AI and ML models.

Seaborn

Seaborn is another Python library built on top of Matplotlib, designed to simplify creating complex and aesthetically pleasing data visualizations. It has several built-in themes and color palettes to make it easy for users to create visually appealing plots. Seaborn also integrates seamlessly with the Pandas library, allowing for efficient data manipulation and analysis.

Plotly

Plotly is a popular open-source library for creating interactive and web-based visualizations in Python, R, and Julia. It offers various chart types, including scatter plots, line charts, bar charts, and more. Plotly's interactive features, such as tooltips, zooming, and panning, make it an excellent choice for presenting and exploring complex datasets in AI and ML projects.

Tableau

Tableau is a powerful data visualization and analysis tool that allows users to create interactive and shareable dashboards. With its intuitive drag-and-drop interface, Tableau enables users to quickly analyze large datasets and create visually appealing visualizations without programming knowledge. Tableau's integration with various data sources, such as databases, spreadsheets, and cloud services, makes it a popular choice for data-driven decision-making in AI and ML projects.

Jupyter Notebook

Jupyter Notebook is an open-source web application that allows users to create and share documents containing live code, equations, visualizations, and narrative text. It is widely used in the AI and ML community for data cleaning, transformation, and visualization, as well as for building and training models. Jupyter Notebook's interactive nature makes it an ideal tool for exploring data, testing hypotheses, and iterating on models.

In conclusion, selecting the right data visualization and analysis tools for your AI and ML projects is essential for effectively communicating your findings and making data-driven decisions. By familiarizing yourself with the various tools available, you can choose the ones that best suit your needs and enhance the overall success of your projects.

Choosing the Right Tools for Your AI and ML Projects

As we have traversed the landscape of artificial intelligence (AI) and machine learning (ML) development, we have encountered many tools and libraries that cater to the diverse needs of coders. The options are vast and varied, from programming languages to machine learning frameworks, deep learning libraries, and data visualization tools. In this concluding section, we provide guidance on selecting the most suitable tools for your AI and ML projects, ensuring you can harness these cutting-edge technologies' full potential.

The first step in choosing the right tools for your AI and ML projects is identifying your specific goals and requirements. Are you looking to develop a simple machine-learning model or delve into the complexities of deep learning? Are you working on a project requiring real-time data analysis or focusing on data visualization? By clearly defining your objectives, you can narrow down the tools and libraries that best serve your needs.

Next, consider your level of expertise and familiarity with programming languages. While Python is widely regarded as the go-to language for AI and ML development, other languages such as R, Java, and C++ offer robust libraries and frameworks. If you are already proficient in a particular language, it may be more efficient to leverage its capabilities rather than learn a new one from scratch. However, if you are starting your AI and ML journey, Python's user-friendly syntax and extensive resources make it an excellent choice.

The choice of machine learning libraries and frameworks largely depends on the type of model you wish to create and the level of customization you require. Scikit-learn is a popular choice for beginners due to its simplicity and ease of use, while Tensor-Flow and PyTorch offer more advanced features and flexibility for experienced developers. Be sure to explore the documentation and community support for each library, as these resources can significantly impact your learning curve and overall experience.

Deep learning libraries and tools like Keras, TensorFlow, and

PyTorch cater to different preferences and use cases. Keras is known for its user-friendly interface and is ideal for those new to deep learning. TensorFlow and PyTorch provide more control over the underlying architecture and are preferred by researchers and professionals. Again, consider your project requirements and personal preferences when making your selection.

Data visualization and analysis tools are crucial for understanding and interpreting the results of your AI and ML models. Libraries such as Matplotlib, Seaborn, and Plotly offer a range of visualization options to suit various data types and presentation styles. Tools like Pandas and NumPy also facilitate data manipulation and analysis, streamlining the development process.

In conclusion, the choice of tools and libraries for your AI and ML projects is a critical decision that can significantly impact the success of your endeavors. By carefully considering your project goals, programming language preferences, and desired level of customization, you can confidently select the tools that will propel you toward achieving your AI and ML aspirations. Remember, mastering AI and ML is an ongoing process, and as you grow and evolve as a developer, so will your toolkit.

Chapter Summary

- AI and ML development involves a diverse range of languages, libraries, and tools that cater to different needs and preferences, making it essential for developers to explore these options and choose the right ones for their projects.
- Popular programming languages for AI and ML include Python, R, Java, C++, and Julia, each with strengths and weaknesses. Python and R are known for their extensive library support and ease of use, while Java and C++ offer robustness and scalability for large-scale projects.

- Machine learning libraries and frameworks like Scikit-learn, TensorFlow, Keras, PyTorch, and XGBoost provide developers with pre-built algorithms, functions, and methods to simplify creating and implementing ML models.
- Deep learning libraries and tools, including TensorFlow, Keras, PyTorch, Caffe, and Theano, enable developers to harness the full potential of deep learning techniques, such as neural networks, for various AI and ML applications.
- Data visualization and analysis tools, like Matplotlib, Seaborn, Plotly, Tableau, and Jupyter Notebook, play a crucial role in understanding and interpreting the vast amounts of data generated by AI and ML technologies.
- Identifying specific goals and requirements is the first step in choosing the right tools for AI and ML projects, followed by considering the level of expertise and familiarity with programming languages.
- The choice of machine learning libraries and frameworks largely depends on the type of model to be created and the level of customization required, while deep learning libraries cater to different preferences and use cases.
- Selecting the right tools and libraries for AI and ML projects is a critical decision that can significantly impact the success of the endeavors, and as developers grow and evolve, so will their toolkit.

4

DATA PREPARATION AND PREPROCESSING TECHNIQUES FOR MACHINE LEARNING

I n the constantly changing world of artificial intelligence (AI) and machine learning (ML), the role of data has become increasingly significant. As coders and developers, we must recognize that our ML models' success relies heavily on the quality and structure of the data we feed them. This chapter delves into the essential aspects of data preparation and preprocessing techniques, which are the foundation for building accurate and efficient ML models.

Data preparation and preprocessing encompass a wide range of techniques that aim to transform raw data into a format easily understood and utilized by ML algorithms. These techniques ensure that our models can extract meaningful insights and make accurate predictions. By investing time and effort into preparing and preprocessing our data, we can significantly enhance the performance of our ML models and, ultimately, the success of our AI applications.

In this chapter, we will explore the importance of data quality in machine learning and discuss various techniques to clean and handle missing values in our datasets. We will also delve into the art of feature engineering and selection, which can significantly impact the performance of our models. Furthermore, we will examine data transformation and scaling techniques that can help standardize and normalize our data for optimal model training.

By the end of this chapter, you will have a comprehensive understanding of the various data preparation and preprocessing techniques essential for successful machine learning projects. With this knowledge, you will be well-equipped to tackle the challenges of working with real-world data and building high-performing ML models. So, let's embark on this exciting journey and uncover the secrets to effective data preparation and preprocessing in AI and ML.

Understanding the Importance of Data Quality in Machine Learning

In the realm of artificial intelligence (AI) and machine learning (ML), the adage "garbage in, garbage out" rings truer than ever. As coders and developers, we must recognize the critical role that data quality plays in the success of our machine-learning models. In this section, we will delve into the significance of data quality, its impact on model performance, and the potential consequences of neglecting this crucial aspect of machine learning.

To begin with, let us consider the foundation of any machine learning project: the data. High-quality data is the lifeblood of machine learning algorithms, enabling them to learn patterns, make predictions, and, ultimately, solve complex problems. Even the most sophisticated algorithms will struggle to produce meaningful results without accurate, reliable, and relevant data. The quality of the data we feed into our models directly influences their ability to make accurate predictions and generate valuable insights.

We must consider several key dimensions of data quality when preparing our datasets for machine learning. These include:

- **Accuracy:** The degree to which the data reflects the true state of the world or the phenomenon being studied. Inaccurate data can lead to incorrect predictions and misguided decision-making.
- **Completeness:** The extent to which all necessary data points are present in the dataset. Missing or incomplete data can hinder the ability of machine learning algorithms to identify patterns and make accurate predictions.
- **Consistency:** The uniformity of data across different sources and formats. Inconsistent data can create confusion and ambiguity, making it difficult for algorithms to learn and generalize effectively.
- **Relevance:** The pertinence of the data to the problem at hand. Irrelevant data can introduce noise and distractions, impeding the ability of machine learning models to focus on the most essential features and relationships.
- **Timeliness:** The currency and freshness of the data. Outdated or stale data can lead to ill-equipped models to handle current or future scenarios.

Neglecting data quality can have far-reaching consequences for machine learning projects. Poor-quality data can result in less accurate, unreliable, and generalizable models for new situations. This, in turn, can lead to misguided decision-making, wasted resources, and, ultimately, a loss of trust in the power of AI and ML.

In conclusion, understanding the importance of data quality in machine learning is paramount for coders and developers who wish to harness the full potential of AI and ML technologies. By ensuring that our datasets are accurate, complete, consistent, relevant, and timely, we can lay the groundwork for machine learning models capable of delivering powerful insights and driving meaningful change. In the following sections, we will explore various data preparation and preprocessing techniques to help us achieve this goal and set our machine learning projects up for success.

Data Cleaning and Handling Missing Values

The adage "garbage in, garbage out" holds true in machine learning. The data quality fed into a model directly impacts its performance and accuracy. Data cleaning, therefore, is a crucial step in the machine learning pipeline. This section will delve into the importance of data cleaning and explore various techniques for handling missing values in your dataset.

The Importance of Data Cleaning

Data cleaning is identifying and correcting errors, inconsistencies, and inaccuracies in datasets. Raw data collected from various sources often contains noise, missing values, and outliers that can negatively affect the performance of machine learning algorithms. Cleaning the data ensures your model is trained on accurate and reliable information, leading to better predictions and insights.

Identifying Missing Values

Before handling missing values, it is essential to identify them in your dataset. Missing values can occur for various reasons, such as data entry errors, equipment malfunctions, or respondents not providing information in surveys. In most programming languages and libraries, missing values are represented as "NaN" (Not a Number) or "null."

Techniques for Handling Missing Values

There are several techniques for handling missing values in a dataset, each with advantages and disadvantages. The choice of technique depends on the nature of the data, the percentage of missing values, and the specific requirements of the machine learning model. Some common techniques include:

- **Deletion:** This method removes rows or columns with missing values from the dataset. While it is the most straightforward approach, deletion can lead to the loss of valuable information, especially if a significant portion of the data is missing.
- **Imputation:** Imputation involves replacing missing values with estimated values based on other available data. There are various imputation techniques, such as mean, median, or mode imputation for numerical data and the most frequent category imputation for categorical data. More advanced techniques include regression imputation and k-nearest neighbors imputation.
- **Interpolation:** This technique is used for time-series data, where missing values are estimated based on the values of neighboring data points. Linear interpolation is the most common method, but more advanced techniques like polynomial or spline interpolation can also be used.

Using algorithms that handle missing values: Some machine learning algorithms, such as decision trees and random forests, can handle missing values without the need for preprocessing. Depending on the specific implementation, these algorithms can either ignore the missing values or use them to make splits in the data.

Evaluating the Impact of Handling Missing Values

After applying a technique to handle missing values, evaluating its impact on the dataset and the machine learning model's performance is essential. This can be done by comparing the performance metrics of the model trained on the original dataset with the performance metrics of the model trained on the cleaned dataset. If the performance improves significantly, it indicates that the chosen technique effectively handles missing values.

In conclusion, data cleaning and handling missing values are critical steps in the machine learning pipeline. By ensuring that your dataset is free of errors and inconsistencies, you can significantly improve the performance and accuracy of your machine-learning models. Remember to carefully consider the nature of your data and your model's specific requirements when choosing a technique for handling missing values.

Feature Engineering and Selection for Optimal Model Performance

The adage "garbage in, garbage out" holds true in machine learning. The quality of the input data directly impacts the performance of the model. As such, feature engineering and selection are crucial in ensuring optimal model performance. In this section, we will delve into the art and science of feature engineering and selection, exploring the various techniques and strategies that can be employed to enhance the performance of machine learning models.

Feature engineering transforms raw data into meaningful and informative features that can be used as input for machine learning algorithms. This process often involves domain knowledge, creativity, and intuition to identify the most relevant features for a given problem. Some standard feature engineering techniques include:

- **Combining features:** This involves creating new features by combining two or more existing features. For example, in a dataset containing information about houses, one could create a new feature called "price per square foot" by dividing the price of the house by its square footage.
- **Binning:** This technique involves grouping continuous variables into discrete categories or bins. For instance, age can be binned into categories such as "young," "middle-aged," and "old."
- **Polynomial features:** This technique involves creating new features by raising existing features to power or combining them multiplicatively. For example, if a dataset contains features x and y, one could create new features x^2, y^2, and $x*y$.
- **One-hot encoding:** This technique converts categorical variables into binary features. For example, a feature representing the color of a car (red, blue, or green) can be converted into three binary features: "is_red," "is_blue," and "is_green."

On the other hand, feature selection identifies the most critical features from the original dataset or the engineered features. This is crucial because irrelevant or redundant features can negatively impact the model's performance. Some common feature selection techniques include:

- **Filter methods:** These techniques involve ranking features based on a specific metric, such as correlation

with the target variable or mutual information, and
selecting the top-ranked features.

- **Wrapper methods:** These techniques involve evaluating
the performance of a machine learning model with
different subsets of features and selecting the subset that
yields the best performance. Examples of wrapper
methods include forward selection, backward
elimination, and recursive feature elimination.
- **Embedded methods:** These techniques involve
selecting features as part of the model training process.
For example, regularization techniques such as Lasso
and Ridge regression can penalize the inclusion of
irrelevant features, effectively performing feature
selection.

In conclusion, feature engineering and selection are essential
steps in the data preparation process for machine learning. By carefully crafting informative features and selecting the most relevant
ones, data scientists can significantly improve the performance of
their models, leading to more accurate predictions and better decision-making.

The Impact of Effective Data Preparation on Machine Learning Success

In conclusion, the significance of data preparation and preprocessing techniques in artificial intelligence and machine learning
cannot be overstated. As we have explored throughout this chapter,
the quality of data fed into machine learning models is a critical
determinant of their success. By ensuring that the data is clean,
well-structured, and appropriately transformed, coders can unlock
the true potential of AI and ML algorithms, leading to more accurate and reliable predictions.

The process of data cleaning and handling missing values is
essential to maintain the integrity of the dataset. By identifying and

addressing inconsistencies, outliers, and inaccuracies, coders can create a solid foundation for their machine-learning models. This step not only improves the algorithms' performance but also helps build trust in the results generated by the models.

Feature engineering and selection play a crucial role in optimizing model performance. By carefully crafting and selecting the most relevant features, coders can ensure that their models can capture the underlying patterns and relationships within the data. This, in turn, leads to more efficient and effective machine learning models that can deliver actionable insights and drive decision-making.

Data transformation and scaling techniques are vital in ensuring that the data is compatible with the requirements of machine learning algorithms. By applying appropriate transformations and scaling methods, coders can ensure that their models can process the data effectively and generate meaningful results. This step is particularly important when dealing with large and complex datasets, as it can significantly impact the speed and accuracy of the machine-learning process.

In summary, effective data preparation and preprocessing techniques are the backbone of successful machine-learning projects. By investing time and effort in these crucial steps, coders can significantly enhance the performance of their AI and ML models, leading to more accurate predictions and valuable insights. As the field of artificial intelligence and machine learning continues to evolve, the importance of data preparation and preprocessing will only grow, making it an essential skill for coders to master.

Chapter Summary

- Data preparation and preprocessing are crucial for building accurate and efficient machine learning (ML) models, as they ensure the quality and structure of the input data.

- Data quality is paramount in ML, directly influencing the model's ability to make accurate predictions and generate valuable insights. Key dimensions of data quality include accuracy, completeness, consistency, relevance, and timeliness.
- Data cleaning and handling missing values are essential steps in the ML pipeline, as they help maintain the integrity of the dataset and improve model performance.
- Feature engineering and selection are critical in optimizing model performance by creating meaningful features and selecting the most relevant ones for the given problem.
- Data transformation and scaling techniques ensure compatibility with ML algorithms, as they standardize and normalize the data for optimal model training.
- Common data transformation techniques include combining features, binning, polynomial features, one-hot encoding, and Box-Cox transformation.
- Common scaling techniques include Min-Max Scaling, Standardization (Z-score normalization), and Log Transformation.
- Effective data preparation and preprocessing techniques lay the foundation for successful ML projects, leading to more accurate predictions, valuable insights, and better decision-making.

5

SUPERVISED LEARNING ALGORITHMS: REGRESSION, CLASSIFICATION, AND DECISION TREES

I n the perpetually transforming world of artificial intelligence (AI) and machine learning (ML), supervised learning algorithms have emerged as a powerful tool for coders seeking to develop intelligent systems capable of making predictions and decisions based on data. As the name suggests, supervised learning involves training a model using labeled data where the correct output is known. This chapter delves into the fascinating realm of supervised learning algorithms, focusing on regression, classification, and decision trees and exploring their practical applications in real-world scenarios.

Supervised learning algorithms can be broadly categorized into two types: regression and classification. Regression algorithms are used to predict continuous values, such as the price of a house or the number of sales in a month. On the other hand, classification algorithms are employed to predict categorical values, such as whether an email is spam or if a customer will make a purchase. Decision trees, a versatile and popular technique, can be used for both regression and classification tasks, making them an essential topic of discussion in this chapter.

The supervised learning process begins with collecting a dataset containing input-output pairs, where the output is the desired outcome or target variable. The dataset is then divided into two parts: the training set and the testing set. The training set is used to build the model, while the testing set is reserved for evaluating the model's performance. The algorithm learns from the training data by adjusting its parameters to minimize errors between its predictions and output. Once the model is trained, it can predict new, unseen data.

Throughout this chapter, we will explore various regression techniques, such as linear regression and polynomial regression, and delve into classification algorithms, including logistic regression, k-nearest neighbors, and support vector machines. We will also unravel the power of decision trees and their ensemble counterparts, such as random forests and gradient-boosting machines. Each section will provide a comprehensive understanding of these algorithms' underlying concepts, mathematical foundations, and practical implementation.

Moreover, we will discuss real-world examples and applications of supervised learning algorithms, showcasing their potential in diverse fields such as finance, healthcare, marketing, and more. By the end of this chapter, you will have a solid grasp of the fundamentals of supervised learning algorithms and be equipped with the knowledge to harness their potential in your coding projects.

In conclusion, supervised learning algorithms offer a robust and versatile approach to solving a wide range of problems in AI and ML. By understanding the principles of regression, classification, and decision trees, coders can unlock the full potential of these powerful techniques and create intelligent systems capable of making accurate predictions and informed decisions based on data. So, let's embark on this exciting journey and delve into the fascinating world of supervised learning algorithms.

Exploring Regression Techniques for Predictive Modeling

Regression techniques hold a special place in supervised learning algorithms as they enable coders to create predictive models that can forecast continuous values. This section will delve into the intricacies of regression techniques, providing a comprehensive understanding of their applications and importance in machine learning.

The Essence of Regression Techniques

At the core of regression techniques is establishing relationships between variables. In the context of machine learning, these variables are often referred to as features or predictors (independent variables) and targets or responses (dependent variables). The primary objective of regression techniques is to create a model that can accurately predict the target variable based on the values of the predictor variables.

Linear Regression: The Foundation

Linear regression is the most fundamental and widely used regression technique in machine learning. It assumes a linear relationship between the predictor and target variables, which can be represented by a straight line. Linear regression aims to find the best-fitting line that minimizes the sum of the squared differences between the actual and predicted target values. This line is represented by the equation:

$$y = \beta_0 + \beta_1 x_1 + \beta_2 x_2 + ... + \beta_n x_n + \varepsilon$$

Here, y is the target variable, x_1, x_2, ..., x_n are the predictor variables, β_0 is the intercept, β_1, β_2, ..., β_n are the coefficients, and ε is the error term.

Expanding Horizons: Non-Linear Regression Techniques

While linear regression is a powerful tool, it may not always be suitable for modeling complex relationships between variables. This is where non-linear regression techniques come into play, allowing coders to model curved relationships between predictor and target variables. Some popular non-linear regression techniques include polynomial regression, exponential regression, and logistic regression.

Regularization Techniques: Tackling Overfitting

In machine learning, overfitting occurs when a model becomes too complex and captures the noise in the data, leading to poor generalization of new, unseen data. Regularization techniques, such as Ridge Regression, Lasso Regression, and Elastic Net, help mitigate overfitting by adding a penalty term to the regression equation. This penalty term discourages the model from assigning large weights to the predictor variables, thus preventing overfitting and improving the model's performance on new data.

Evaluating Regression Models: Performance Metrics

To assess the performance of regression models, coders can use various metrics, such as Mean Absolute Error (MAE), Mean Squared Error (MSE), Root Mean Squared Error (RMSE), and R-squared. These metrics provide valuable insights into the accuracy and reliability of the model, enabling coders to fine-tune their models and select the most appropriate regression technique for their specific problem.

In conclusion, regression techniques are indispensable tools for coders working with supervised learning algorithms. By understanding the nuances of linear and non-linear regression techniques, regularization methods, and performance metrics, coders can harness the power of predictive modeling to tackle a wide array of real-world problems.

Delving into Classification Algorithms for Categorical Data

As we venture deeper into supervised learning algorithms, it is essential to understand the significance of classification algorithms in handling categorical data. This section will explore the various classification techniques, their underlying principles, and how coders can effectively employ them to create powerful machine-learning models.

Classification algorithms are a subset of supervised learning techniques that focus on predicting categorical outcomes. In other words, these algorithms are designed to classify data points into distinct categories or classes based on their features. Some common examples of classification tasks include spam detection, medical diagnosis, and image recognition.

Let's now delve into some of the most widely used classification algorithms in machine learning.

- **Logistic Regression**: Despite its name, logistic regression is a classification algorithm that is particularly well-suited for binary classification problems, where the target variable has only two possible outcomes. It estimates the probability of an instance belonging to a specific class using the logistic function, which outputs a value between 0 and 1. The predicted class is then determined based on a threshold value, typically set at 0.5.

- **K-Nearest Neighbors (KNN):** KNN is a simple yet powerful classification algorithm that can be used for both binary and multi-class problems. It operates on the principle of proximity, where an instance is classified based on the majority class of its 'k' nearest neighbors. The value of 'k' is a user-defined parameter that determines the number of neighbors to consider when making predictions. KNN is particularly effective when dealing with datasets that have well-defined boundaries between classes.

- **Support Vector Machines (SVM):** SVM is a versatile classification algorithm that handles linear and non-linearly separable data. It works by finding the optimal hyperplane that best separates the classes in the feature space. For non-linearly separable data, SVM employs the kernel trick to transform the data into a higher-dimensional space where a linear separation is possible. SVM is known for its robustness and ability to handle high-dimensional data.

- **Naïve Bayes:** This classification algorithm is based on the Bayes theorem and assumes that the features are conditionally independent given the class label. Despite its simplicity and the naïve assumption of feature independence, Naïve Bayes has proven effective in various real-world applications, particularly in text classification and sentiment analysis.

- **Decision Trees:** As discussed in the previous section, decision trees are a powerful classification algorithm that can handle both categorical and continuous data. They work by recursively splitting the data based on the feature that provides the highest information gain, resulting in a tree-like structure with decision nodes and leaf nodes representing the class labels.

In conclusion, classification algorithms are crucial in machine learning, enabling coders to tackle various categorical data problems. By understanding each algorithm's underlying principles and strengths, you can make informed decisions when selecting the most appropriate technique for your specific use case. In the next section, we will unravel the power of decision trees in machine learning and explore their numerous applications.

Unraveling the Power of Decision Trees in Machine Learning

Decision trees hold a special place in the fascinating world of machine learning due to their simplicity, interpretability, and versatility. As a coder, understanding the power of decision trees will enable you to easily harness their potential in solving complex problems. In this section, we will delve into the inner workings of decision trees, their advantages, and how they can be applied in various machine learning tasks.

The Essence of Decision Trees

At their core, decision trees are flowchart-like structures that help in making decisions based on certain conditions. They consist of nodes representing the conditions or attributes and branches, which signify the possible outcomes of those conditions. The tree starts with a root node, which branches into subsequent nodes until a final decision is reached at the leaf nodes.

In the context of machine learning, decision trees are used for both regression and classification tasks. They work by recursively splitting the input data into subsets based on the most significant attribute, ultimately leading to a prediction. The elegance of decision trees lies in their ability to mimic human decision-making processes, making them easily interpretable and relatable.

Advantages of Decision Trees

Decision trees offer several benefits that make them a popular choice among coders and data scientists:

- **Interpretability:** Decision trees are easy to understand and visualize, even for those with limited knowledge of machine learning. This transparency allows stakeholders to trust and validate the model's predictions.
- **Minimal Data Preprocessing:** Unlike other algorithms, decision trees do not require extensive data preprocessing, such as normalization or scaling. They can handle missing values, outliers, and categorical data with ease.
- **Non-Parametric Nature:** Decision trees make no assumptions about the underlying data distribution, making them suitable for various applications.
- **Fast Training and Prediction:** Decision trees can be trained quickly and provide predictions in logarithmic time, making them efficient for large datasets.

Practical Applications of Decision Trees

The versatility of decision trees allows them to be employed in various domains, including:

- **Healthcare:** Decision trees can predict the likelihood of a disease based on patient symptoms, aiding in early diagnosis and treatment.
- **Finance:** In the financial sector, decision trees can help assess credit risk, detect fraudulent transactions, and predict stock prices.

- **Marketing:** Decision trees can assist in customer segmentation, enabling targeted marketing campaigns and personalized recommendations.
- **Manufacturing:** In the manufacturing industry, decision trees can be used for quality control, identifying the root cause of defects, and optimizing production processes.

Unleashing the Power of Decision Trees

As a coder, mastering decision trees will equip you with a powerful tool in your machine-learning arsenal. By understanding their inner workings and leveraging their strengths, you can confidently tackle a wide array of problems. In the next section, we will explore practical applications and real-world examples of supervised learning, further solidifying your knowledge and skills in this exciting field.

Practical Applications and Real-World Examples of Supervised Learning

As we delve deeper into artificial intelligence (AI) and machine learning (ML), it is essential to understand the practical applications and real-world examples of supervised learning algorithms. These algorithms have been successfully employed in various industries, solving complex problems and enhancing decision-making processes. This section will explore some of the most notable applications of regression, classification, and decision trees in different domains.

- **Healthcare:** Supervised learning algorithms have revolutionized the healthcare industry by enabling the development of predictive models for disease diagnosis and treatment. For instance, regression techniques are used to predict patient outcomes based on their medical history and vital signs, while classification algorithms help identify diseases such as cancer, diabetes, and heart disorders. Decision trees, on the other hand, are employed to determine the most effective treatment plans for patients based on their unique medical conditions.

- **Finance:** In the financial sector, supervised learning algorithms play a crucial role in predicting stock prices, assessing credit risk, and detecting fraudulent transactions. Regression models are used to forecast future stock prices based on historical data, while classification algorithms help banks and financial institutions determine the creditworthiness of borrowers. Decision trees identify potential fraud patterns and flag suspicious transactions for further investigation.

- **Marketing:** The marketing domain has also benefited from the power of supervised learning algorithms. Regression techniques predict customer lifetime value, allowing businesses to allocate resources more effectively and target high-value customers. Classification algorithms help in customer segmentation and the identification of potential target markets. Decision trees optimize marketing campaigns by identifying the most effective channels and strategies for reaching specific customer segments.

- **Manufacturing:** In the manufacturing industry, supervised learning algorithms are used to optimize production processes, reduce waste, and improve product quality. Regression models help predict equipment failure and maintenance requirements, while classification algorithms are employed to detect defects in products during the quality control process. Decision trees optimize production schedules and resource allocation, ensuring manufacturing operations run smoothly and efficiently.

- **Transportation:** Supervised learning algorithms have also significantly contributed to the transportation sector. Regression techniques predict travel times and optimize route planning, while classification algorithms help identify traffic patterns and congestion hotspots. Decision trees are employed to improve traffic signal timings and enhance the overall efficiency of transportation systems.

In conclusion, supervised learning algorithms have proven invaluable tools for coders in various industries, enabling them to develop predictive models and make data-driven decisions. By harnessing the potential of regression, classification, and decision trees, coders can create innovative solutions to complex problems and contribute to advancing AI and ML technologies. As we continue to explore the capabilities of these algorithms, we can expect to see even more groundbreaking applications and real-world examples in the future.

Harnessing the Potential of Supervised Learning Algorithms for Coders

In this final section of our exploration into supervised learning algorithms, we shall reflect on these techniques' immense potential for coders and the broader world of artificial intelligence and machine learning. By understanding and mastering regression, classification, and decision trees, coders can unlock a treasure trove of opportunities to create innovative solutions and contribute to the ever-evolving field of AI and ML.

Throughout this chapter, we have delved into the intricacies of supervised learning algorithms, beginning with an introduction to the fundamental concepts and techniques. We then explored the world of regression techniques, which enable coders to create predictive models for continuous data. By understanding linear and logistic regression, coders can harness the power of these algorithms to make accurate predictions and inform decision-making processes.

As we ventured further into supervised learning, we examined classification algorithms essential for handling categorical data. Techniques such as k-Nearest Neighbors, Support Vector Machines, and Naïve Bayes allow coders to classify data points into distinct categories, creating models that can predict outcomes and identify patterns in complex datasets.

Our journey then led us to the fascinating world of decision trees, a powerful and versatile tool in the machine learning toolbox. By understanding the principles of entropy, information gain, and tree pruning, coders can create robust and interpretable models that can be applied to a wide range of real-world problems.

This chapter also highlighted practical applications and real-world examples of supervised learning algorithms, demonstrating their immense potential in various industries and sectors. From healthcare and finance to marketing and transportation, these techniques are revolutionizing how we approach problem-solving and decision-making.

As we conclude our exploration into supervised learning algorithms, coders need to recognize the importance of continuous learning and adaptation in the ever-evolving world of AI and ML. By staying abreast of the latest developments and refining their skills, coders can harness the full potential of these powerful techniques and contribute to advancing this exciting field.

In summary, the world of supervised learning algorithms offers a wealth of opportunities for coders eager to make their mark in AI and ML. By mastering regression, classification, and decision trees, coders can create innovative solutions that have the potential to transform industries and improve the lives of people around the world. The future of AI and ML is bright, and with the power of supervised learning algorithms at their fingertips, coders are poised to play a pivotal role in shaping this exciting frontier.

Chapter Summary

- Supervised learning algorithms are powerful tools in AI and ML, enabling coders to develop intelligent systems capable of making predictions and decisions based on data. They can be broadly categorized into regression and classification techniques, with decision trees being versatile enough for both tasks.

- Regression techniques focus on predicting continuous values and involve establishing relationships between variables. Linear regression is the most fundamental technique, while non-linear regression techniques, such as polynomial regression, can model more complex relationships.

- Classification algorithms are designed to classify data points into distinct categories based on their features. Some widely used classification techniques include logistic regression, k-nearest neighbors, support vector machines, and naïve Bayes.

- Decision trees are flowchart-like structures that help make decisions based on certain conditions. They are simple, interpretable, and versatile, making them popular in machine learning for both regression and classification tasks.

- Supervised learning algorithms have practical applications in various industries, such as healthcare, finance, marketing, manufacturing, and transportation. They help in solving complex problems and enhancing decision-making processes.

- Performance metrics, such as Mean Absolute Error (MAE), Mean Squared Error (MSE), Root Mean Squared Error (RMSE), and R-squared, are essential for evaluating the performance of regression models and fine-tuning them for optimal results.

- Regularization techniques, such as Ridge Regression, Lasso Regression, and Elastic Net, help mitigate overfitting in regression models by adding a penalty term to the regression equation, preventing overfitting and improving the model's performance on new data.
- Continuous learning and adaptation are crucial for coders in the ever-evolving world of AI and ML. By mastering regression, classification, and decision trees, coders can create innovative solutions that have the potential to transform industries and improve the lives of people around the world.

6

UNSUPERVISED LEARNING ALGORITHMS: CLUSTERING, DIMENSIONALITY REDUCTION, AND ASSOCIATION RULES

I n the continuously evolving landscape of artificial intelligence (AI) and machine learning (ML), unsupervised learning algorithms have emerged as a powerful tool for coders seeking to uncover hidden patterns and structures within complex datasets. Unlike supervised learning, where algorithms are trained on labeled data to make predictions, unsupervised learning algorithms work with unlabeled data, allowing them to identify patterns and relationships that may not be immediately apparent. This chapter delves into the fascinating realm of unsupervised learning, exploring its various techniques, applications, and real-world examples.

Unsupervised learning algorithms can be broadly categorized into three main types: **clustering, dimensionality reduction**, and **association rules.** Each technique serves a unique purpose in data analysis, offering valuable insights that can be harnessed to drive decision-making and optimize processes.

Clustering techniques, such as K-Means, Hierarchical, and DBSCAN, are used to group similar data points together based on their features. This can be particularly useful in tasks like customer segmentation, anomaly detection, and image segmentation, where understanding the underlying structure of the data is crucial.

Dimensionality reduction methods, including Principal Component Analysis (PCA), t-Distributed Stochastic Neighbor Embedding (t-SNE), and Uniform Manifold Approximation and Projection (UMAP), are designed to reduce the number of features in a dataset while preserving its essential characteristics. By simplifying high-dimensional data, these techniques can improve the performance of other machine-learning algorithms and facilitate data visualization.

Association rules, such as the Apriori and Eclat algorithms, are employed to discover relationships between variables in large datasets. These rules can identify frequent item sets and generate insights into the associations between different items, which can be invaluable in fields like market basket analysis and recommender systems.

This chapter will delve deeper into these unsupervised learning techniques, providing a comprehensive understanding of their inner workings, strengths, and limitations. We will also explore practical applications and real-world examples, demonstrating the immense potential of unsupervised learning algorithms in various industries and domains.

In conclusion, unsupervised learning algorithms offer a

powerful means of extracting valuable insights from complex, unlabeled data. By mastering these techniques, coders can unlock the full potential of AI and ML, harnessing the power of unsupervised learning to drive innovation and create a better future.

Clustering Techniques: K-Means, Hierarchical, and DBSCAN

In unsupervised learning algorithms, clustering techniques hold a prominent position. These methods aim to identify and group similar data points based on their features, thereby unveiling hidden patterns and structures within the data. This section will delve into three popular clustering techniques: K-Means, Hierarchical, and DBSCAN. By understanding their underlying principles and applications, coders can harness the power of these algorithms to tackle complex problems in AI and ML.

K-Means Clustering

K-Means is a widely-used clustering algorithm known for its simplicity and efficiency. The primary goal of this method is to partition the data into 'K' distinct clusters, where each data point belongs to the cluster with the nearest mean. The algorithm follows an iterative process, which includes:

1. **Initialization:** Randomly select 'K' data points as the initial cluster centroids.
2. **Assignment:** Assign each data point to the nearest centroid.
3. **Update:** Calculate the new centroid for each cluster by taking the mean of all the data points within that cluster.
4. **Repeat steps 2 and 3** until convergence is achieved, i.e., the centroids no longer change significantly.

Despite its popularity, K-Means has some limitations. The algorithm is sensitive to the initial placement of centroids and may converge to a local minimum. Additionally, it assumes that clusters are spherical and evenly sized, which may not always be the case in real-world data.

Hierarchical Clustering

Hierarchical clustering is another powerful technique that builds a tree-like structure to represent the relationships between data points. This method can be classified into two types: agglomerative (bottom-up) and divisive (top-down). In agglomerative clustering, each data point starts as an individual cluster, and the algorithm iteratively merges the closest clusters until only one cluster remains. Conversely, divisive clustering begins with a single cluster containing all data points and recursively splits it into smaller clusters.

The key to hierarchical clustering is the choice of distance metric and linkage criteria. Common distance metrics include Euclidean, Manhattan, and cosine distances, while linkage criteria can be single, complete, average, or Ward's method. The resulting hierarchical structure can be visualized using a dendrogram, which helps determine the optimal number of clusters.

DBSCAN (Density-Based Spatial Clustering of Applications with Noise)

DBSCAN is a density-based clustering algorithm that identifies clusters as dense regions of data points separated by areas of lower point density. Unlike K-Means and hierarchical clustering, DBSCAN does not require specifying the number of clusters beforehand. Instead, it relies on two parameters: a distance 'ε' and a minimum number of points 'MinPts'.

The algorithm defines a neighborhood around each data point within the distance 'ε'. If a data point has at least 'MinPts' neighbors, it is considered a core point and forms a cluster. Border points, which have fewer than 'MinPts' neighbors but are within the 'ε' distance of a core point, are also assigned to the cluster. All other points are considered noise.

DBSCAN is particularly useful for discovering clusters of arbitrary shapes and filtering out noise. However, it may struggle with clusters of varying densities and is sensitive to the choice of parameters.

In conclusion, clustering techniques such as K-Means, Hierarchical, and DBSCAN offer powerful tools for uncovering hidden structures within data. By understanding their principles and limitations, coders can effectively apply these algorithms to various AI and ML problems. As we explore unsupervised learning algorithms, we will delve into dimensionality reduction methods and association rules, further expanding our toolkit for tackling complex data-driven challenges.

Dimensionality Reduction Methods: PCA, t-SNE, and UMAP

In artificial intelligence and machine learning, data is the lifeblood that fuels the algorithms and models that drive innovation. However, as the volume and complexity of data increase, it becomes increasingly challenging to process and analyze it effectively. This is where dimensionality reduction methods come into play. In this section, we will delve into three popular techniques: Principal Component Analysis (PCA), t-Distributed Stochastic Neighbor Embedding (t-SNE), and Uniform Manifold Approximation and Projection (UMAP).

Principal Component Analysis (PCA)

PCA is a widely used linear dimensionality reduction technique that aims to identify the most significant variables in a dataset while preserving as much information as possible. It transforms the original data into a new set of orthogonal variables called principal components. These components are linear combinations of the original variables, ordered by the amount of variance they explain. The first principal component accounts for the largest possible variance, while each subsequent component explains the highest possible remaining variance under the constraint of being orthogonal to the preceding components.

In practical terms, PCA can reduce the computational cost and noise in the data, making it easier to visualize and analyze. It is particularly useful when dealing with high-dimensional datasets, such as image or gene expression data.

t-Distributed Stochastic Neighbor Embedding (t-SNE)

While PCA is a linear technique, t-SNE is a non-linear method designed to visualize high-dimensional data in a low-dimensional space, typically two or three dimensions. It minimizes the divergence between two probability distributions: one that measures pairwise similarities in the high-dimensional space and another that measures pairwise similarities in the low-dimensional space.

The main advantage of t-SNE over PCA is its ability to preserve local structures in the data, making it particularly suitable for visualizing complex datasets with non-linear relationships. However, t-SNE can be computationally expensive and sensitive to hyperparameters, which may require fine-tuning to achieve optimal results.

Uniform Manifold Approximation and Projection (UMAP)

UMAP is a relatively new dimensionality reduction technique that combines the strengths of both PCA and t-SNE. It is a non-linear method that aims to preserve both local and global structures in the data while being computationally efficient. UMAP works by constructing a high-dimensional graph representation of the data and optimizing a low-dimensional graph to be as structurally similar as possible.

One of the key advantages of UMAP is its scalability, making it suitable for large datasets. It is also less sensitive to hyperparameters than t-SNE, making it easier to use and interpret.

In conclusion, dimensionality reduction methods such as PCA, t-SNE, and UMAP are powerful tools that help coders and data scientists navigate the complexities of high-dimensional data. By understanding the strengths and limitations of each technique, practitioners can harness their potential to uncover hidden patterns, simplify data visualization, and, ultimately, enhance the performance of machine learning models.

Association Rules: Apriori and Eclat Algorithms

This section will delve into the fascinating world of association rules, a powerful unsupervised learning technique that can help us uncover hidden patterns and relationships within large datasets. We will focus on two widely used algorithms, Apriori and Eclat, and explore their inner workings, strengths, and limitations. By the end of this section, you will have a solid understanding of these algorithms and be well-equipped to apply them in your AI and ML projects.

Association rules are unsupervised learning algorithms that aim to discover interesting relationships between variables in large datasets. These relationships, often represented as "if-then" rules, can provide valuable insights into the underlying structure of the data and help us make better decisions. For example, an association rule in a retail dataset might reveal that customers who purchase diapers are also likely to buy baby wipes. This information can be used to optimize product placement, marketing strategies, and inventory management.

Apriori Algorithm

The Apriori algorithm, introduced by Rakesh Agrawal and Ramakrishnan Srikant in 1994, is a classic method for mining frequent item sets and generating association rules. The algorithm operates iteratively, starting with single-item sets and gradually expanding to larger itemsets while pruning the search space based on a user-defined minimum support threshold.

The key idea behind the Apriori algorithm is the Apriori principle, which states that if an itemset is frequent, then all its subsets must also be frequent. Conversely, if an itemset is infrequent, all its supersets must also be infrequent. This principle allows the algorithm to efficiently prune the search space and focus only on the most promising itemsets.

The Apriori algorithm consists of two main steps:

1. **Frequent Itemset Generation:** In this step, the algorithm iteratively generates candidate itemsets and computes their support (i.e., the proportion of transactions containing the itemset). Itemsets that meet the minimum support threshold are considered frequent and are used to generate larger candidate itemsets in the next iteration.

2. **Rule Generation:** Once all frequent item sets have been identified, the algorithm generates association rules by considering all possible combinations of items within each item set. Rules that meet the user-defined minimum confidence threshold (i.e., the conditional probability of the consequent given the antecedent) are considered valid and are returned as output.

Eclat Algorithm

The Eclat algorithm, proposed by Christian Borgelt in 1999, is another popular method for mining frequent item sets and generating association rules. Unlike the Apriori algorithm, which uses a horizontal data representation (i.e., transactions and their items), the Eclat algorithm employs a vertical data representation (i.e., items and their transactions).

The main advantage of the Eclat algorithm is its efficiency, as it avoids the repeated computation of itemset supports and leverages set intersection operations to identify frequent itemsets quickly. The algorithm operates in a depth-first search manner, recursively exploring the itemset lattice and pruning the search space based on the minimum support threshold.

In summary, association rules are a powerful unsupervised learning technique that can help us uncover hidden patterns and relationships within large datasets. The Apriori and Eclat algorithms are two widely used methods for mining frequent item sets and generating association rules, each with strengths and limitations. By understanding the inner workings of these algorithms and applying them to your projects, you can harness the power of unsupervised learning algorithms to gain valuable insights and make better decisions.

Practical Applications and Real-World Examples

Unsupervised learning algorithms have been making waves in artificial intelligence and machine learning, proving invaluable tools for coders and data scientists. These algorithms can uniquely identify patterns and relationships within data without the need for explicit guidance or labeled data. This section will explore some practical applications and real-world examples of unsupervised learning algorithms, showcasing their versatility and potential to revolutionize various industries.

Customer Segmentation in Marketing

Understanding customer behavior is crucial for developing targeted and effective campaigns in marketing. Clustering techniques, such as K-Means and Hierarchical clustering, can segment customers based on their purchasing habits, demographics, and preferences. This segmentation allows businesses to tailor their marketing strategies to specific customer groups, increasing customer satisfaction and loyalty.

Anomaly Detection in Finance

The finance industry is no stranger to the importance of identifying unusual patterns and activities. Unsupervised learning algorithms, particularly clustering methods like DBSCAN, can detect anomalies in financial data, such as fraudulent transactions or irregular trading activities. Financial institutions can swiftly mitigate potential risks and protect their clients' assets by identifying these outliers.

Recommender Systems in E-commerce

Online shopping platforms constantly seek ways to enhance the user experience and increase sales. Dimensionality reduction techniques, such as PCA and t-SNE, can be utilized to analyze customer browsing and purchasing data, enabling the development of personalized recommender systems. These systems provide users with tailored product suggestions based on their preferences and behavior, ultimately driving sales and customer satisfaction.

Natural Language Processing

The field of natural language processing (NLP) has dramatically benefited from unsupervised learning algorithms. Techniques like topic modeling, which employs dimensionality reduction methods like Latent Dirichlet Allocation (LDA), can analyze and categorize large volumes of text data. This can be particularly useful for sentiment analysis, document classification, and information retrieval.

Bioinformatics and Genomics

The rapidly growing field of bioinformatics and genomics has embraced unsupervised learning algorithms to make sense of the vast amounts of data generated by modern sequencing technologies. Clustering and dimensionality reduction techniques can be applied to identify patterns and relationships within genetic data, leading to new insights into gene function, disease mechanisms, and potential therapeutic targets.

In conclusion, unsupervised learning algorithms have demonstrated immense potential across various industries and applications. By harnessing the power of these algorithms, coders and data scientists can uncover hidden patterns and relationships within data, leading to innovative solutions and a deeper understanding of the world around us. As the field of artificial intelligence and machine learning continues to evolve, there is no doubt that unsupervised learning algorithms will play an increasingly prominent role in shaping our future.

Harnessing the Power of Unsupervised Learning Algorithms

As we reach the end of our exploration into the fascinating world of unsupervised learning algorithms, we must reflect on the immense potential these techniques hold for coders and data scientists alike. By delving into clustering, dimensionality reduction, and association rules, we have uncovered powerful tools that can transform how we analyze and interpret data, ultimately leading to more informed decision-making and innovative solutions.

This chapter has examined various clustering techniques, such as K-Means, Hierarchical, and DBSCAN, each with unique strengths and applications. These methods enable us to group data points based on their similarities, revealing hidden patterns and structures within the data. By harnessing the power of clustering algorithms, coders can develop more efficient and targeted solutions to complex problems, ranging from customer segmentation to image recognition.

Dimensionality reduction methods, including PCA, t-SNE, and UMAP, have further broadened our understanding of unsupervised learning algorithms. By reducing the number of variables in a dataset while preserving its essential features, these techniques allow us to visualize high-dimensional data more comprehensively.

This not only aids in data exploration and interpretation but also helps improve the performance of other machine-learning models by reducing noise and computational complexity.

Lastly, we delved into association rules, focusing on the Apriori and Eclat algorithms. These techniques enable us to uncover relationships between items in a dataset, providing valuable insights into customer behavior, market trends, and more. By leveraging the power of association rules, coders can develop intelligent recommendation systems, optimize marketing strategies, and enhance the overall user experience.

Throughout this chapter, we have also highlighted practical applications and real-world examples, demonstrating the versatility and relevance of unsupervised learning algorithms in today's data-driven world. From healthcare and finance to retail and social media, these techniques are revolutionizing how we approach problem-solving and decision-making.

In conclusion, unsupervised learning algorithms offer a wealth of opportunities for coders and data scientists to unlock the hidden potential within their data. By mastering these techniques, you will be well-equipped to tackle complex challenges, drive innovation, and contribute to the ever-evolving field of artificial intelligence and machine learning. So, as you embark on your journey into unsupervised learning, remember to harness the power of these algorithms and let your creativity and curiosity guide you toward new discoveries and breakthroughs.

Chapter Summary

- Unsupervised learning algorithms work with unlabeled data, allowing them to identify patterns and relationships that may not be immediately apparent.
- Clustering techniques, such as K-Means, Hierarchical, and DBSCAN, group similar data points together based

on their features, revealing hidden patterns and structures within the data.

- Dimensionality reduction methods, including PCA, t-SNE, and UMAP, reduce the number of features in a dataset while preserving its essential characteristics, simplifying high-dimensional data, and improving the performance of other machine learning algorithms.

- Association rules, such as the Apriori and Eclat algorithms, discover relationships between variables in large datasets, providing valuable insights into customer behavior, market trends, and more.

- Unsupervised learning algorithms have practical applications across various industries, including marketing, finance, e-commerce, natural language processing, and bioinformatics.

- Clustering techniques can be used for tasks like customer segmentation, anomaly detection, and image segmentation, while dimensionality reduction methods can facilitate data visualization and analysis.

- Association rules can be employed in market basket analysis and recommender systems, helping businesses optimize product placement, marketing strategies, and inventory management.

- Mastering unsupervised learning techniques can equip coders and data scientists to tackle complex challenges, drive innovation, and contribute to the ever-evolving field of artificial intelligence and machine learning.

7

DEEP LEARNING AND NEURAL NETWORKS: ARCHITECTURES, ACTIVATION FUNCTIONS, AND TRAINING TECHNIQUES

W ithin the ceaselessly advancing realm of technology, artificial intelligence (AI) and machine learning (ML) have emerged as powerful tools transforming how we live, work, and interact with the world around us. Deep learning is at the heart of this revolution, a subset of machine learning that has garnered significant attention and investment in recent years. This chapter delves into the fascinating realm of deep learning and neural networks, exploring their architectures, activation functions, and training techniques that enable coders to harness their full potential.

Deep learning is a machine learning technique that teaches computers to learn by example, much like humans. It involves using artificial neural networks, which are inspired by the structure and function of the human brain. These networks consist of interconnected layers of nodes or neurons that work together to process, analyze, and make sense of vast data. The ability of deep learning algorithms to automatically learn and improve from experience without being explicitly programmed has made them indispensable in various applications, ranging from natural language processing and computer vision to speech recognition and recommendation systems.

Neural networks are the backbone of deep learning, and their architectures play a crucial role in determining their performance and capabilities. This chapter will explore various neural network architectures, such as feedforward networks, recurrent networks, and convolutional networks, each with unique strengths and applications. Understanding these architectures will enable coders to select the most suitable one for their specific tasks and challenges.

Activation functions are another essential component of neural networks, as they determine the output of a neuron based on its input. These functions introduce non-linearity into the network, allowing it to learn complex patterns and relationships in the data. We will discuss different types of activation functions, such as sigmoid, ReLU, and softmax, and their applications in various contexts.

Training a neural network is a critical step in the deep learning process, as it involves adjusting the weights and biases of the network to minimize the error between the predicted and actual outputs. This chapter will cover various training techniques, such as gradient descent, backpropagation, and regularization, which are essential for achieving optimal performance in deep learning models.

Finally, we will examine real-world applications of AI and ML in coding, showcasing how deep learning and neural networks solve complex problems and create innovative solutions across various industries. This will provide a glimpse into the future of deep learning and neural networks, highlighting their potential to revolutionize the way we approach coding and problem-solving in the future.

Join us on this exciting journey as we unravel the mysteries of deep learning and neural networks, equipping you with the knowledge and skills to harness their power and transform the world of coding.

Exploring Various Neural Network Architectures

In artificial intelligence and machine learning, deep learning has emerged as a powerful tool for solving complex problems. At the heart of deep learning lies the concept of neural networks, which are inspired by the structure and function of the human brain. In this section, we will delve into the world of neural network architectures, exploring their various forms and understanding how they contribute to the development of intelligent systems.

Feedforward Neural Networks

The most basic and widely used neural network architecture is the feedforward neural network (FNN). In this type of network, information flows in one direction, from the input layer through one or more hidden layers and finally to the output layer. Each layer consists of interconnected nodes or neurons, which process the input data and pass it on to the next layer. FNNs are particularly useful for pattern recognition, classification, and regression tasks.

Convolutional Neural Networks

Convolutional neural networks (CNNs) are a specialized type of neural network designed to process grid-like data, such as images or speech signals. CNNs consist of multiple layers, including convolutional layers, pooling layers, and fully connected layers. The convolutional layers apply filters to the input data, extracting features such as edges, corners, and textures. Pooling layers reduce the spatial dimensions of the data, while fully connected layers combine the extracted features to make predictions. CNNs have achieved state-of-the-art results in image recognition, natural language processing, and speech recognition tasks.

Recurrent Neural Networks

Recurrent neural networks (RNNs) are designed to handle sequential data, such as time series or text. Unlike feedforward networks, RNNs have connections that loop back, allowing them to maintain a hidden state that can capture information from previous time steps. This architecture enables RNNs to learn patterns and dependencies in the input data over time. RNNs have been successfully applied to language modeling, machine translation, and speech recognition tasks. However, they can suffer from issues like vanishing or exploding gradients, hindering their ability to learn long-range dependencies.

Long Short-Term Memory Networks

To address the limitations of RNNs, long short-term memory (LSTM) networks were introduced. LSTMs are a type of RNN that incorporates a more sophisticated memory cell capable of learning long-range dependencies in the data. This is achieved through gating mechanisms, which control the flow of information into and out of the memory cell. LSTMs have been widely adopted in various applications, such as text generation, sentiment analysis, and video classification.

Generative Adversarial Networks

Generative adversarial networks (GANs) are a relatively recent addition to the neural network landscape. GANs consist of two neural networks, a generator and a discriminator, which are trained simultaneously in a competitive fashion. The generator learns to create realistic data samples, while the discriminator learns to distinguish between real and generated samples. This adversarial process generates high-quality data, making GANs particularly useful for tasks such as image synthesis, style transfer, and data augmentation.

In conclusion, the diverse range of neural network architectures available today enables researchers and practitioners to tackle many complex problems in artificial intelligence and machine learning. By understanding the strengths and limitations of each architecture, coders can make informed decisions about which approach is best suited for their specific application. As deep learning continues to evolve, we expect to see even more innovative and powerful neural network architectures emerge, further expanding the possibilities for AI and ML in coding.

Activation Functions: Types and Applications

In the fascinating world of deep learning and neural networks, activation functions play a crucial role in determining the output of a neuron. These functions introduce non-linearity into the network, allowing it to learn complex patterns and solve intricate problems. In this section, we will delve into the various types of activation functions, their applications, and how they contribute to the overall performance of a neural network.

Understanding Activation Functions

An activation function is a mathematical equation that determines the output of a neuron based on its input. It takes the weighted sum of the inputs and biases and then applies a specific function to produce the final output. The primary purpose of an activation function is to introduce non-linearity into the network, enabling it to learn and adapt to complex data patterns.

Types of Activation Functions

Several activation functions are used in deep learning, each with unique characteristics and applications. Some of the most commonly used activation functions include:

- **Sigmoid Function:** The sigmoid function is a smooth, S-shaped curve that maps input values to a range between 0 and 1. It is widely used in binary classification problems, as it can easily differentiate between two classes. However, it is susceptible to the vanishing gradient problem, which can slow down the learning process.
- **Hyperbolic Tangent (tanh) Function:** The tanh function is similar to the sigmoid function but maps input values to a range between -1 and 1. It is more suitable for problems where the output needs to be centered around zero. Like the sigmoid function, it also suffers from the vanishing gradient problem.
- **Rectified Linear Unit (ReLU) Function:** The ReLU function is a popular choice for deep learning, as it is computationally efficient and helps mitigate the vanishing gradient problem. It outputs the input value if it is positive and zero otherwise. However, it can suffer from the "dying ReLU" problem, where neurons become inactive and stop learning.
- **Leaky ReLU Function:** To address the dying ReLU issue, the leaky ReLU function was introduced. It allows

a small, non-zero gradient for negative input values, ensuring neurons remain active and continue learning.

- **Softmax Function:** The softmax function is used in multi-class classification problems, as it converts a vector of input values into a probability distribution over multiple classes. It is commonly used in the output layer of a neural network.

Applications of Activation Functions

Activation functions are essential components of neural networks and significantly impact their performance. They are used in various applications, such as:

- **Image Recognition:** Convolutional Neural Networks (CNNs) use activation functions like ReLU to detect and classify objects within images.
- **Natural Language Processing:** Recurrent Neural Networks (RNNs) and Long Short-Term Memory (LSTM) networks use activation functions like tanh and sigmoid to process and generate text.
- **Reinforcement Learning:** Deep Q-Networks (DQNs) use activation functions like ReLU to learn optimal strategies for decision-making in complex environments.
- **Generative Adversarial Networks (GANs):** GANs use activation functions like Leaky ReLU to generate realistic images, music, and other creative outputs.

In conclusion, activation functions are vital elements in the design and performance of neural networks. By understanding their types and applications, coders can harness the power of AI and ML to create innovative solutions that tackle complex problems and shape the future of technology.

Training Techniques for Optimal Performance

In artificial intelligence and machine learning, training techniques are pivotal in achieving optimal performance for deep learning models and neural networks. As we delve into this section, we will explore various training techniques to help coders fine-tune their models and enhance their efficiency. By understanding and implementing these methods, developers can harness the full potential of AI and ML in their coding projects.

Gradient Descent and its Variants

Gradient descent is a fundamental optimization algorithm used to minimize the error or loss function in a neural network. It works by iteratively adjusting the model's parameters to find the optimal combination that minimizes the error. There are three primary variants of gradient descent:

- **Batch Gradient Descent:** This method computes the gradient of the entire dataset and updates the model's parameters accordingly. While it provides a stable convergence, it can be computationally expensive for large datasets.
- **Stochastic Gradient Descent (SGD):** Unlike batch gradient descent, SGD updates the model's parameters using only a single training example at a time. This approach is faster and can escape local minima but may result in a less stable convergence.
- **Mini-batch Gradient Descent:** This technique balances the previous two methods by updating the model's parameters using a small batch of training examples. It offers a good trade-off between computational efficiency and convergence stability.

Adaptive Learning Rate Techniques

Adaptive learning rate techniques adjust the learning rate during training, allowing the model to converge more quickly and accurately. Some popular adaptive learning rate methods include:

- **AdaGrad:** This method adapts the learning rate for each parameter based on the historical gradients, allowing for a more fine-tuned optimization.
- **RMSprop:** Similar to AdaGrad, RMSprop adjusts the learning rate for each parameter but uses an exponentially decaying average of squared gradients to prevent the learning rate from diminishing too quickly.
- **Adam (Adaptive Moment Estimation):** Combining the concepts of momentum and adaptive learning rates, Adam is a widely-used optimization algorithm that computes adaptive learning rates for each parameter while also considering the first and second moments of the gradients.

Regularization Techniques

Regularization techniques help prevent overfitting in neural networks by adding a penalty term to the loss function. This encourages the model to learn simpler and more generalizable patterns in the data. Common regularization techniques include:

- **L1 and L2 Regularization:** These methods add a penalty term proportional to the model's parameters' absolute value (L1) or the square (L2). This encourages the model to have smaller weights, reducing the risk of overfitting.
- **Dropout:** This technique randomly "drops out" a proportion of neurons during training, forcing the network to learn redundant representations and improving generalization.
- **Early Stopping:** By monitoring the model's performance on a validation set, early stopping halts the

training process when the validation error starts to
increase, preventing overfitting.

In conclusion, understanding and implementing these training techniques can significantly improve the performance of deep learning models and neural networks. By experimenting with various optimization algorithms, adaptive learning rates, and regularization methods, coders can fine-tune their AI and ML models to achieve optimal results. As we continue to explore the vast potential of deep learning and neural networks, these training techniques will undoubtedly play a crucial role in shaping the future of AI and ML in coding.

Real-World Applications of AI and ML in Coding

As we delve deeper into the fascinating world of artificial intelligence (AI) and machine learning (ML), it becomes increasingly evident that these technologies have the potential to revolutionize the way we approach coding and software development. In this section, we will explore some of the most promising real-world applications of AI and ML in coding, showcasing how these cutting-edge techniques are employed to solve complex problems, optimize performance, and create more efficient, intelligent systems.

Automated Code Generation and Optimization

One of the most exciting applications of AI and ML in coding is the ability to generate and optimize code automatically. By leveraging deep learning algorithms and neural networks, developers can create systems that analyze existing codebases, identify patterns and best practices, and generate new, optimized code based on these insights. This can significantly reduce the time and effort required to write and maintain code, allowing developers to focus on more strategic, high-level tasks.

Bug Detection and Resolution

AI and ML can also be employed to improve the bug detection and resolution process in software development. By training neural networks on large datasets of code with known issues, these systems can learn to identify potential bugs and vulnerabilities in new code. Moreover, AI-powered tools can suggest possible fixes for these issues, streamlining the debugging process and reducing the likelihood of human error.

Intelligent Code Completion

Another promising application of AI and ML in coding is the development of intelligent code completion tools. These tools leverage natural language processing and machine learning algorithms to predict and suggest the most likely next line of code as a developer is typing. This can significantly speed up the coding process and help developers avoid common syntax errors and typos.

Code Review and Quality Assurance

Ensuring the quality and maintainability of code is a critical aspect of software development. AI and ML can automate and enhance the code review process by analyzing code for adherence to best practices, consistency, and potential performance issues. By providing developers with real-time feedback and suggestions for improvement, these tools can help maintain high-quality codebases and reduce the likelihood of technical debt.

Personalized Learning and Skill Development

As AI and ML continue to evolve, developers need to stay up-to-date with the latest techniques and best practices. AI-powered learning platforms can analyze a developer's existing skill set and recommend personalized learning paths, resources, and exercises to help them grow and stay competitive in the rapidly changing tech landscape.

In conclusion, integrating AI and ML into the coding process holds immense potential for improving efficiency, reducing errors, and fostering innovation in software development. As these technologies continue to advance, we can expect to see even more groundbreaking applications emerge, further transforming the way we approach coding and shaping the future of the software development industry.

The Future of Deep Learning and Neural Networks

As we reach the end of this enlightening journey through the world of artificial intelligence and machine learning, it is essential to take a moment to reflect on the incredible advancements that have been made in the field of deep learning and neural networks. The potential of these technologies is immense, and their coding applications are only beginning to be explored. In this conclusion, we will discuss the future of deep learning and neural networks and how they will continue to shape the world of coding and beyond.

The rapid progress in deep learning and neural networks has been astounding. From their humble beginnings as simple models of the human brain, these powerful tools have evolved into complex systems capable of solving some of the most challenging problems in computer science. As we continue to push the boundaries of what is possible with AI and ML, it is clear that deep learning and neural networks will play a central role in shaping the future of coding.

One of the most exciting aspects of deep learning and neural networks is their ability to learn and adapt. As these systems become more sophisticated, they can tackle increasingly complex tasks, making them invaluable tools for coders. In the future, we expect to see AI and ML integrated into a wide range of applications, from software development and data analysis to cybersecurity and natural language processing.

Furthermore, developing new neural network architectures and activation functions will continue to drive innovation in the field. As researchers and engineers experiment with novel approaches, we expect to see more powerful and efficient models emerge. These advancements will improve the performance of existing applications and open up new possibilities for AI and ML in coding.

In addition to these technical advancements, the future of deep learning and neural networks will also be shaped by the ethical considerations surrounding their use. As AI and ML become more prevalent daily, we must develop a robust ethical framework to guide their development and deployment. This will ensure that these powerful tools are used responsibly and for the benefit of all.

Finally, the future of deep learning and neural networks will be characterized by increased collaboration between researchers, engineers, and coders. As the field continues to grow and evolve, we must foster cooperation and knowledge-sharing. By working together, we can unlock the full potential of AI and ML and create a brighter future for coding and beyond.

In conclusion, the future of deep learning and neural networks is incredibly promising. As these technologies continue to advance, they will revolutionize the world of coding, opening up new possibilities and transforming how we approach problem-solving. By embracing the power of AI and ML, we can look forward to a future where coding is more efficient, effective, and accessible than ever before.

Chapter Summary

- Deep learning, a subset of machine learning, uses artificial neural networks inspired by the human brain to process and analyze vast amounts of data, making them indispensable in various applications such as natural language processing and computer vision.

- Neural network architectures, including feedforward networks, recurrent networks, and convolutional networks, play a crucial role in determining the performance and capabilities of deep learning models.
- Activation functions, such as sigmoid, ReLU, and softmax, introduce non-linearity into neural networks, allowing them to learn complex patterns and relationships in the data.
- Training techniques, including gradient descent, backpropagation, and regularization, are essential for achieving optimal performance in deep learning models.
- Real-world applications of AI and ML in coding include automated code generation, bug detection and resolution, intelligent code completion, code review and quality assurance, and personalized learning and skill development.
- The future of deep learning and neural networks will be shaped by advancements in neural network architectures, activation functions, and ethical considerations surrounding their use.
- Increased collaboration between researchers, engineers, and coders will be essential for unlocking the full potential of AI and ML in coding and beyond.
- As deep learning and neural networks continue to advance, they will revolutionize the world of coding, making it more efficient, practical, and accessible than ever before.

8

NATURAL LANGUAGE PROCESSING: TEXT ANALYSIS, SENTIMENT ANALYSIS, AND CHATBOTS

I n the rapidly shifting domain of artificial intelligence (AI) and machine learning (ML), one area that has garnered significant attention and growth is Natural Language Processing (NLP). As coders, it is essential to understand the fundamentals of NLP and its applications to stay ahead in the game and create innovative solutions for a wide range of industries. In this chapter, we will delve into the fascinating realm of NLP, exploring text analysis, sentiment analysis, and chatbots while also discussing how to integrate AI and ML into your NLP projects.

At its core, natural language processing is the intersection of computer science, AI, and linguistics. It focuses on enabling computers to understand, interpret, and generate human language in a meaningful and helpful way. This is no small feat, as human language is incredibly complex, filled with nuances, idioms, and context-dependent meanings. However, the advancements in AI and ML have made it possible for computers to process and analyze large volumes of text, opening up a world of possibilities for coders.

As a coder, you might wonder why NLP is relevant to you. The answer lies in the vast array of applications to which NLP techniques can be applied. From sentiment analysis that helps businesses understand customer feedback to chatbots that provide seamless customer support, NLP is revolutionizing how we interact with technology. By incorporating NLP into your skillset, you will be better equipped to create cutting-edge applications that cater to the growing demand for intelligent and intuitive systems.

In the following sections, we will explore various NLP techniques and their applications, starting with text analysis. Text analysis is the foundation of NLP, which involves breaking down and understanding language structure. This knowledge can then be applied to more advanced NLP tasks, such as sentiment analysis, which aims to decipher the emotions and opinions expressed in a piece of text. Finally, we will discuss chatbots and how they utilize NLP to engage in meaningful conversations with users.

As we journey through the world of Natural Language Processing, you will gain valuable insights into the power of AI and ML in transforming how we interact with technology. By the end of this chapter, you will have a solid understanding of NLP and its applications, empowering you to create innovative solutions that harness the power of language and communication. So, let's embark on this exciting adventure and discover the limitless potential of Natural Language Processing for coders.

Text Analysis Techniques and Applications

This section will delve into the fascinating world of text analysis, exploring various techniques and their applications in artificial intelligence and machine learning. As coders, understanding these methods will enable you to harness the power of natural language processing (NLP) to create innovative solutions and enhance user experiences.

Tokenization and Text Preprocessing

The first step in text analysis is breaking down the text into smaller units, known as tokens. Tokenization is converting a text sequence into individual words, phrases, symbols, or other meaningful elements. This technique allows for easier manipulation and analysis of the text data.

Text preprocessing is another crucial aspect of text analysis. It involves cleaning and transforming raw text data into a structured format that machine learning algorithms can easily understand. Common preprocessing tasks include:

- **Lowercasing:** Converting all text to lowercase to ensure uniformity.
- **Removing special characters and numbers:** Eliminating any irrelevant elements that may hinder analysis.
- **Stopword removal:** Filtering out common words (e.g., 'and', 'the', 'is') that do not contribute to the meaning of the text.
- **Stemming and Lemmatization:** Reducing words to their root form to consolidate similar terms and reduce dimensionality.

Feature Extraction and Representation

Once the text data is preprocessed, the next step is to extract relevant features and represent them in a format that can be fed into machine learning models. Two popular techniques for feature extraction and representation are:

- **Bag of Words (BoW):** This approach represents text data as a 'bag' (unordered set) of its words, disregarding grammar and word order but keeping track of frequency. Each document is represented as a vector, with the length of the vector being the total number of unique words in the corpus (collection of documents). The value at each position in the vector indicates the frequency of the corresponding word in the document.
- **Term Frequency-Inverse Document Frequency (TF-IDF):** This method is an extension of the BoW approach, taking into account the frequency of a word in a document and its importance across the entire corpus. The idea is to give higher weight to words more specific to a particular document and lower weight to words common across documents.

Text Classification and Clustering

With the text data preprocessed and represented in a suitable format, we can now apply machine learning algorithms to perform various tasks, such as:

- **Text Classification:** Assigning predefined categories (labels) to a given text based on its content. Typical applications include spam detection, sentiment analysis, and topic identification. Popular algorithms for text classification include Naive Bayes, Support Vector Machines, and Deep Learning models such as Convolutional Neural Networks (CNNs) and Recurrent Neural Networks (RNNs).

- **Text Clustering:** Grouping similar text documents based on their content without any prior knowledge of categories or labels. This unsupervised learning technique is helpful for discovering hidden patterns and structures in the data. Standard algorithms for text clustering include K-means, Hierarchical Clustering, and Latent Dirichlet Allocation (LDA).

In conclusion, text analysis techniques play a vital role in harnessing the power of NLP for various AI and ML applications. By understanding and implementing these methods, coders can unlock new possibilities and create innovative solutions that leverage the vast potential of natural language data.

Sentiment Analysis: Understanding Emotions in Text

In today's digital age, understanding and interpreting human emotions in text has become increasingly important. Sentiment analysis, also known as opinion mining or emotion AI, is a subfield of natural language processing (NLP) that focuses on identifying and extracting subjective information from textual data. This section will delve into sentiment analysis, exploring its techniques, applications, and significance for coders working with AI and ML.

The Basics of Sentiment Analysis

Sentiment analysis aims to determine the sentiment or emotion behind a piece of text, be it positive, negative, or neutral. This can be achieved through various techniques, including machine learning, lexicon-based approaches, and deep learning. The primary goal is to gain insights into the opinions and emotions expressed by users, which can be invaluable for businesses, researchers, and developers alike.

Techniques for Sentiment Analysis

- **Machine Learning:** Supervised machine learning algorithms, such as Naïve Bayes, Support Vector Machines (SVM), and Decision Trees, can be trained on labeled datasets to classify text based on sentiment. These algorithms learn from the input data and make predictions based on patterns and relationships they identify.
- **Lexicon-Based Approaches:** This technique relies on predefined sentiment lexicons, lists of words, and phrases associated with specific emotions or sentiments. The overall sentiment can be determined by analyzing the frequency and context of these words in a given text.
- **Deep Learning:** Neural networks, such as Convolutional Neural Networks (CNN) and Recurrent Neural Networks (RNN), can capture complex patterns and relationships in textual data. These models can be particularly effective in handling large datasets and understanding the nuances of human language.

Applications of Sentiment Analysis

- **Social Media Monitoring:** Sentiment analysis can be used to track public opinion on social media platforms, helping businesses and organizations understand how the audience perceives their products, services, or campaigns.
- **Customer Feedback Analysis:** By analyzing customer reviews and feedback, businesses can identify areas of improvement, address customer concerns, and enhance their overall customer experience.
- **Market Research:** Sentiment analysis can provide valuable insights into market trends and consumer preferences, enabling businesses to make informed decisions and stay ahead of the competition.

- **Political Analysis:** By gauging public sentiment on political issues, candidates, and campaigns, sentiment analysis can help predict election outcomes and inform political strategies.

The Role of Coders in Sentiment Analysis

As AI and ML advance, the demand for skilled coders in sentiment analysis will only grow. Coders play a crucial role in developing and refining algorithms, creating and maintaining sentiment lexicons, and integrating sentiment analysis tools into various applications. By staying up-to-date with the latest techniques and developments in NLP, coders can contribute to the evolution of sentiment analysis and its impact on industries worldwide.

In conclusion, sentiment analysis is a powerful tool for understanding emotions in text, with numerous applications across various domains. As a coder working with AI and ML, mastering sentiment analysis techniques and staying informed about the latest advancements in NLP will enhance your skillset and open doors to exciting opportunities in this rapidly evolving field.

Building Chatbots: Conversational AI and User Interaction

Chatbots have become a powerful tool for businesses and developers in today's fast-paced digital world. These intelligent virtual assistants are designed to interact with users through natural language processing (NLP), providing a seamless and efficient communication experience. This section will delve into the fascinating world of chatbots, exploring the underlying technology, user interaction, and the steps to build your own conversational AI.

The Essence of Chatbots

At their core, chatbots are AI-driven programs that can understand, interpret, and respond to human language. They can be integrated into various platforms, such as websites, messaging apps, or even social media, to provide instant support, answer queries, or engage users in conversation. The primary goal of chatbots is to mimic human-like interactions, making them an invaluable asset in enhancing user experience and customer satisfaction.

Conversational AI: The Driving Force Behind Chatbots

Conversational AI is the technology that enables chatbots to understand and process human language. It combines NLP, machine learning (ML), and artificial intelligence (AI) to analyze text or speech input, extract meaning, and generate appropriate responses. This intricate process involves several steps, including tokenization, parsing, and entity recognition, which help the chatbot comprehend the user's intent and respond accordingly.

User Interaction: The Key to Successful Chatbots

For a chatbot to be effective, it must be able to engage users naturally and intuitively. This involves understanding the context of the conversation, providing relevant information, and maintaining a consistent tone. To achieve this, developers must focus on the following aspects:

- **Personalization:** Tailoring the chatbot's responses to the user's preferences and needs can significantly enhance the interaction experience. This can be achieved by analyzing user data, such as browsing history or previous interactions, to provide personalized recommendations or support.
- **Context-awareness:** Chatbots should be able to understand the context of the conversation and respond accordingly. This may involve maintaining the

conversation history, recognizing user emotions, or
detecting sarcasm to ensure appropriate responses.
- **Natural language generation:** Crafting human-like
responses is crucial for a chatbot's success. This can be
achieved through natural language generation (NLG),
which involves converting structured data into coherent
and engaging text.

Building Your Own Chatbot: A Step-by-Step Guide

1. **Define the purpose:** Before diving into the development
process, it is essential to identify the primary goal of
your chatbot. This could range from customer support
to product recommendations or even entertainment.
2. **Choose a platform:** Select a suitable platform for your
chatbot, such as Facebook Messenger, Slack, or your
own website. This decision will influence the
development process and the tools you will need.
3. **Design the conversation flow:** Map out the potential
conversation paths, including user inputs, chatbot
responses, and fallback options for unrecognized
queries.
4. **Develop the NLP model:** Utilize NLP libraries and
frameworks, such as TensorFlow or spaCy, to build your
chatbot's underlying language processing model.
5. **Train and test the chatbot:** Use a dataset of sample
conversations to train your chatbot and evaluate its
performance. Continuously refine the model to improve
its accuracy and responsiveness.
6. **Integrate and deploy:** Once your chatbot is ready,
integrate it into the chosen platform and monitor its
performance. Gather user feedback and make necessary
adjustments to enhance the overall experience.

In conclusion, chatbots have revolutionized how businesses and users interact, offering a more personalized and efficient communication channel. By understanding the intricacies of conversational AI and user interaction, developers can harness the power of NLP, AI, and ML to create engaging and effective chatbots that cater to a wide range of applications. As technology advances, the potential for natural language processing and its impact on coders is limitless, opening up new avenues for innovation and growth.

Integrating AI and ML into Your NLP Projects

As we delve deeper into the fascinating world of Natural Language Processing (NLP), it becomes increasingly evident that the integration of Artificial Intelligence (AI) and Machine Learning (ML) is crucial for the development of advanced NLP projects. In this section, we will explore the process of incorporating AI and ML techniques into your NLP projects, enabling you to create more sophisticated and efficient applications.

Identifying the Problem and Setting Goals

Before diving into the technical aspects of AI and ML integration, it is essential to identify the specific problem you aim to solve with your NLP project. This involves defining clear objectives and determining the desired outcomes. For instance, you may want to create a sentiment analysis tool that accurately gauges customer opinions on a product or service, or you may want to develop a chatbot capable of providing personalized recommendations to users.

Selecting the Right AI and ML Techniques

Once you have established your project's goals, the next step is choosing the appropriate AI and ML techniques to help you achieve those objectives. Various algorithms and models are available, each with strengths and weaknesses. Some popular techniques include:

- **Supervised Learning:** This approach involves training a model using labeled data, where the input-output pairs are known. Supervised learning is particularly useful for text classification and sentiment analysis tasks.
- **Unsupervised Learning:** In this method, the model learns from unlabeled data by identifying patterns and structures within the dataset. Unsupervised learning is often employed for tasks like topic modeling and clustering.
- **Deep Learning:** This subset of ML involves using artificial neural networks to model complex patterns in data. Deep learning techniques, such as recurrent neural networks (RNNs) and transformers, have proven highly effective in various NLP tasks, including machine translation and text generation.

Preprocessing and Feature Engineering

To ensure the success of your AI and ML integration, it is vital to preprocess your text data and extract relevant features. This process typically involves cleaning and tokenizing the text, removing stop words, and stemming or lemmatizing words to reduce them to their root forms. Additionally, you may need to convert the text into numerical representations, such as word embeddings or bag-of-words representations, which ML algorithms can efficiently process.

Model Training and Evaluation

You can train your model after preprocessing your data and

selecting the appropriate AI and ML techniques. This involves feeding the processed data into the chosen algorithm and adjusting the model's parameters to minimize the error between the predicted and actual outputs. Evaluating your model's performance using various metrics, such as accuracy, precision, recall, and F1 score, is crucial to ensure that it meets your project's objectives.

Fine-tuning and Optimization

Once your model has been trained and evaluated, you may need to fine-tune its parameters or optimize its architecture to improve its performance further. This process may involve adjusting hyperparameters, employing regularization techniques to prevent overfitting, or exploring more advanced AI and ML techniques, such as transfer learning or ensemble methods.

In conclusion, integrating AI and ML into your NLP projects can significantly enhance their capabilities and efficiency. By following the steps outlined in this section, you will be well-equipped to develop cutting-edge NLP applications that harness the power of AI and ML, ultimately shaping the future of language processing and its impact on coders.

The Future of Natural Language Processing and Its Impact on Coders

As we reach the end of this enlightening journey through the world of Natural Language Processing (NLP), it is essential to take a moment to reflect on the future of this rapidly evolving field and its impact on coders. Artificial Intelligence (AI) and Machine Learning (ML) advancements have already transformed how we interact with technology, and NLP is at the forefront of this revolution.

In the coming years, we can expect NLP to become even more sophisticated and versatile, enabling machines to understand and process human language with unprecedented accuracy. This will open up many opportunities for coders, who will be instrumental in shaping the future of NLP and its applications.

One of the most significant growth areas in NLP will be the development of more advanced and intuitive chatbots. As conversational AI continues to improve, chatbots will become increasingly capable of understanding complex language patterns and providing more accurate and personalized responses. This will lead to a higher demand for skilled coders who can design, develop, and maintain these intelligent systems.

Moreover, integrating AI and ML into NLP projects will become more seamless, allowing coders to harness the power of these technologies more efficiently. This will result in the creation of more advanced tools and applications for text analysis, sentiment analysis, and other NLP tasks. Consequently, coders must stay up-to-date with the latest developments in AI and ML to remain competitive in the job market.

Another exciting prospect for the future of NLP is the potential for cross-disciplinary collaboration. As NLP techniques become more refined, they will be increasingly applied to various fields, such as healthcare, finance, and education. This will create new opportunities for coders to work alongside professionals from diverse backgrounds, fostering innovation and driving progress in multiple domains.

Furthermore, as NLP evolves, ethical considerations will become increasingly important. Coders must be mindful of the potential biases and ethical implications of the algorithms they develop, ensuring that their work promotes fairness and inclusivity. This will require a deep understanding of NLP's technical and social aspects, highlighting the importance of a well-rounded education for aspiring coders.

In conclusion, the future of Natural Language Processing is undoubtedly bright, and its impact on coders will be profound. As NLP techniques become more advanced and widespread, coders will play a crucial role in shaping how we communicate with machines and unlocking the full potential of AI and ML. By staying informed about the latest developments in NLP and honing their skills, coders will be well-equipped to navigate this exciting and ever-changing landscape.

Chapter Summary

- Natural Language Processing (NLP) is the intersection of computer science, AI, and linguistics, focusing on enabling computers to understand, interpret, and generate human language meaningfully and usefully.
- Text analysis is the foundation of NLP, involving techniques such as tokenization, text preprocessing, feature extraction, and representation, which can be applied to more advanced NLP tasks like sentiment analysis and chatbots.
- Sentiment analysis, a subfield of NLP, focuses on identifying and extracting subjective information from textual data, helping businesses understand customer feedback, monitor social media, and conduct market research.
- Powered by conversational AI, chatbots are intelligent virtual assistants designed to interact with users through NLP, providing seamless and efficient communication experiences across various platforms.
- Integrating AI and ML into NLP projects involves identifying the problem, selecting the right techniques, preprocessing and feature engineering, model training and evaluation, and fine-tuning and optimization.
- The future of NLP will see more advanced and intuitive chatbots, seamless integration of AI and ML, and cross-disciplinary collaboration, creating new opportunities for coders in various fields.
- Ethical considerations will become increasingly important in NLP, with coders needing to be mindful of

potential biases and ethical implications of the algorithms they develop.

- As NLP continues to evolve, coders must stay up-to-date with the latest developments in AI and ML to remain competitive in the job market and contribute to the growth of NLP applications.

9

COMPUTER VISION AND IMAGE RECOGNITION: CONVOLUTIONAL NEURAL NETWORKS AND OBJECT DETECTION

In the dynamic and changing sphere of artificial intelligence (AI) and machine learning (ML), computer vision and image recognition have emerged as two of the most fascinating and rapidly growing subfields. These technologies can revolutionize various industries, from healthcare and agriculture to security and entertainment. This chapter will delve into the intricacies of computer vision and image recognition, exploring the underlying concepts, techniques, and applications that make these technologies so powerful and transformative.

Computer vision is a multidisciplinary field that aims to enable computers to interpret and understand the visual world, much like humans do. By processing and analyzing digital images and videos, computer vision algorithms can extract valuable information, recognize patterns, and make intelligent decisions based on the visual data. This ability to "see" and comprehend the world around us has far-reaching implications, as it can significantly enhance the capabilities of AI and ML systems across various domains.

Image recognition, a subset of computer vision, focuses on identifying and classifying objects within images. This process involves detecting specific features, such as shapes, colors, and textures, and using them to distinguish between different objects or categories. The ultimate goal of image recognition is to teach machines to recognize and understand images' content, enabling them to perform tasks that were once exclusive to human perception.

One of the most groundbreaking advancements in computer vision and image recognition has been the development of Convolutional Neural Networks (CNNs). These deep learning models have demonstrated remarkable success in various image recognition tasks, outperforming traditional methods and setting new benchmarks in the field. In this chapter, we will explore the architecture and applications of CNNs and other object detection techniques that have shaped the landscape of computer vision.

As we journey through the world of computer vision and image recognition, we will also examine real-world applications and case studies that showcase the transformative power of these technologies. From self-driving cars and facial recognition systems to medical imaging and wildlife conservation, computer vision and image recognition are poised to redefine how we live, work, and interact with our environment.

Finally, we will discuss the future of computer vision and image recognition in AI and ML, highlighting the challenges, opportunities, and emerging trends shaping the next generation of intelligent systems. As we continue to push the boundaries of what machines can see and understand, there is no doubt that computer vision and image recognition will play a pivotal role in the evolution of AI and ML, unlocking new possibilities and transforming the world as we know it.

Exploring Convolutional Neural Networks: Architecture and Applications

In artificial intelligence and machine learning, computer vision has emerged as a powerful tool for enabling computers to perceive and interpret visual information from the world. At the heart of this revolution lies the Convolutional Neural Network (CNN), a class of deep learning models specifically designed for image recognition and analysis. In this section, we will delve into the architecture and applications of CNNs, shedding light on their remarkable capabilities and potential impact on computer vision.

The Architecture of Convolutional Neural Networks

Convolutional Neural Networks are artificial neural networks that have been explicitly tailored for processing grid-like data structures, such as images. The architecture of a CNN is composed of several interconnected layers, each designed to perform a specific function in the image recognition process. These layers can be broadly categorized into convolutional layers, pooling layers, and fully connected layers.

- **Convolutional Layers:** The primary building blocks of a CNN, convolutional layers detect local features within an image, such as edges, corners, and textures. They achieve this by applying a series of filters, or kernels, to the input image, which results in a set of feature maps.

These feature maps represent the presence of specific features at different locations within the image.

- **Pooling Layers:** Following the convolutional layers, pooling layers reduce the spatial dimensions of the feature maps, effectively summarizing the information contained within them. This process, known as downsampling, helps to reduce the computational complexity of the network and improve its robustness to small variations in the input data.
- **Fully Connected Layers:** In the final stage of a CNN's architecture, fully connected layers integrate the information extracted by the preceding convolutional and pooling layers. These layers are responsible for producing the network's final output, which typically takes the form of a probability distribution over the possible classes or objects present in the input image.

Applications of Convolutional Neural Networks

The unique architecture of CNNs has made them particularly well-suited for a wide range of computer vision tasks. Some of the most notable applications of CNNs include:

- **Image Classification:** Perhaps the most fundamental application of CNNs, image classification involves assigning an input image to one of several predefined categories. CNNs have demonstrated remarkable success in this domain, achieving state-of-the-art performance on benchmark datasets such as ImageNet.
- **Object Detection:** Building upon the capabilities of image classification, object detection tasks require CNNs to identify the objects present in an image and localize them within the image frame. This is typically achieved by predicting bounding boxes around the detected objects and their corresponding class labels.

- **Semantic Segmentation:** In semantic segmentation tasks, CNNs assign a class label to each pixel in an input image, effectively partitioning the image into distinct regions corresponding to different objects or scene elements. This level of granularity enables a more detailed understanding of the image content and has applications in areas such as autonomous vehicles and robotics.
- **Image Generation and Style Transfer:** CNNs have also been utilized for creative purposes, such as generating new images or transferring the artistic style of one image onto another. This is achieved through generative models, such as Generative Adversarial Networks (GANs), which leverage the feature extraction capabilities of CNNs to synthesize visually compelling images.

In conclusion, Convolutional Neural Networks have emerged as a cornerstone of modern computer vision, enabling machines to perceive and interpret visual information with unprecedented accuracy and efficiency. As we continue to explore the potential of CNNs in various applications, it is clear that their impact on the field of AI and ML will be both profound and far-reaching.

Object Detection Techniques: From Traditional Methods to Deep Learning Approaches

The realm of object detection has witnessed a remarkable evolution over the years, transitioning from traditional methods to deep learning approaches. In this section, we will delve into the intricacies of these techniques, highlighting their strengths and limitations and exploring how they have shaped the landscape of computer vision and image recognition.

Traditional Object Detection Methods

Before the advent of deep learning, computer vision researchers relied on traditional methods for object detection. These techniques typically involved feature extraction and applying machine learning algorithms to classify objects. Some of the most prominent traditional methods include:

- **Viola-Jones Algorithm:** This groundbreaking method, introduced in 2001, employed Haar-like features and a cascaded classifier to detect objects, particularly faces, in real time. The Viola-Jones algorithm's success can be attributed to its speed and efficiency, which paved the way for further advancements in object detection.
- **Scale-Invariant Feature Transform (SIFT):** SIFT is a robust feature extraction technique that identifies key points and their corresponding descriptors in an image. These features are invariant to scale, rotation, and illumination changes, making SIFT suitable for various object recognition tasks.
- **Histogram of Oriented Gradients (HOG):** HOG is another popular feature extraction method that captures the distribution of gradients and edge directions in an image. It has been widely used for pedestrian detection and other object recognition applications.

Despite their contributions to the field, traditional object detection methods have certain limitations. They often struggle with variations in object appearance, occlusions, and complex backgrounds. Moreover, these techniques require manual feature engineering, which can be time-consuming and may not always yield optimal results.

Deep Learning Approaches to Object Detection

The emergence of deep learning has revolutionized object

detection, offering improved accuracy and efficiency. Convolutional Neural Networks (CNNs) have been at the forefront of this transformation, with several architectures and techniques being developed to tackle object detection tasks. Some of the most notable deep learning approaches include:

- **Region-based CNNs (R-CNN):** R-CNNs combine the power of CNNs with region proposal methods to detect objects in an image. The R-CNN framework generates region proposals, extracts feature using a CNN, and classifies objects using a support vector machine (SVM) classifier. Variants of R-CNN, such as Fast R-CNN and Faster R-CNN, have been developed to address the computational inefficiencies of the original R-CNN.
- **You Only Look Once (YOLO):** YOLO is a real-time object detection system that frames object detection as a single regression problem. It divides the input image into a grid and predicts bounding boxes and class probabilities for each grid cell. YOLO's end-to-end architecture allows for faster processing and real-time detection.
- **Single Shot MultiBox Detector (SSD):** SSD is another real-time object detection technique that eliminates the need for region proposals. It predicts bounding boxes and class probabilities directly from feature maps at different scales, resulting in a more efficient and accurate detection process.

Deep learning approaches have significantly outperformed traditional methods in object detection tasks thanks to their ability to learn hierarchical features automatically. These techniques have proven more robust and adaptable, handling relative ease variations in object appearance, occlusions, and complex backgrounds.

In conclusion, the transition from traditional methods to deep learning approaches has been instrumental in advancing the field of object detection. As we continue to explore the potential of AI and ML for coders, it is crucial to understand and appreciate the techniques that have shaped the landscape of computer vision and image recognition. The future of this domain promises even more exciting developments as researchers and practitioners strive to push the boundaries of what is possible with AI and ML.

Implementing Convolutional Neural Networks for Image Recognition Tasks

This section delves into the practical aspects of implementing Convolutional Neural Networks (CNNs) for image recognition tasks. We will discuss the essential components of a CNN, the process of building a model, and the tools and frameworks available for coders to develop and deploy these networks efficiently.

Essential Components of a Convolutional Neural Network

A typical CNN consists of several layers, each designed to perform a specific function in the image recognition process. These layers include:

- **Input Layer:** This layer receives the input image and preprocesses it to a suitable format for further processing. Preprocessing may involve resizing, normalization, and data augmentation techniques.
- **Convolutional Layer:** The core component of a CNN, the convolutional layer applies a series of filters to the input image, detecting various features such as edges, corners, and textures. These filters, also known as kernels, slide over the image and perform element-wise multiplication, generating feature maps.
- **Activation Layer:** Following the convolutional layer, the activation layer introduces non-linearity into the network by applying an activation function, such as the

Rectified Linear Unit (ReLU), to the feature maps. This step enhances the network's ability to learn complex patterns.

- **Pooling Layer:** The pooling layer reduces the spatial dimensions of the feature maps, thereby decreasing computational complexity and preventing overfitting. Common pooling techniques include max pooling and average pooling.

- **Fully Connected Layer:** After several iterations of convolutional, activation, and pooling layers, the fully connected layer flattens the feature maps into a single vector. This vector is then fed into a classifier, such as a softmax function, to generate the final output probabilities for each class.

Building a Convolutional Neural Network Model

To implement a CNN for image recognition tasks, follow these general steps:

1. **Data Preparation:** Collect and preprocess a dataset of labeled images. Split the dataset into training, validation, and testing sets.

2. **Model Architecture:** Design the CNN architecture by stacking the appropriate layers in a sequential manner. Determine the number of filters, kernel sizes, and other hyperparameters based on the specific problem and dataset.

3. **Model Training:** Train the CNN using the training set, adjusting the weights and biases through backpropagation and optimization algorithms such as stochastic gradient descent. Monitor the model's performance on the validation set to prevent overfitting and fine-tune hyperparameters.

4. **Model Evaluation:** Assess the trained CNN's performance on the testing set using accuracy, precision, recall, and F1 score metrics.

5. **Model Deployment:** Integrate the trained CNN into an application or system for real-time image recognition tasks.

Tools and Frameworks for Implementing Convolutional Neural Networks

Several tools and frameworks are available to facilitate the implementation of CNNs for image recognition tasks. Some popular options include:

- **TensorFlow:** An open-source machine learning library developed by Google, TensorFlow offers a comprehensive ecosystem for building, training, and deploying CNNs.
- **Keras:** A high-level neural networks API, Keras simplifies the process of building and training CNNs by providing an intuitive interface and pre-built layers. Keras can run on top of TensorFlow, Microsoft Cognitive Toolkit, or Theano.
- **PyTorch:** Developed by Facebook's AI Research lab, PyTorch is a flexible and efficient deep learning framework that supports dynamic computation graphs, making it particularly suitable for research purposes.
- **Caffe:** A deep learning framework developed by the Berkeley Vision and Learning Center, Caffe is specifically designed for image recognition tasks and offers a fast and efficient implementation of CNNs.

In conclusion, implementing Convolutional Neural Networks for image recognition tasks involves understanding the essential components, building and training the model, and utilizing the appropriate tools and frameworks. As AI and ML continue to advance, we can expect further improvements in the accuracy and efficiency of CNNs, paving the way for more sophisticated and diverse applications in computer vision.

Real-World Applications and Case Studies in Computer Vision

The advancements in artificial intelligence (AI) and machine learning (ML) have significantly impacted various industries, with computer vision and image recognition playing a crucial role in this transformation. In this section, we will delve into real-world applications and case studies that demonstrate the power of computer vision and image recognition in solving complex problems and enhancing our daily lives.

Healthcare and Medical Imaging

One of the most promising applications of computer vision lies in the healthcare industry, particularly in medical imaging. By leveraging convolutional neural networks (CNNs) and other deep learning techniques, computer vision algorithms can analyze medical images, such as X-rays, MRIs, and CT scans, to accurately detect and diagnose diseases. For instance, researchers have developed AI models to identify early signs of diabetic retinopathy, lung cancer, and Alzheimer's disease, enabling timely intervention and treatment.

Autonomous Vehicles

Integrating computer vision and image recognition technologies has revolutionized the automotive industry. Self-driving cars rely heavily on these techniques to navigate safely and efficiently. CNNs process and analyze data from cameras, LiDAR, and other sensors, allowing the vehicle to recognize and track objects like pedestrians, other vehicles, and traffic signs. This real-time object detection and tracking capability is essential for autonomous vehicles to make informed decisions and avoid accidents.

Retail and E-commerce

Computer vision has also found its way into the retail and e-commerce sectors, enhancing customer experiences and streamlining operations. For example, image recognition algorithms can analyze customer preferences and shopping habits, enabling retailers to offer personalized product recommendations. Additionally, computer vision-powered checkout systems can automatically identify and track items, reducing the need for manual barcode scanning and speeding up the checkout process.

Agriculture and Precision Farming

The agriculture industry has benefited from adopting computer vision and image recognition technologies, leading to the emergence of precision farming. By analyzing images captured by drones or satellites, AI algorithms can identify crop health, monitor growth, and detect signs of pests or diseases. This information allows farmers to make data-driven decisions, optimize resource usage, and improve crop yields.

Surveillance and Security

Computer vision plays a vital role in enhancing security and surveillance systems. Advanced image recognition algorithms can analyze real-time video feeds, detecting and tracking suspicious activities, such as unattended bags, trespassing, or loitering. Furthermore, facial recognition technology has become increasingly prevalent in various security applications, from unlocking smartphones to identifying criminals in public spaces.

In conclusion, the real-world applications and case studies discussed in this section highlight the immense potential of computer vision and image recognition in transforming industries and improving our daily lives. As AI and ML evolve, we can expect even more innovative and impactful use cases for these technologies.

The Future of Computer Vision and Image Recognition in AI and ML

As we reach the end of our exploration into the fascinating world of computer vision and image recognition, we must take a step back and consider the potential future developments in this field. The rapid advancements in artificial intelligence (AI) and machine learning (ML) have already transformed how we interact with technology, and the impact of these innovations on computer vision is no exception.

In this concluding section, we will delve into the possible future trajectories of computer vision and image recognition, highlighting the potential breakthroughs and challenges. By understanding the direction in which this technology is headed, we can better prepare ourselves for the exciting opportunities in AI and ML.

One of the most promising areas of development in computer vision is the continued improvement of convolutional neural networks (CNNs) and other deep learning techniques. We expect to see even more accurate and efficient image recognition systems as researchers refine these algorithms. This will enable a wide range of applications, from autonomous vehicles to advanced medical diagnostics, to become increasingly sophisticated and reliable.

Another exciting prospect for the future of computer vision is integrating other sensory data, such as audio and touch, to create more comprehensive and intuitive AI systems. By combining multiple sources of information, these systems can better understand and interpret the world around them, leading to more accurate and versatile applications.

In addition to these technological advancements, the future of computer vision will also be shaped by ethical considerations. As

AI and ML systems become more prevalent in our daily lives, it is crucial to ensure that they are designed and implemented to respect privacy, fairness, and transparency. This will require ongoing collaboration between researchers, policymakers, and industry leaders to establish best practices and guidelines for the responsible development and deployment of computer vision technologies.

Finally, the future of computer vision and image recognition will be heavily influenced by the availability of high-quality, diverse datasets. As AI and ML systems rely on vast amounts of data to learn and improve, ensuring that these datasets represent a diverse range of human experiences and perspectives is essential. This will not only lead to more accurate and effective AI systems but also help mitigate potential biases and promote fairness in developing and deploying these technologies.

In conclusion, the future of computer vision and image recognition in AI and ML has exciting possibilities and challenges. As we continue to push the boundaries of what is possible with these technologies, it is essential to remain mindful of the ethical implications and strive to create AI systems that are not only powerful but also responsible and inclusive. By doing so, we can unlock the full potential of computer vision and image recognition, transforming how we live, work, and interact with the world around us.

Chapter Summary

- Computer vision and image recognition are rapidly growing subfields of AI and ML, with the potential to revolutionize various industries, such as healthcare, agriculture, security, and entertainment.
- Convolutional Neural Networks (CNNs) are deep learning models specifically designed for image recognition tasks, consisting of convolutional layers, pooling layers, and fully connected layers.

- CNNs have demonstrated remarkable success in various image recognition tasks, including image classification, object detection, semantic segmentation, image generation, and style transfer.
- Object detection techniques have evolved from traditional methods like Viola-Jones Algorithm, SIFT, and HOG to deep learning approaches like R-CNN, YOLO, and SSD.
- Implementing CNNs for image recognition tasks involves understanding the essential components, building and training the model, and utilizing appropriate tools and frameworks like TensorFlow, Keras, PyTorch, and Caffe.
- Real-world applications of computer vision and image recognition include healthcare and medical imaging, autonomous vehicles, retail and e-commerce, agriculture and precision farming, and surveillance and security.
- The future of computer vision and image recognition will likely see continued improvement of CNNs, integration of other sensory data, addressing ethical considerations, and ensuring the availability of high-quality, diverse datasets.
- As AI and ML continue to evolve, it is crucial to remain mindful of the ethical implications and strive to create AI systems that are not only powerful but also responsible and inclusive, unlocking the full potential of computer vision and image recognition.

10

ETHICAL CONSIDERATIONS AND RESPONSIBLE AI DEVELOPMENT

I n today's rapidly evolving technological landscape, artificial intelligence (AI) and machine learning (ML) have emerged as powerful tools transforming how we live, work, and interact with the world around us. From self-driving cars and personalized healthcare to advanced robotics and natural language processing, AI and ML have the potential to revolutionize countless industries and improve the quality of life for millions of people. However, as with any groundbreaking technology, the development and deployment of AI and ML systems also raise a host of ethical questions and concerns that must be carefully considered by coders, researchers, and policymakers alike.

The importance of ethics in AI and ML development cannot be overstated. As these technologies become increasingly integrated into our daily lives, they have the potential to either reinforce or challenge existing social norms, values, and power structures. By taking a proactive approach to ethical considerations, coders can help ensure that AI and ML systems are designed and implemented fairly, transparently, and beneficial to all members of society.

This chapter will explore some key ethical considerations that coders must consider when working with AI and ML technologies. We will begin by examining the concepts of bias and fairness in AI and ML algorithms, discussing how these issues can arise and what steps can be taken to mitigate their impact. Next, we will delve into the critical topics of privacy and data security, highlighting the importance of safeguarding user information and maintaining trust in AI systems. We will then focus on transparency and explainability, exploring the need for clear communication and understanding of AI decision-making processes. Finally, we will discuss the role of accountability and regulation in promoting responsible AI development, touching upon the various legal and ethical frameworks emerging to guide the future of AI and ML for coders.

By engaging with these important ethical considerations, coders can play a crucial role in shaping the development of AI and ML technologies in a manner that is both responsible and beneficial to society. As we continue to push the boundaries of what is possible with AI and ML, we must do so with a keen awareness of the ethical implications of our work and a commitment to fostering a more just, equitable, and inclusive future for all.

Understanding Bias and Fairness in AI and ML Algorithms

As we delve into artificial intelligence (AI) and machine learning (ML), coders must understand the importance of addressing bias and ensuring fairness in their algorithms. In this section, we will explore the concept of bias, its impact on AI and ML systems, and the steps developers can take to promote fairness in their work.

Defining Bias in AI and ML

Bias in AI and ML refers to the presence of systematic errors in the algorithms, data, or decision-making processes that lead to unfair or discriminatory outcomes. These biases can stem from various sources, such as the training data, the algorithm's design, or even the developer's unconscious beliefs and assumptions. When left unchecked, biased AI and ML systems can perpetuate and exacerbate existing inequalities, causing harm to individuals and society as a whole.

The Impact of Bias on AI and ML Systems

The consequences of biased AI and ML algorithms can be far-reaching and detrimental. For instance, biased algorithms in hiring processes may discriminate against certain demographic groups, leading to a lack of diversity and perpetuating stereotypes. In facial recognition technology, biased algorithms have been shown to misidentify people of color more than their white counterparts, raising concerns about privacy and civil liberties.

Moreover, biased AI and ML systems can erode public trust in technology as people become increasingly wary of the potential harm these systems can cause. This distrust can hinder the adoption of beneficial AI and ML applications, ultimately stalling progress and innovation.

Promoting Fairness in AI and ML Development

To ensure fairness in AI and ML algorithms, developers must proactively address and mitigate bias. Here are some steps to consider:

- **Curate diverse and representative data:** Ensure that the training data used in developing AI and ML algorithms is diverse and representative of the population it serves. This helps to minimize the risk of biased outcomes and ensures that the system performs fairly across different demographic groups.
- **Regularly evaluate and test for bias:** Continuously monitor and assess AI and ML systems for potential biases during development and after deployment. This can be done through various techniques, such as fairness metrics, bias audits, and third-party evaluations.
- **Encourage interdisciplinary collaboration:** Collaborate with experts from various fields, such as social sciences, ethics, and law, to gain a broader perspective on potential biases and their implications. This interdisciplinary approach can help developers better understand the societal context in which their algorithms operate and make more informed decisions about fairness.
- **Foster a culture of ethical development:** Encourage a culture of ethical AI and ML development within your organization, emphasizing the importance of fairness and the potential consequences of biased algorithms. This can be achieved through training, workshops, and the establishment of ethical guidelines and best practices.
- **Advocate for transparency and openness:** Be transparent about the development process, the data used, and the potential limitations of AI and ML systems. This openness can help build trust with users and stakeholders and facilitate a more informed

dialogue about the ethical implications of AI and ML technologies.

In conclusion, understanding and addressing bias in AI and ML algorithms is crucial to responsible development. By taking the necessary steps to promote fairness, developers can create AI and ML systems that are effective and ethical, ensuring a more equitable future for all.

Privacy and Data Security: Safeguarding User Information

As AI and ML technologies advance and become more integrated into our daily lives, the importance of privacy and data security cannot be overstated. In this section, we will explore the significance of safeguarding user information and the steps coders can take to ensure that their AI and ML systems are designed with privacy and data security in mind.

The rapid growth of AI and ML has led to unprecedented data being collected, stored, and analyzed. This data often includes sensitive personal information, such as financial records, health data, and location data. As a result, the potential for misuse or unauthorized access to this information is a significant concern. In addition to the potential harm to individuals, data breaches can lead to significant financial and reputational damage for companies.

To address these concerns, coders must prioritize privacy and data security when developing AI and ML systems. This can be achieved through technical measures, organizational policies, and adherence to relevant regulations and industry standards.

One of the critical technical measures that can be implemented is data anonymization. This involves removing personally identifiable information (PII) from datasets, making it more difficult for individuals to be identified. Data masking, pseudonymization, and aggregation can be used to achieve this goal.

Another critical aspect of data security is encryption. By

encrypting data at rest and in transit, coders can help protect sensitive information from unauthorized access. Additionally, implementing strong access controls and authentication mechanisms can reduce the data breach risk.

Organizational policies also play a crucial role in safeguarding user information. Companies should establish precise data collection, storage, and usage guidelines and procedures for handling data breaches. Regular audits and assessments ensure that these policies are followed and that potential vulnerabilities are identified and addressed.

Compliance with relevant regulations and industry standards is another essential aspect of privacy and data security. In many jurisdictions, specific laws govern the collection, storage, and use of personal information, such as the European Union's General Data Protection Regulation (GDPR) and the California Consumer Privacy Act (CCPA). By familiarizing themselves with these regulations and adhering to industry best practices, coders can help ensure their AI and ML systems are legally compliant and secure.

In conclusion, privacy and data security are critical considerations for coders working with AI and ML technologies. By implementing technical measures, establishing organizational policies, and adhering to relevant regulations and industry standards, developers can help safeguard user information and build trust in their AI and ML systems. As the field continues to evolve, coders must remain vigilant and proactive in addressing these concerns, ensuring that AI and ML technologies are developed and deployed responsibly.

Transparency and Explainability: Building Trust in AI Systems

As AI and ML systems become increasingly integrated into our daily lives, developers must prioritize transparency and explainability in their creations. These two factors play a crucial role in building trust between users and AI systems, ensuring that the technology is effective and ethically sound. This section will explore the importance of transparency and explainability in AI and ML development and discuss strategies for achieving these goals.

Transparency refers to the openness and clarity with which an AI system operates. It involves providing users with information about how the system works, the data it uses, and the decision-making processes it employs. This level of openness allows users to understand the rationale behind the AI's actions and decisions, fostering trust and confidence in the technology.

Explainability, on the other hand, refers to the ability of an AI system to provide clear, understandable explanations for its decisions and actions. This is particularly important when AI systems are used in critical decision-making processes, such as medical diagnoses, financial investments, or legal judgments. Users must comprehend the reasoning behind the AI's decisions to trust the technology and feel confident in its capabilities.

To achieve transparency and explainability in AI and ML systems, developers should consider the following strategies:

- **Design with transparency in mind:** From the outset, developers should prioritize transparency in their AI systems. This includes selecting easily interpretable algorithms and designing user interfaces that clearly communicate the system's processes and decision-making rationale.
- **Provide clear documentation:** Comprehensive documentation is essential for transparency and explainability. Developers should create user guides, technical documents, and other resources that explain the AI system's inner workings, data sources, and decision-making processes in an accessible and understandable manner.
- **Implement explainable AI techniques:** Explainable AI (XAI) is an emerging field focusing on developing AI systems that provide clear, human-understandable

explanations for their decisions and actions. Developers can improve explainability and foster user trust by incorporating XAI techniques into their AI systems.

- **Engage in open communication:** Developers should be open to feedback and questions from users, regulators, and other stakeholders. By engaging in open communication and addressing concerns, developers can demonstrate their commitment to transparency and explainability and build trust in their AI systems.
- **Collaborate with ethicists and other experts:** To ensure that AI systems are developed with transparency and explainability, developers should collaborate with ethicists, social scientists, and other experts who can provide valuable insights and guidance on ethical considerations.

In conclusion, transparency and explainability are essential for responsible AI and ML development. By prioritizing these factors and implementing the strategies discussed in this section, developers can build AI systems that are not only effective but also ethically sound, fostering trust and confidence among users. As AI and ML technologies continue to advance, developers must remain committed to these principles, ensuring that the future of AI is both innovative and ethically responsible.

Accountability and Regulation: Ensuring Responsible AI Development

As we delve deeper into artificial intelligence (AI) and machine learning (ML), it becomes increasingly crucial for coders to understand the importance of accountability and regulation in the development process. In this section, we will explore the role of these two factors in ensuring responsible AI development and discuss how coders can contribute to a more ethical AI landscape.

Accountability in AI development refers to the responsibility of developers, organizations, and other stakeholders to ensure that AI systems are designed, implemented, and used in a manner that adheres to ethical principles and guidelines. This includes being answerable for the consequences of AI systems, whether intended or unintended, and taking necessary steps to mitigate any potential harm.

One of the key aspects of accountability is the need for developers to be aware of the potential biases and ethical implications of their AI systems. This involves conducting thorough assessments of AI algorithms and datasets to identify and address potential issues related to fairness, privacy, and transparency. By doing so, developers can ensure that their AI systems are effective and ethically sound.

Regulation, on the other hand, refers to establishing and enforcing rules and guidelines that govern the development and use of AI systems. These regulations are typically set by governments, industry bodies, or other relevant authorities and are designed to ensure that AI development adheres to ethical standards and best practices.

In recent years, there has been a growing call for more robust and comprehensive AI regulations, as concerns about the potential misuse of AI technologies and their impact on society continue to rise. Some key areas where regulation is needed include data privacy, algorithmic fairness, and transparency.

As a coder working in AI and ML, staying informed about the latest developments in AI regulations and guidelines is essential. This helps you ensure that your work complies with the relevant rules and enables you to contribute to the ongoing conversation about responsible AI development.

One way to stay updated on AI regulations is by following the work of organizations and initiatives focusing on AI ethics, such as the AI Ethics Guidelines by the European Commission, the AI Now Institute, and the Partnership on AI. These organizations often publish research, recommendations, and guidelines that can help

445

inform your work and ensure you are responsibly developing AI systems.

In conclusion, accountability and regulation are crucial in ensuring responsible AI development. As a coder working in AI and ML, it is your responsibility to be aware of your work's ethical implications and adhere to the relevant guidelines and regulations. By doing so, you can contribute to developing effective and ethically sound AI systems, paving the way for a more responsible and inclusive AI landscape.

The Future of Ethical AI and ML for Coders

As we conclude this chapter, it is essential to reflect on the critical role that ethics plays in the development of artificial intelligence and machine learning technologies. The rapid advancements in these fields have brought numerous benefits, from automating mundane tasks to revolutionizing industries. However, these advancements also come with a responsibility for coders to ensure that the AI and ML systems they create are ethical, fair, and transparent.

This chapter has explored various ethical considerations, such as understanding bias and fairness, privacy and data security, transparency and explainability, and accountability and regulation. By addressing these concerns, coders can contribute to developing AI and ML systems that are both efficient and morally sound.

The future of ethical AI and ML for coders lies in the continuous pursuit of knowledge and understanding of the ethical implications of their work. As technology evolves, so must the ethical frameworks that guide its development. Coders must remain vigilant about the latest ethical concerns and best practices in AI and ML development.

Moreover, collaboration between coders, ethicists, policymakers, and other stakeholders is crucial in shaping the future of ethical AI and ML. By working together, these groups can develop comprehensive guidelines and regulations that ensure AI and ML technologies are used responsibly and for the betterment of society.

In addition, fostering a culture of ethical awareness within the coding community is vital. This can be achieved through education, mentorship, and sharing resources and experiences. By cultivating an environment where ethical considerations are integral to the development process, coders can ensure that AI and ML technologies are built on a foundation of responsibility and integrity.

Ultimately, the future of ethical AI and ML for coders has immense potential and opportunity. By embracing the ethical considerations outlined in this chapter and committing to responsible development practices, coders can play a pivotal role in shaping a world where AI and ML technologies are used to enhance our lives, promote fairness, and uphold the values that define our humanity.

Chapter Summary

- Ethics in AI and ML development is crucial, as these technologies have the potential to either reinforce or challenge existing social norms, values, and power structures.
- Understanding and addressing bias in AI and ML algorithms is essential for responsible development, ensuring fairness, and avoiding perpetuating inequalities.
- Privacy and data security are critical considerations for coders working with AI and ML technologies, requiring technical measures, organizational policies, and adherence to relevant regulations and industry standards.
- Transparency and explainability are essential components of responsible AI and ML development, fostering trust and confidence among users.

- Accountability in AI development refers to the responsibility of developers, organizations, and other stakeholders to ensure that AI systems adhere to ethical principles and guidelines.
- Regulation is necessary to establish and enforce rules and guidelines that govern the development and use of AI systems, ensuring adherence to ethical standards and best practices.
- Collaboration between coders, ethicists, policymakers, and other stakeholders is crucial in shaping the future of ethical AI and ML, developing comprehensive guidelines and regulations.
- Fostering a culture of ethical awareness within the coding community is vital, achieved through education, mentorship, and sharing resources and experiences, ensuring AI and ML technologies are built on a foundation of responsibility and integrity.

THE FUTURE OF AI AND ML IN CODING AND BEYOND

In recent years, the world has witnessed a technological revolution that has transformed the way we live, work, and interact with one another. At the forefront of this revolution are artificial intelligence (AI) and machine learning (ML), two rapidly evolving fields that have the potential to revolutionize not only the coding industry but also the very fabric of our society. As we stand on the cusp of a new era, coders, developers, and technology enthusiasts must embrace the AI and ML revolution and harness its power to create a smarter, more efficient world.

This chapter aims to provide a comprehensive overview of the current state of AI and ML in coding and explore the potential implications of these technologies for the future of the industry and beyond. By examining major themes and findings, we will unravel the core insights of AI and ML for coders, highlighting the significance of these advancements in shaping the future of technology and society. Furthermore, we will address the limitations and critiques surrounding AI and ML development, offering recommendations for overcoming these challenges and paving the way for a more sustainable, ethical, and inclusive technological landscape.

As we delve into the world of AI and ML, it is essential to recognize that these technologies are not merely tools for coders to wield; they are powerful forces that have the potential to redefine the way we approach problem-solving, decision-making, and innovation. By embracing the AI and ML revolution, we can unlock new possibilities for growth and development, empowering individuals and organizations to reach new heights of success and efficiency.

In the following sections, we will explore the major themes and findings of AI and ML for coders, discussing the implications and significance of these technologies for the industry's future and beyond. We will also address the limitations and critiques of AI and ML development, offering insights and recommendations for overcoming these challenges and fostering a more sustainable, ethical, and inclusive technological landscape.

As we embark on this journey, let us remember that the future of AI and ML in coding and beyond is not predetermined; it is up to us to shape it. By embracing the AI and ML revolution and harnessing its power for good, we can create a smarter, more efficient, and more connected world than ever before.

Unraveling the Core Insights of AI and ML for Coders

As we delve into artificial intelligence (AI) and machine learning (ML), we must understand the major themes and findings that have emerged in recent years. These insights provide a solid foundation for coders looking to incorporate AI and ML into their work and offer a glimpse into the future of these transformative technologies.

The Power of Data

One of the most significant revelations in AI and ML is the importance of data. Data is the lifeblood of these technologies, as it provides the necessary information for algorithms to learn, adapt, and improve. Coders must recognize the value of collecting, processing and analyzing vast amounts of data to create intelligent systems capable of making informed decisions and predictions.

The Rise of Deep Learning

Deep learning, a subset of ML, has emerged as a game-changer in AI. Deep learning algorithms can process and analyze complex data with remarkable accuracy by utilizing artificial neural networks that mimic the human brain's structure and function. This breakthrough has led to significant advancements in areas such as image and speech recognition, natural language processing, and autonomous vehicles.

The Integration of AI and ML in Various Industries

AI and ML have transcended the boundaries of computer science and are now being integrated into a wide range of industries. These technologies are revolutionizing our lives and work, from healthcare and finance to agriculture and entertainment. Coders must be prepared to adapt their skills and knowledge to meet the demands of an increasingly AI-driven world.

The Ethical Considerations of AI and ML

As AI and ML continue to advance, ethical considerations have come to the forefront of the conversation. Coders, researchers, and policymakers must address issues such as data privacy, algorithmic bias, and the potential loss of jobs due to automation. Understanding and addressing these concerns ensures that AI and ML are developed and implemented responsibly.

The Need for Collaboration and Interdisciplinary Approaches

The development of AI and ML requires a collaborative and

interdisciplinary approach, combining elements of computer science, mathematics, psychology, and other fields. Coders must be willing to work with experts from various disciplines to create innovative solutions that push the boundaries of what is possible with AI and ML.

In conclusion, understanding these major themes and findings is crucial for coders harnessing AI and ML's power. By embracing the importance of data, deep learning, industry integration, ethical considerations, and interdisciplinary collaboration, coders can play a vital role in shaping the future of technology and society. As we continue to explore the potential of AI and ML, the possibilities are limitless, and the impact on our world will be profound.

Shaping the Future of Technology and Society

As we delve into the third chapter of our conclusion, it is crucial to understand the far-reaching implications and significance of artificial intelligence (AI) and machine learning (ML) in coding and beyond. The transformative power of these technologies has the potential to reshape not only the way we develop software and applications but also the very fabric of our society. In this section, we will explore the various ways AI and ML are poised to revolutionize the world of technology and the broader implications for our society.

First and foremost, the integration of AI and ML into coding practices will lead to a significant increase in efficiency and productivity. By automating repetitive tasks and streamlining complex processes, developers can focus on more creative and innovative aspects of their work. This, in turn, will lead to the creation of more advanced and sophisticated software capable of solving problems and addressing challenges that were once considered impossible.

Moreover, adopting AI and ML in coding will result in more personalized and user-centric applications. As these technologies become more adept at understanding and predicting user behavior, developers will be able to create software that caters to individual users' unique needs and preferences. This will enhance the overall user experience and foster a more inclusive and accessible digital landscape.

However, the implications of AI and ML extend far beyond coding. As these technologies continue to advance and permeate various sectors, we expect to see a profound impact on the job market and the economy at large. While some fear that the rise of AI and ML will lead to widespread job displacement, others argue that these technologies will give rise to new industries and employment opportunities. In either case, governments, businesses, and educational institutions must adapt and prepare for the inevitable changes the AI and ML revolution brings.

Furthermore, integrating AI and ML into our daily lives will also have significant ethical and societal implications. As we become increasingly reliant on these technologies, privacy, security, and accountability questions will become more pressing. It is crucial for stakeholders to engage in open and honest dialogue about the potential risks and benefits of AI and ML and to establish guidelines and regulations that ensure these technologies' responsible and equitable development.

In conclusion, the implications and significance of AI and ML in coding and beyond are vast and far-reaching. As we embrace the AI and ML revolution, we must remain cognizant of the potential challenges and concerns accompanying these advancements. By fostering a culture of innovation, collaboration, and responsibility, we can harness the power of AI and ML to shape a brighter, more efficient, and more inclusive future for all.

Addressing the Challenges and Concerns in AI and ML Development

As we delve into the fascinating world of artificial intelligence (AI) and machine learning (ML), we must acknowledge the limitations and critiques accompanying these groundbreaking technologies. By addressing the challenges and concerns in AI and ML development, we can better understand the potential risks and work towards creating a more responsible and ethical future for these technologies.

Data Quality and Bias

One of the most significant challenges in AI and ML development is ensuring the data quality used to train algorithms. Data is the lifeblood of AI and ML systems, and the quality of the data directly impacts the performance and accuracy of these systems. Poor data quality can lead to biased or inaccurate results, which can have severe consequences in real-world applications.

Moreover, AI and ML systems are susceptible to biases in the data used to train them. These biases can result from human prejudices, cultural norms, or systemic issues. Developers need to be aware of potential biases and work towards creating more diverse and representative datasets to minimize the risk of perpetuating harmful stereotypes or discrimination.

Security and Privacy Concerns

As AI and ML technologies become more integrated into our daily lives, concerns about security and privacy have become increasingly prevalent. The vast amounts of data collected and processed by AI and ML systems can pose significant risks if improperly protected. Developers must prioritize data security and privacy, ensuring that sensitive information is not compromised or misused.

Additionally, the rise of deepfake technology, which uses AI and ML to create realistic but fake images and videos, has raised concerns about the potential for misinformation and manipulation. Addressing these concerns requires a combination of technological advancements, legal frameworks, and public awareness to mitigate the risks associated with deepfakes and other AI-generated content.

Ethical Considerations

The development of AI and ML technologies raises numerous ethical questions, such as the potential for job displacement, the impact on human decision-making, and the responsibility for AI-generated outcomes. As AI and ML systems become more autonomous, it is crucial to establish ethical guidelines and frameworks to ensure that these technologies are developed and deployed responsibly.

Developers, policymakers, and society must engage in ongoing discussions about the ethical implications of AI and ML, striving to strike a balance between innovation and the potential consequences of these technologies.

Technical Limitations

Despite the impressive advancements in AI and ML, technical limitations still hinder their full potential. For instance, AI and ML systems often require vast computational power and energy, which can be costly and environmentally unsustainable. Additionally, many AI and ML algorithms struggle with understanding context and nuance, which can lead to misinterpretations or incorrect conclusions.

Addressing these technical limitations requires continued research and development and collaboration between academia, industry, and government to drive innovation and overcome these challenges.

In conclusion, while AI and ML technologies hold immense promise for revolutionizing the world of coding and beyond, addressing the limitations and critiques accompanying these advancements is essential. Acknowledging and addressing these challenges, we can work towards a more responsible, ethical, and sustainable future for AI and ML technologies.

Paving the Way for a Smarter, More Efficient World

As we conclude our exploration into the world of artificial intelligence (AI) and machine learning (ML) for coders, it is essential to reflect on the transformative potential of these technologies. Integrating AI and ML into the coding landscape has already begun to revolutionize how we approach problem-solving, decision-making, and the development of innovative solutions. In this final section, we will summarize our key findings and offer recommendations for harnessing the power of AI and ML to create a smarter, more efficient world.

Throughout this book, we have delved into the intricacies of AI and ML, examining their applications, benefits, and challenges. We have seen how these technologies can enhance the capabilities of coders, enabling them to create more sophisticated and intelligent software systems. By automating repetitive tasks, optimizing algorithms, and facilitating the analysis of vast amounts of data, AI and ML can significantly improve the efficiency and effectiveness of coding processes.

However, integrating AI and ML into the coding sphere is challenging, as with any technological revolution. Concerns surrounding data privacy, security, and ethical considerations must be addressed to ensure the responsible development and deployment of these technologies. Additionally, the potential for job displacement and the need for upskilling and reskilling in the workforce must be considered as AI and ML continue to advance.

With these considerations in mind, we offer the following recommendations for paving the way toward a smarter, more efficient world:

- **Encourage collaboration and knowledge-sharing:**
  Fostering a culture of collaboration and knowledge-

sharing among coders, researchers, and industry professionals will be crucial in driving innovation and overcoming the challenges associated with AI and ML. By working together, we can develop best practices, share resources, and create a strong foundation for the responsible growth of these technologies.

- **Invest in education and training:** As AI and ML continue to reshape the coding landscape, investing in education and training programs is essential to equip coders with the skills and knowledge necessary to thrive in this new era. This includes not only technical skills but also a strong understanding of the ethical and societal implications of AI and ML.

- **Develop ethical guidelines and regulations:** To ensure the responsible development and deployment of AI and ML, it is crucial to establish ethical guidelines and regulations that govern their use. This will help to address concerns surrounding data privacy, security, and the potential for bias and discrimination in AI-driven systems.

- **Promote transparency and accountability:** Encouraging transparency and accountability in developing and deploying AI and ML systems will be essential in building trust and fostering responsible innovation. This includes communicating the capabilities and limitations of AI-driven systems and ensuring that developers and organizations are held accountable for their actions.

- **Embrace a human-centric approach:** As we continue integrating AI and ML into the coding sphere, it is essential to remember the importance of maintaining a human-centric approach. By prioritizing human values, needs, and experiences, we can ensure that these technologies are used to enhance our lives and create a more equitable, inclusive, and sustainable future.

457

In conclusion, the future of AI and ML in coding and beyond holds immense promise and potential. By embracing the AI and ML revolution and addressing its challenges and concerns, we can pave the way for a smarter, more efficient world that benefits all of humanity. The journey has only just begun, and the possibilities are truly limitless.

ABOUT THE AUTHOR

Andrew Hinton is a prolific author specializing in Artificial Intelligence (AI). With a background in computer science and a passion for making complex concepts accessible, Andrew has dedicated his career to educating others about the rapidly evolving world of AI. His debut series, AI Fundamentals, is a comprehensive guide for those seeking to understand and apply AI in various professional settings. Andrew's work caters to a broad audience, from managers to coders, breaking down AI basics, essential math, machine learning, and generative AI clearly and engagingly. His ability to demystify the complexities of AI has made him a trusted voice in the tech industry. Andrew's work imparts knowledge and empowers his readers to navigate and innovate in an AI-driven world.

$~~10.99~~ FREE EBOOK

Receive Your Free Copy of The Power of AI

SCAN ME

Or visit:
bookboundstudios.wixsite.com/andrew-hinton

Made in United States
North Haven, CT
23 October 2024

59345030R00261